Preface

This book covers the syllabus for the City and
Guilds 205 part II Course: Mechanical Engineering
Craft Studies. It will also be useful for the City and
Guilds 205 part II Course: Mechanical Engineering
Maintenance Craft Studies, TEC units and for the
CSE in workshop technology. This book is
dedicated to my family: Arlene, Angela and David.

August 1983   *A. Thomas*

Acknowledgements

The author wishes to acknowledge with grate-
ful thanks the help and assistance given by
colleagues at Luton College of Higher Educa-
tion, especially Mr C. Shotbolt, Mr M. Lewis
and Mrs Singh.

The author and publishers would also like to
thank the City and Guilds of London Institute
for permission to use past examination
questions and the British Standard Institution
for permission to quote and reproduce their
standards.

Extracts from BS 5378: Part 1: 1980 are
reproduced by permission of the British
Standards Institution, 2 Park Street, London,
W1A 2BS from whom complete copies can be
obtained.

Contents

1 Health and safety

Objectives

(a) A student should be able to identify potential health and safety hazards when handling and using materials and equipment in a workshop.

(b) A student will have a knowledge of the responsibilities both employer and employee have for themselves, for each other and for third parties.

(c) A student will understand and be familiar with and carry out safe working methods, and safety precautions relating to the workshop at all times.

(d) A student will be able to apply first-aid treatment in the event of an accident.

The Health and Safety at Work Act 1974

The basic aim of this new Act is that employers, with the co-operation of their employees, should do all that is reasonably practicable to ensure the safety of their employees and to see that the general public are not adversely affected by their activities. The provisions of the Act are briefly and simply explained in the following sections.

Introduction

The aims of the Act are:

1 To secure the health, safety and welfare of people at work.
2 To prevent risks to the health and safety of the general public arising from work activities.
3 To control the acquisition, possession and use of dangerous substances.
4 To control atmospheric pollution.

The protection of the Act extends to all persons at work and to members of the general public who may be affected by work activities.

Duties imposed by the Act

Employers

Particular matters within the general duty to which an employer must give attention are:

1 The provision and maintenance of safe plant and equipment and safe systems of work.

2 Safety and absence of risk to health in connection with the use, handling, storage and transport of articles and substances.
3 The provision of adequate instruction, training and supervision.
4 The provision and maintenance of a safe place to work and means of access and egress (exit).
5 The provision and maintenance of a safe and healthy working environment with adequate provision for employees' welfare.
6 Employers will be well advised to maintain an adequate written record to prove that they have taken steps to cover maintenance and training.

Employers are required to prepare and publish a written statement of their general policy with respect to health and safety and the organisation and arrangements for carrying out the policy.

Employees

Employees have the following duties:

1 To take reasonable care for their own health and safety.
2 To take reasonable care for the health and safety of others who may be affected by their activities at work.
3 To co-operate with employers and others in meeting statutory requirements.

4   Not to intentionally or recklessly interfere with or misuse anything which is provided for their health, safety or welfare.

Manufacturers, designers, suppliers, etc.
Anyone who designs, manufactures, supplies or imports any article for use at work will have to take all reasonable steps, carry out tests and provide such information as is necessary to ensure that the article will not cause injury or be a risk to the health of the people who use it.

What happens to existing legislation?
The existing health and safety legislation, e.g. *the Factories Act 1961*; *the Offices, Shops and Railway Premises Act 1963* and Regulations made under these Acts, will remain in force but will be gradually replaced by an improved and up-dated system of regulations to be made under the new Act.

Who will enforce the new rules?
Two new bodies have been set up to adminster the Act:
1   The Health and Safety Commission.
2   The Health and Safety Executive.

For all practical purposes the Health and Safety Executive is an integration of the existing Inspectorates. The Executive appoint Inspectors to carry out its enforcement functions.

Under the new Act, the Inspectors will retain all the powers previously held by Factory Inspectors but they will have important additional powers. If Inspectors are of the opinion that an activity involves a risk of serious personal injury, they may serve a Prohibition Notice on the person who is in control of the activity. The notice has the effect of prohibiting the activity from the time stated in the notice. It is probable that most such notices will take immediate effect. If Inspectors are of the opinion that any statutory provisions are being contravened, then they may serve an Improvement Notice, requiring that the matter be remedied and specifying the time in which the remedy must be made.

There is provision for appeal against either notice to an Industrial Tribunal, providing the appeal is made within twenty-one days of the notice being served. Improvement Notices are suspended from the bringing of the appeal until the appeal has been heard. On the other hand, Prohibition Notices will remain effective until the appeal has been heard.

Who can be held responsible?
The Act has created criminal liabilities on both employers and employees alike. There is little doubt that management will bear the main brunt of the new procedures and the increased penalties that go with them, but it must be clearly understood that *everyone* connected with work activities has duties placed upon them and will be liable to prosecution if they fail to follow them. Furthermore, it is no longer possible to simply claim innocence of the regulations — in future it will be necessary to prove that innocence. Hence the importance and desirability of written records.

It will be for the Inspector to decide who shall be charged and since the phrase 'similar officer or any one purporting to act . . .' can and may well be read to extend to anyone with managerial responsibility, however junior, the Inspector's choice will be a wide one.

What are the penalties?
The majority of prosecutions for alleged offences will be tried summarily, i.e. before a Magistrates Court, and will be subject to penalties of up to £400, multiplied by the number of people held to be responsible.

What are offences?

The list of offences is impressive and includes:

1 Failure to comply with a duty imposed by the Act.
2 Interference with or misuse of things provided under the Act contravening a regulation.
3 Attempting to prevent a person appearing before an Inspector.
4 Contravening a Prohibition or Improvement Notice.
5 Obstructing an Inspector.
6 Failing to give lawfully required information.
7 Making false statements.
8 Making false entries in registers etc.
9 Forgery or use of forged documents.
10 Failure to comply with a Court Order.
11 Falsely pretending to be an Inspector.

What power does an Inspector have?

Inspectors will always carry with them their warrants of appointment and these will specify that they are authorised to exercise some or all of the following powers:

1 To enter premises at any reasonable time.
2 To take a constable with them if they suspect serious obstruction.
3 To take with them other authorised persons and any equipment or materials necessary for their purposes.
4 To make any necessary examinations and investigations.
5 To direct that premises or parts be left undisturbed for as long as necessary for examination.
6 To take measurements, photographs and recordings.
7 To take samples.
8 To cause articles of danger to be dismantled or subjected to process or test.
9 To take possession of and detain such articles.
10 To require persons to answer questions and sign declarations.
11 To require the production of books and documents.
12 To require facilities and assistance to enable them to exercise their powers.
13 To issue Prohibition or Improvement Notices.
14 To seize, render harmless or destroy any article or substance which they have reason to believe is a cause of imminent danger.

Check list — The Health and Safety at Work Act 1974

Examples of specific points and areas of danger that require regular and specific checking by duly appointed and responsible staff include:

Buildings

1 *Fire exits and doors*
Including panic bars and all mechanisms.
2 *Roller shutters*
Operating mechanism.
3 *Staircases*
(a) Steps and risers: nose of steps,
(b) Banisters and hand-rails,
(c) Under-stair areas (cleanliness and combustible materials).
4 *Passages and clearways*
Kept clear of obstacles.
5 *Electrical Installations and wirings*
Serviceability and wear.

6   *Windows*
Opening/closing; broken glass; cleanliness.

7   *Fabric and fittings*
  (a)   Security of chimney stacks,
  (b)   Fixtures and fastening of slates, tiles, gutters, etc.

8   *Boundary walls*
Safe and secure (including coping stones).

9   *Stock storing*
Safe stacking and stacking heights; shelves — racks not over-loaded.

10   *Floors*
Safety — cracks and holes — polished surfaces.

Plant

1   *Boilers and furnaces*
  (a)   Safety valves and vents,
  (b)   Burner units and fire baskets,
  (c)   Lagging on pipes.

2   *Fixtures*
Safety fixings.

Machinery and equipment

1   *Lifts and hoists*
Safety locks and all mechanisms including emergency stops; clearance.

2   *Electrical, mechanical and other equipment and appliances*
Regular testing and servicing in accordance with manufacturers' instructions.

3   *Conveyor belts*
Mechanism and emergency stop functions.

4   *Fork-lift Equipment*
  (a)   Driver's controls,
  (b)   Steering mechanism,
  (c)   Lifting gear,
  (d)   Safety (chain/belts) guards; cages.

5   *Bulk Petrol and similar stores*
  (a)   Serviceable pump; hose and fittings,
  (b)   Sand/fire Extinguisher available,
  (c)   No parking area.

6   *Vehicles*
Regular servicing and inspection with specific reference to:
  (a)   Tyres,
  (b)   Mechanisms,
  (c)   Bodywork,
  (d)   Commercial vehicles — internal body fittings.

Offices

1   Office machinery — regular servicing.
2   Doors; passages; windows — as in 'Buildings'.

External areas

1   Car parking — clear of exit doors and hydrants.
2   Speed limits of vehicle movements in yards.
3   Clearly defined 'exits' and 'entrances' and 'one way' systems.

Fire precautions

1   Fire drill — to take place at least once in every three months.
2   Fire appliance:
  (a)   Hoses and connections inspected and tested every month,
  (b)   Fire extinguishers inspected every month and properly tested by fire appliance engineers at least once every twelve months.
3   Fire notices, fire exits, fire doors and 'panic bars' inspected and tested every week.
4   Safety clearways — ensure that no impediments or obstructions of any sort are ever permitted in gangways, accesses, doors, on or near staircases or fire exits.

First aid

Ensure that first-aid facilities are available and ready at all times, e.g.

1. That first-aid boxes are complete with clean and fresh medicaments.
2. That safety posters and notices are at all times on view in appropriate places.
3. That suitable facilities (e.g. rest rooms) are provided to accommodate a person pending the arrival of skilled medical aid.
4. That one responsible person per branch/depot has received first-aid training by having attended a recognised course.

Provision for non-slip flooring

Tool rooms

The following safety guidelines apply to tool rooms that have wood block floors.

1. The use of emery type adhesive backed sheets is recommended.
2. It is important that coolant or oil does not come into contact with the floor.
3. The remaining wood block must be kept dry and free from polish.
4. All personnel should wear shoes or boots with dry leather soles and heels to obtain a safe grip on the floor.

General engineering workshop

For a general engineering workshop, the floor should have:

1. A good finish and should be an even, concrete floor.
2. A dustless surface — this can be obtained by treatment.
3. A structure impervious to water.
4. A dry surface at all times. Coolant or oil which is spilt on the floor should be cleaned up by using absorbent granules, which must then also be removed. Any liquid causes a dangerous, slippery floor.

The personnel must have safe working shoes or boots, with dry leather soles and heels. Dry leather on dry concrete has a very high coefficient of friction. It gives the operator the safest, surest and quickest means of starting to move, walking and stopping. A lubricant on the floor causes 'wet' conditions between floor and leather, a low coefficient of friction results, with slippery and dangerous consequences.

Protective clothing

Boiler type overalls
1 They must be the correct size.
2 Tight fitting at the wrists.
3 Buttoned up at the front as high as possible for comfort, and to retain any tie or necklace in the overall.
4 Belted at the waist.
5 Always clean and in a good state of repair.

Footwear
1 Sturdy boots or shoes.
2 Correct fitting.
3 Steel toecaps give added safety against falling parts.
4 Footwear should be treated to withstand oil or coolant splashes.

Eye protection
1 Goggles of approved standard complete with side shields.
2 Eye shields.
3 Must always be worn in a machine shop.

Hair protection
1 Protective hat, complete with peak and hairnet.
2 All hair must be inside the hat and the hairnet. The hair is therefore kept clear and there is no danger of long pieces of hair being caught in rotating machine parts.
3 Must always be worn in a machine shop.

Special clothing
1 When handling swarf, leather gloves with metal reinforcing strips and a leather apron should be worn.
2 When handling coolant mixtures and oils, heavy duty PVC aprons and rubber gloves should be worn.

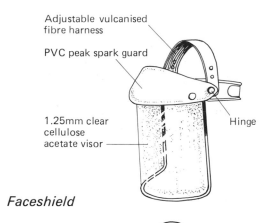

Adjustable vulcanised fibre harness
PVC peak spark guard
1.25mm clear cellulose acetate visor
Hinge

Faceshield

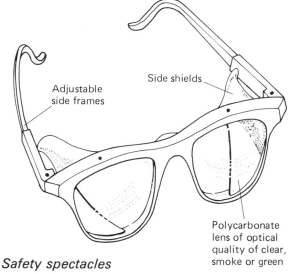

Side shields
Adjustable side frames
Polycarbonate lens of optical quality of clear, smoke or green

Safety spectacles

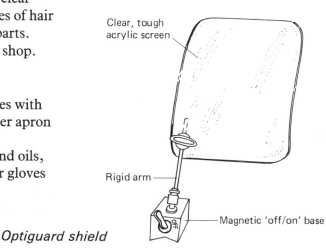

Clear, tough acrylic screen
Rigid arm
Magnetic 'off/on' base

Optiguard shield

Safety signs

The main idea of the large safety signs, is that:
1   The safety message is noted quickly by the drawing displayed rather than by the use of words.
2   The bright colours attract attention.
3   They are similar to international traffic signs.

The following signs are illustrated: from BS 5378: Part 1: 1980: Safety signs and colours.

Mandatory signs
Eye protection must be worn

Foot protection must be worn

Hand protection must be worn

Hearing protection must be worn

Prohibition signs
Do not extinguish with water

Not drinking water

Warning signs
Caution, risk of electric shock

Caution, corrosive substance

Safe condition signs
The symbol is in white, and the background in light green, e.g. symbols of a cross and an arrow — denotes first aid and a direction in a corridor.

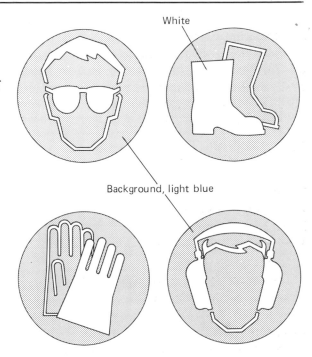

Mandatory signs

Prohibition signs

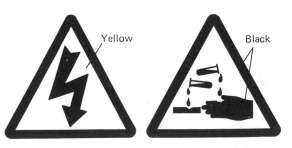

Warning signs

Machine guards

Vertical milling machine guards

1   Made up of two half assemblies.
2   Constructed of steel members which are coated with epoxy nylon and carry acrylic extension visors.
3   Visors can be adjusted vertically and horizontally.

4   Can form three sides of a box shape, as shown, or can be arranged in a straight line across the front of the machine table.
5   Release of locking devices gives easy access to the work or cutter.

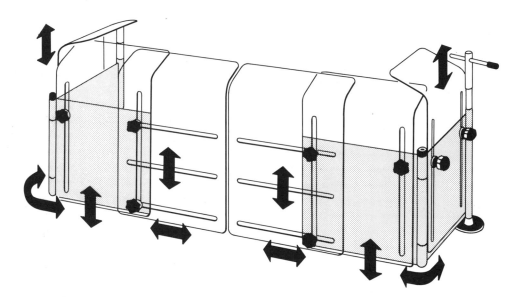

Drill guards

1   These are strongly constructed to be suitable for heavy duty pedestal drilling machines.
2   The plan views show two methods of attachment to the machine.
3   Releasing the wing nuts allows the extension of the guard.
4   When drilling is completed the wing nuts can be slackened to allow the bottom two sections to slide upwards into the top section. They are then locked in position by the wing nuts.

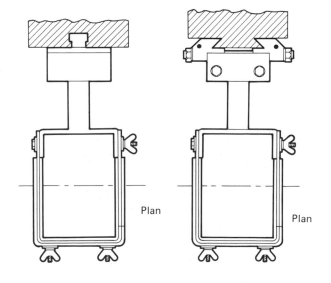

Plan

Plan

5　For lighter drilling machines a similar
　design is used, but the material is of
　thinner gauge, possibly aluminium. In
　plan view the guard is of circular section.
　The bottom section has a window of
　transparent acrylic. The top section is
　clamped to the machine spindle casting.

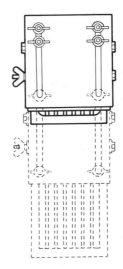

Lathe guards

Static type

1　Construction is of aluminium die cast
　frame and replaceable acrylic vision panels.
　The guard rotates on the steel spindle. The
　spindle bracket is bolted to the headstock
　casting of the lathe.
2　When the guard is in the down position,
　with the chuck or face plate securing the
　work, the operator is protected from the
　rotation of the parts. When the work is
　rotated the work is visible through the
　visor. During cutting the guard also pro-
　tects the operator from swarf and coolant
　spray.
3　When the machine is stopped the guard is
　rotated up and over on the spindle.

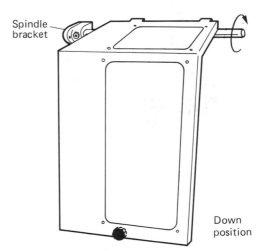

Spindle bracket

Down position

Saddle mounted traversing latheguard

1　This guard is used when work such as a
　long shaft is to be turned.
2　The rod A is carried on the column. The
　column is set in the mounting bracket,
　which is secured to the saddle.
3　The frame is similar to the static type,
　complete with a hinge bracket assembly. It
　is clamped and located to the horizontal
　rod A.
4　When the frame is in the down position the
　operator is guarded during the continuous
　turning of the shaft.
5　When work is completed, and the lathe is
　stopped, the frame is rotated up and over.

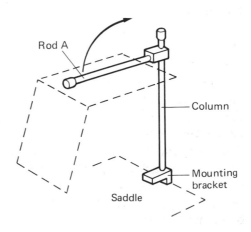

Rod A

Column

Mounting bracket

Saddle

Positioning

The drives and moving parts of materials-handling devices should be positioned out of reach of operators.

Large presses and guillotines
The electric motors and flywheels on the machines are positioned high above the floor level. The guarding of these moving parts is not necessary, due to their remote positions from the ground floor operators.

Shafts and gears inside machine tools
The shafts and gears are encased in housings. They are therefore inaccessible to the operators of the machines.

Overhead conveyors
Overhead conveyor systems are used a great deal in factories that mass-produce cars, machinery, electric washing machines, cookers, refrigerators etc. Components and sub-assemblies are suspended from the conveyor and are moved along the bays high above the shop floor operator. At stations in the bays, work has to be carried out on the components/sub-assembly at floor level. The conveyor is set to slope down to this station where wire mesh barriers and hand barriers are set into the floor alongside the track.

Roof cranes
Roof cranes are situated in the roofs of bays. Therefore guarding is not necessary as the crane passes the length of the bay, high above the floor operators. However, when a load is moved, operators *must not* stand underneath it or in its path.

General note
For maintenance to be carried out on the materials-handling devices mentioned, strict safety rules apply; i.e. the electrical supply must be cut off and fuses removed. Warning notices must be displayed, e.g. *'Maintenance Work in Progress'*, *'Danger'*, *'Do not switch on the Power'* etc. and temporary barriers should be erected around the machines.

Machine shop layout

When designing for a safe, efficient machine shop, the following points are important.

1 The machine tools should be spaced an adequate distance apart and at an angle to each other. Operators are therefore open to less danger should a tool or component break away from a machine.
2 Gangways should be marked with white edge lines. Gangways are painted in a different colour, say green, from all other areas, say grey. Materials, machine parts etc. must never be parked on the gangways. They must be kept clear at all times.

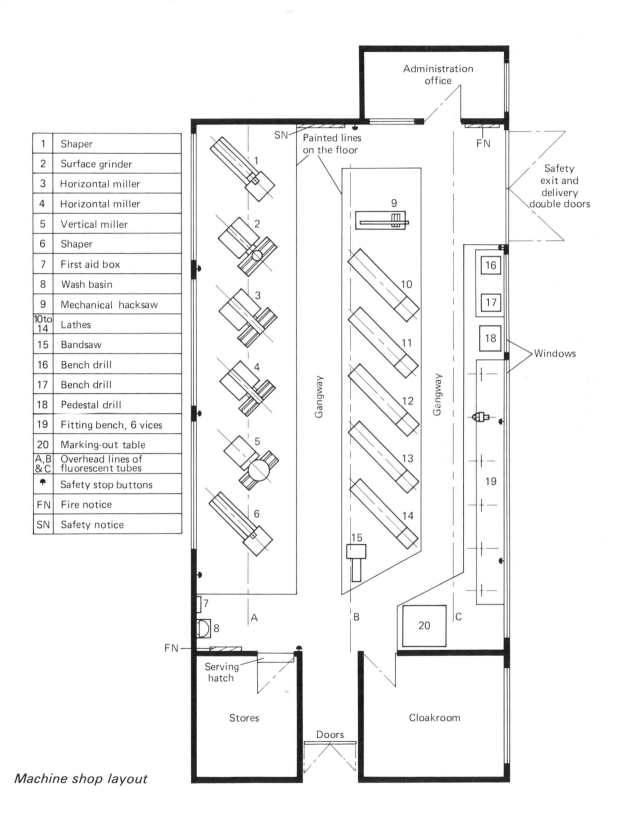

1	Shaper
2	Surface grinder
3	Horizontal miller
4	Horizontal miller
5	Vertical miller
6	Shaper
7	First aid box
8	Wash basin
9	Mechanical hacksaw
10 to 14	Lathes
15	Bandsaw
16	Bench drill
17	Bench drill
18	Pedestal drill
19	Fitting bench, 6 vices
20	Marking-out table
A,B &C	Overhead lines of fluorescent tubes
☂	Safety stop buttons
FN	Fire notice
SN	Safety notice

Machine shop layout

3   Machine accessories and finished works should be kept in cupboards or tables in the work area.
4   The shop should have adequate overhead lighting, with individual lamps on the machines and benches. Natural light from windows helps efficiency, accuracy and safety.
5   An adequate number of *power stop buttons* should be located on the walls as well as in the centre of the shop if necessary.

6   The following facilities are also required — an adequately stocked stores; a cloakroom for changing and rest periods; an administration office for supervisors, receipt of goods and general enquiries.
7   A first-aid box and wash basin are also essential.

Safety in the workshop

Each machine has its own special safety requirements and should be added, in each case, to the following safety regulations and displayed on each machine.

Safety regulations
Any person operating this machine *must*:
1   Have received sufficient training and instruction in its operation and use.
2   Use all safety regulations as applied to this machine.

Students please note:
1   No student must switch on this machine until the lecturer in charge has checked the machine for safe operation.
2   Safety hat, goggles and overalls *must* be worn at all times. Overalls must be in good condition, buttoned up, with no loose or ragged cuffs, ties should be placed securely inside the overalls.
3   No rings on fingers.
4   Sturdy working shoes must be worn.
5   Only one student to operate the machine.

6   Correct cutting speed and coolant supply to be used.
7   If any coolant, oil or swarf is dropped on the floor the machine must be stopped and the coolant/oil/swarf mopped up.
8   Correct standing position at all times.
9   To inspect job, tool or other part of machine:
    (a)   Switch clutch lever to OFF.
    (b)   Press stop button.
    (c)   Switch machine off by throwing the isolating switch to OFF.
    (d)   Leave the job or tool to stop and move the job a safe working distance away from the cutter, using scraper and swarf brush to clean job or cutter. Beware of sharp edges.
10   If in doubt at any time, stop the machine and request the aid of a lecturer.
11   You must know the location of the main stop buttons in the shop.
12   You must know the fire drill procedure.
13   You must know the location of the first-aid box.

Power supply 'stop' buttons

These emergency stop buttons are a bright red colour. They are normally mounted on the walls, joists or columns of the workshop.

When a power stop button is pressed all the power to the shop is cut off and all the machine tools will stop. When this happens the *no volt release* comes into action, which means that all machine tools are now in the OFF position. When the power supply is turned on, the START button on each machine will have to be pressed in order to operate the machine.

The following recommendations apply:
1   Only to be operated in an emergency.
2   Pressing any one of the large mushroom buttons automatically switches off all power to all the machines.
3   Large notices are positioned above each switch — in large print with the words STOP or STOP BUTTON in red on a white background.
4   The notices should be secured at or above head height, and must not be obscured by machines or cupboards.

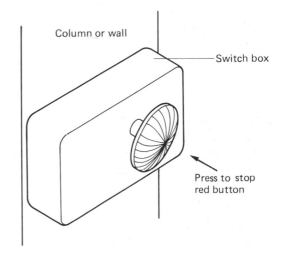

Power stop button

Machine 'start' buttons
1   To be located at a position for easy reach by the operator.
2   The green button is housed in a 'bush' in the switchbox casing.
3   When the top of the button is in the recessed position the machine is switched off.
4   To start the motor, the operator has to put a finger into the recess and press. This is a safety feature.

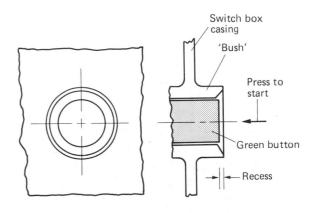

Machine start button

Machine 'stop' buttons
1   To be located in a position for easy reach
    by the operator.
2   The large red buttons are clearly visible.
3   On many machine tools the switch box is
    located at about knee height. This enables
    operators to switch off the machine by
    pressing either with their hands or their
    knees in an emergency.

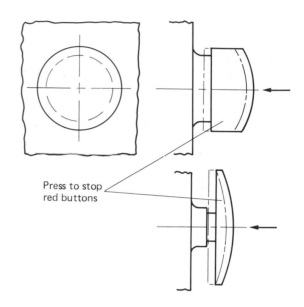

Press to stop
red buttons

Machine stop button

Toxic and septic properties of metals and non-metallic materials, liquids and gases

The human body is susceptible to attack by
chemical and physical means.

The three routes of chemical attack are via:
1   The nose (inhalation).
2   The mouth (ingestion).
3   The skin or eyes (skin or eye contact).

Physical attack could be by various radiations,
e.g. ultra-violet radiation, from electric arc
welding processes, microwaves, radio-
frequency waves and laser beams.

Inhalation
This causes the majority of cases of industrial
poisoning and disease. Cases occur over a long
period of time, such as with coal dust in mines,
or very suddenly as is the case of gassing with
carbon monoxide in a steel works.

Inhaled substances are:
1   *Dust*: asbestos, lead, silica.
2   *Fumes*: zinc and lead.
3   *Vapour*: mercury, organic solvents.
4   *Mist*: chromic acid.
5   *Gas*: chlorine, carbon monoxide, carbon
    dioxide, hydrogen sulphide.

Ingestion
The swallowing of harmful substances can
take place when the hands become contami-
nated with liquids or materials and are not
washed before eating food.

Accidental ingestion can also occur if a
dangerous liquid is put in an unlabelled bottle,
e.g. weedkiller or other chemicals.

Skin hazards
In a machine shop, a craftsman can receive cuts, abrasions and irritations to the skin through contact with metal swarf, sharp edges on work and tools and rubbing friction on the skin. Bacteria of various kinds can then enter these wounds and a septic condition can result.

Oil dermatitis
This is an inflammation of the skin due to irritation from oil and abrasive matter. Medical advice must be obtained. The condition may clear up if the person avoids the irritant for a short period of time. If on returning, the inflammation occurs again then further medical advice must be sought.

Oil folliculitis
This is caused by the irritation of the hair follicles by oil and foreign matter. It occurs mainly on the backs of arms and forearms when correct washing and skin hygiene are neglected. Treatment is usually straightforward.

Oil acne
This skin condition arises from blockage of the sebaceous glands which may well have started as an oil folliculitis. The remedy is the same as for oil dermatitis.

Eczematous type rash
This inflammation of the skin arises from continued contact with soluble oil emulsions, with the hands and forearms being most commonly affected. The skin becomes macerated and may develop small eczematous eruptions — dry red patches which itch. Proper medical treatment is necessary. If it recurs the condition could be due to an allergy and therefore the craftsman must be removed from contact with the oil emulsions.

Mineral oil cancer
Long exposure to certain mineral oils can give rise to a localised thickening of the skin, known as *keratosis*, whereby warty elevations develop over a period of years. They either remain, disappear or become malignant. In the prevention of this disease it is important to always pay attention to personal cleanliness. Oil-soaked clothing should be changed as soon as possible and regular medical inspection is advised. Cancer of the skin is curable if detected and professionally treated early in its development.

De-fatting of the skin
This problem arises when the hands are in prolonged contact with mineral oils, particularly those of lower viscosity. The skin loses some of its natural fat which causes dryness, loss of pliability and fissuring, with resulting inflammation and infection. Following work, the skin must be thoroughly washed, dried and a suitable conditioning cream applied. This restores the natural fat removed during the working day.

Important note
Whenever skin has been cut, becomes inflamed, or irritation occurs you should immediately report to the first-aid station. Professional medical advice must always be sought in these cases.

Treatment of burns

Heat burn
1 Cool the burn at once and keep it cold until the pain stops.
2 For a minor burn, place under a slow-running tap or in clean cold water for up to ten minutes.
3 Then cover the burnt area with a clean sterile dressing.
4 Remove any constrictions such as rings and bracelets.
5 A badly burned patient should be made to lie down, kept still, wrapped in a clean sheet and kept warm.
6 Summon a doctor or an ambulance as soon as possible for transport to a hospital.

Chemical burn
1 Flood the area with large amounts of running water, protecting unaffected parts and avoid contaminating other people.
2 Similar following treatment as for heat burn.

Important note
Professional medical advice should be sought as soon as possible in all cases of burns, no matter how minor.

Safe working procedures when operating pneumatic and electric portable tools

Pneumatic tools
Examples of portable pneumatic tools are drills, zip guns, grinders and sanders. The following safe working procedures are advised:

1 Read the manufacturer's literature before use.
2 Always appreciate that the speed and power of compressed air operated devices make them potentially dangerous.
3 Always wear safety goggles to avoid the danger of dust and chips being thrown into the eyes. Bystanders should also wear safety goggles.

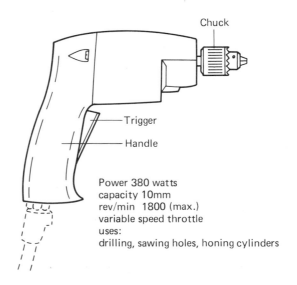

Chuck

Trigger

Handle

Power 380 watts
capacity 10mm
rev/min 1800 (max.)
variable speed throttle
uses:
drilling, sawing holes, honing cylinders

Pneumatic drill

4   Wear a safety cap (with all hair tucked in), overalls, safe working shoes, dust masks, ear protectors and gloves to suit the operation.
5   Keep fingers clear of moving parts.
6   Make sure guards are in position.
7   Before connecting the tool to the air supply, blow out the air line to clear it of any dirt or moisture.
8   Check the position of the job thoroughly, so that the air hose is long enough to reach all parts without pulling on the hose.
9   Connect the *throttling valve* with the *leader* hose into the pneumatic tool and tighten up.
10   With the throttling valve set to zero, plug the leader hose into the air hose which is connected into the wall supply.
11   The throttling valve can then be adjusted to obtain the correct operating conditions for the tool when it is switched on.
12   When the work is completed, switch off, turn the valve to zero and disconnect the line.

Electric tools

A number of portable electric tools are common in workshops, e.g. electric drills (pistol, handle and breast types), portable saws, sanders, suction cleaners and angle grinders. Double insulated tools have greatly increased the safety factor. The following safe working procedures are advised:
1   Read the manufacturer's literature before use.
2   Check power tool for correct voltage, correct fuse protection and correct speed of operation.
3   Avoid holding the tool's contact button when carrying it.
4   Never 'snatch' the plug.
5   Check that the electrical lead is in good condition.

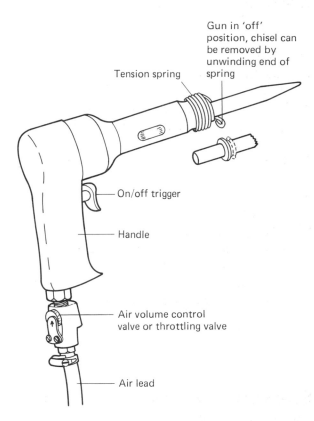

Zip gun

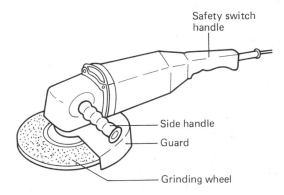

Complies with the Abrasive Wheels Regulations 1970

Electric angle grinder

6   Remove the plug when fitting an attachment.
7   Wear a safety cap, eye protection, overalls, safe working shoes, dust masks, ear protectors and gloves to suit the operation.
8   Keep fingers clear of moving parts.
9   Make sure guards are fitted.
10   Be aware of other people.
11   Never force the work-rate of the power tool.
12   Protect cable leads from mechanical damage.
13   Do not over-reach with the tool.
14   Keep drill chucks clean and tighten with the correct chuck key. Remove the key before starting.
15   Keep the tool and cable clear of water.
16   When the operation is complete, press to stop and when rotation has finished place the tool on a table.
17   Switch off at the socket and remove the plug. Clean the tool and replace it in its box or holder and return it to the stores.

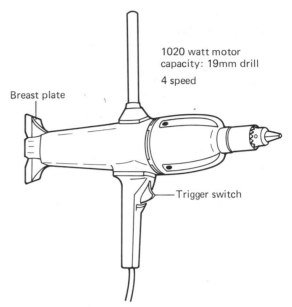

1020 watt motor capacity: 19mm drill

4 speed

Breast plate

Trigger switch

Side handles and breast plate, allow firm control on large capacity deep drilling and boring operations

Large capacity electric drill

Questions

Safety

1   On lathe parts such as the tool, work, chuck, chuck key, guard and light holder, what could be unsafe and what effects could they produce?
2   What injuries do the wearing of safety hat, goggles and overalls help to protect you against?
3   If a ring on a finger catches on a corner of a workpiece or machine, what could happen to the finger?
4   Industrial boots with steel toe-caps give good protection. What injuries could result from wearing unsuitable footwear?
5   On a machine tool there is an isolator switch, 'stop and start' button and a 'stop and start' clutch lever. What could happen if the operator had the work at stop, to measure it, when the motor is still running, the gears not in neutral and clutch lever in the off position?
6   Why can you slip on a wet surface more easily than a dry surface? State two potential dangers with swarf on the floor.

7   Where would you stand when operating:
   (a)   a lathe,
   (b)   a horizontal miller,
   (c)   a pedestal drilling machine,
   (d)   a shaping machine,
   (e)   filing on a bench.
   Indicate feet outlines on plan views.

8   How many *main stop buttons* are in your shop?
   Where are they located?
   Are they easily visible when standing in different areas?
   Are they painted red, with a large white disc behind them and large notices saying 'STOP BUTTON' displayed?
   What happens if a stop button is pressed?
   If it is safe to switch on the power for the workshop, is it correct or incorrect that the machine motors switch on and rotate?

9   Where are your *fire drill procedure* notices displayed?
   What type of fire fighting equipment is available and for what type of fires can they be used?

Questions

Portable electric and pneumatic tools

1   What can happen if a plug is snatched by pulling on the cable?

2   What operation would require the wearing of
   (a)   dust masks and
   (b)   ear protectors?

3   If the work-rate on a portable drill was excessive, what are the effects on the machine itself and the drill?

4   If a lead of pipeline lies along the floor, what can be done to protect it from damage, e.g. people walking on it?

5   What are the dangers to the operator and to the portable tool if 'over-reaching' occurs?

6   Why is it so very dangerous to leave a key in a chuck? What force would be exerted in the key if the tool was switched on?

7   What is the great danger of electricity coming into contact with water?

8   Why is it good practice to keep machines and tools in a good clean condition?

9   If a rotating tool is placed on a table top before it stops, what are the possible dangers?

10   When using a zip gun to chisel a corroded nut off a bolt, what safety items would you wear on the head?

11   Design and draw a safety sign for the following:
   (a)   dust mask protection must be worn,
   (b)   safety helmet must be worn. Indicate colours on the signs.

2 Dimensional control

Objectives

(a) The student should be able to understand the need for, and the usefulness of standardisation.

(b) The student should be able to understand, and use, a system of limits and fits.

(c) The student will be able to use correct gauges when checking components for finish, shape and size.

(d) The student will understand the operation of a screw and nut mechanism, as used in machine tools and measuring equipment.

(e) The student will be able to understand the vernier reading and its application to linear and angular measurements.

(f) The student should be able to understand, appreciate and operate a comparator.

(g) The student will be able to set up and measure angles and tapers.

(h) The student will be able to calculate, and set-out centres from two faces at right-angles to each other.

Standardisation

Imagine that four different factories are all making a particular component, 38.62 mm long; and that these are used in an assembly carried out in a fifth factory, such that all the components wherever they are made, 'mate' with another component made in the fifth factory.

For this to occur satisfactorily then, apart from the skill of the craftsman, something else is necessary; namely, that the measuring devices in all five factories shall be in complete accord — that is 38.62 mm on a gauge in Factory A means exactly the same as 38.62 mm on a gauge (perhaps of a different type) in Factory B. If, because the gauge had not been properly checked, it read 38.62 mm when the true length was, say, 38.51 mm, it could be that the whole output of the component from that factory could finish up on the scrap heap.

Thus it is an economic necessity that craftsmen should at all times be able to trust the accuracy of the devices used to measure their work. To bring this about the following things must happen:

1 The unit of length must be agreed.

2 It must then be defined in such a way that a *universal standard* is thereby achieved.

3 It must be reproducible with such a degree of accuracy that for all industrial and scientific purposes the reproduced standard may be regarded as absolute.

4 Gauges used in factories should be checked, using devices which have themselves been manufactured, within very close limits, as sub-multiples of the agreed standard (e.g. slip gauges).

With regard to (1), two systems, imperial and metric were in use for many years. Their standards, the *standard yard* and the *standard metre*, were distances between marks made on special metal bars (between gold plugs in a bronze bar in the case of the yard, and a platinum-iridium bar for the metre). But in 1960 it was internationally agreed to use, for all measurements, the Système International d'Unités, commonly referred to as SI.

In this system, the unit of length is the *metre*; of mass the *kilogram*; of time the *second*; of temperature the *Kelvin*; of electric current the *ampere*; and of luminous intensity the *candela*. Each is very closely defined.

For example, the length standard, the metre, was previously defined as the length of a bar; and this length would be subject to variations in physical condition. But the rare gas krypton gives off an orange-red radiation the wavelength of which is *completely stable*. So the number of such wavelengths needed to make up a metre (by the old bar standard) has been taken as defining the standard metre. Thus the *standard metre* is defined as $1\,650\,763.73 \times \lambda$, where λ is the wavelength in vacuum of the orange-red radiation of the isotope krypton 86. This is accurately reproducible.

Note that the UK has adopted the SI system. But craftsmen concerned with the repair and maintenance of older equipment may find that drawings are dimensioned in imperial units and it may be necessary, for some years to come, to use slip gauges, micrometers etc. based on these units.

Most industrialised countries have a national body which either controls, or recommends the adoption of, specific standards or codes of practice over a wide variety of activity. In the UK, the organisation is the British Standards Institution. The 'kite-mark' symbol

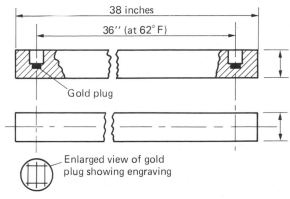

Composition of metal — bronze: 82% copper, 13% tin and 5% zinc

The imperial standard yard

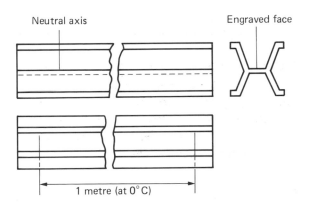

Composition of metal — 90% platinum 10% iridium

The standard metre

on a product indicates that the item has been made to conform to BSI requirements.

The BSI also produces many codes of practice, a good example of which is BS:308 Parts 1, 2 and 3 '*Engineering Drawing Practice*'. These booklets recommend drawing conventions, symbols, abbreviations etc. which, adopted by all UK draughtsmen, are nationally understood. Indeed, as they conform very closely to 'Recommendations of the International Organisation for Standardisation' (ISO), they can be regarded as of international currency. Another good example is BS:4500 on *Limits and Fits*, which is dealt with later in this chapter.

Technical terms and symbols

This is the means of communication between engineers. The BS 308: Part 1: 1972: General principles: '*Engineering Drawing Practice*' gives details and explanations of symbols and abbreviations which are understood by all.

Dimensional

For example, a shaft and hole produced to a system of limits of fits. Thus a coupling could be manufactured by a firm and a motor from another firm. On assembly the fit would be guaranteed.

Performance or quality

Metals such as steel are supplied in many different compositions, e.g. mild, stainless and high speed steel. A standard approved for each of these when supplied to a manufacturer would guarantee: (a) its composition, (b) its strength, (c) its modulus of elasticity, (d) its modulus of rigidity, (e) its thermal resistance and its resistance to corrosion properties, (f) its machineability, etc.

Testing methods

This enables materials and components to be tested by the same procedure. When testing sheet metal or round bar, standard size specimems are made and then tested for the tensile properties of the metal.

Codes of practice

There are standard practices laid down for a great variety of activities, for example the installation and maintenance of plant. Boilers to produce steam under pressure have to be installed correctly on a foundation, with easy access to manhole covers, and lifting tackle should be available to remove tubes etc. During the periodic inspection, methods of testing for corrosion of tubes, correct functioning of pressure gauges, etc. are followed as laid down in the code of practice.

Table 2 Types of lines

	Type	Example
────────────	Continuous (thick)	Visible outlines
────────────	Continuous (thin)	Dimension and leader lines, hatching
──── — ── — ──	Chain (thin)	Centre lines

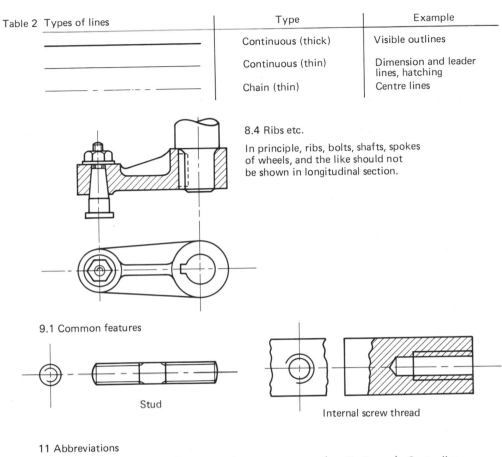

8.4 Ribs etc.

In principle, ribs, bolts, shafts, spokes of wheels, and the like should not be shown in longitudinal section.

9.1 Common features

Stud

Internal screw thread

11 Abbreviations

Term	Across flats	Centres	Radius	Centre line
Abbreviations or symbol	A/F	CRS	R	℄ or CL

Part 2
6.1 Diameters

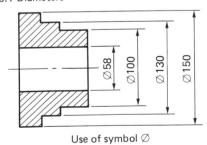

Use of symbol ∅

A dimension indicating the diameter of a circle or cylinder should be preceded by the symbol ∅.

Engineering drawing practice

End standards of length

There are two types of end standard — slip gauges and length bars.

Slip gauges

These were first introduced about seventy years ago by C. E. Johansson. They are rectangular blocks of steel that have been hardened and stabilised. The opposite faces have a lapped finish, and are flat and parallel to a high degree of accuracy. They are supplied in boxes in carefully selected sets. When a certain size is required the gauges are combined together to make up this length.

Sets of slip gauges are manufactured in four basic grades of accuracy: *workshop, inspection, calibration* and *reference*. The highest grade is the reference.

One useful workshop set of slip gauges has 47 pieces, (metric dimensions — width of blocks in mm) as shown in the table below:

Pieces	Range	Steps
1	1.005	—
9	1.01–1.09	0.01
9	1.1–1.9	0.1
24	1–24	1.0
4	25,50,75,100	25.0

Total 47

Wringing

This is the method of assembling the slip gauges. The two mating faces, which must be clean, are pressed together at right angles to each other and then twisted. To break them the procedure is reversed.

Care and use of slip gauges

1 When not in use the gauges are greased and kept in the box.
2 Before wringing they should be wiped with a clean, soft cloth.
3 Fingering of the lapped faces should be avoided to reduce the risk of tarnishing. Unnecessary handling of the gauges in use should be avoided as they can take up heat from the hands.
4 The correct method of wringing must be followed. They should be parted in a similar manner immediately the work has been completed.
5 Slip gauges should not be dropped, subjected to heat or damp, or wrung together in the presence of abrasive dust.
6 With refined work, it must be remembered that they are accurate at a temperature of 20°C; but for ordinary purposes a sufficient degree of accuracy can be obtained if the following precautions are taken. The work to be tested and the gauge blocks which have to be used should both be allowed to assume the prevailing temperature of the room. Thus, a piece of work should not be tested directly after cutting, grinding or other operations have just been completed, nor should large combinations of gauge blocks be used immediately after they have been wrung together.
7 Slip gauges are used to check the accuracy of measuring instruments, e.g. micrometer and vernier calipers, and for the setting of comparators and sine bars. They are also used when checking vee slots with rollers and internal and external tapers with balls.

Example

The method of assembling slip gauges to give a particular overall length should be done systematically, as illustrated in the following example.

A length of 37.315 mm is required.

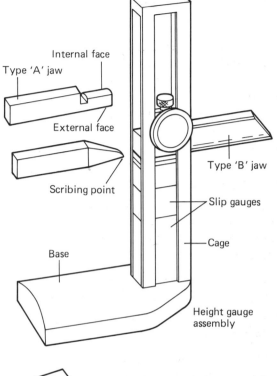

Internal face

Type 'A' jaw

External face

Scribing point

Type 'B' jaw

Slip gauges

Base

Cage

Height gauge assembly

		mm
1 Eliminate the last decimal place		1.005
		37.315
	−	1.005
	remainder =	36.310
2 Eliminate the second decimal place	−	1.010
	remainder =	35.300
3 Eliminate the remaining decimal place	−	1.300
	remainder =	34.000
4 Complete with suitable whole numbers say 9.0 and 25.0		34.000
		00.000

Therefore, for a length of 37.315 mm, the following slip gauges would be used: 1.005, 1.010, 1.3, 9.0 and 25.0.

The total can be checked:

1.005
1.010
1.300
9.000
25.000
37.315 mm

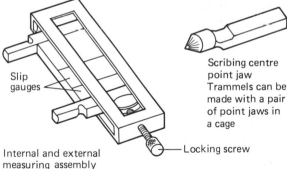

Slip gauges

Internal and external measuring assembly

Locking screw

Scribing centre point jaw Trammels can be made with a pair of point jaws in a cage

Slip gauge accessories — BS 888: 1950

Slip gauge accessories

To make a height gauge for marking-out on a surface plate or table, the scribing point jaw would be selected in place of the type 'B' jaw shown. The height of the scribing point above the table would be equal to the thickness of the base plus the total length of the slip gauges.

The internal face on a type 'A' jaw can be used for checking the bores on a plate or casting.

Two type 'A' jaws in a cage make an accurate internal and external caliper gauge. By substituting two scribing centre point jaws in a cage a very accurate set of trammels can be produced.

Length bars BS:1990: 1961

Length bars are made from high grade steel. They are hardened at the ends only and then stabilised by heat treatment.

The *workshop grade* bars have internally threaded ends and can be used with slip gauges, comparators and their own accessories for measuring gauges, jigs, workpieces, height gauges, etc. As their name implies, they are intended for use in the workshop.

General dimensions, tolerances on length and standards of accuracy for flatness, parallelism and squareness of faces are specified for all grades of bars.

Inspection grade bars have internally threaded ends and can thus be used in combination with each other. They are intended for use in the inspection room and tool room.

Airy positions
When in use the length bar must be supported at its *Airy positions*. The Airy positions are those points at which a bar of uniform cross-section must be supported, when used with its axis horizontal, to bring the end faces of the bar parallel. When it is so supported, the flexure of the bar under its own weight is reduced almost to a minimum. When using length bars the same care and attention must be given to them as with slip gauges.

The use of length bars
To measure the length between datum faces A and B, as shown in the diagram, the following procedure would be used:

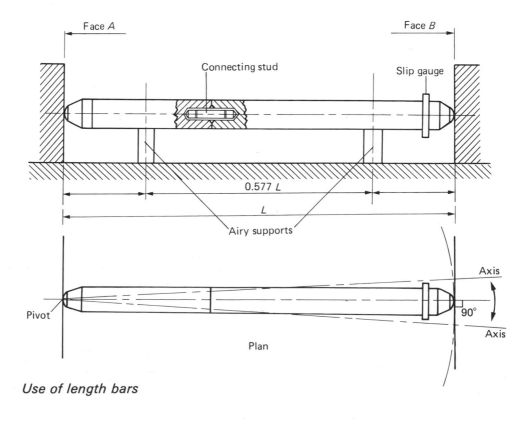

Use of length bars

1 Support the length bar at its Airy positions on two blocks of equal height (Airy supports).
2 Add slip gauges onto the bar to obtain the correct length L. The correct 'feel' is obtained when the bar is rotated about one end, as shown in the plan.
3 The distance between faces A and B, length L = lengths of bars + slip gauges + lengths of spherical ends.

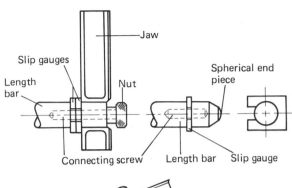

Length bar accessories
Length bars can be assembled together with a base, slip gauges, jaw and nut to make a *height gauge*. When a length bar is assembled to make an *internal gauge*, care must be taken to support the bar at its Airy positions so that the jaw's faces are parallel to each other.

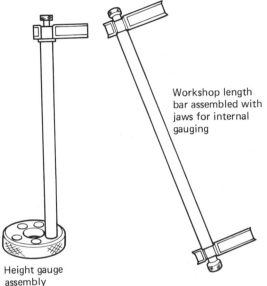

*Length bars: assembly of accessories —
BS 1790: 1961*

Reference temperature

In the 1930's international agreement was reached that the true lengths of standards and workpieces were those determined at a temperature of 20°C. This is a temperature that can be easily maintained in a standards room in a country having a temperate climate.

If the temperature is slightly above or below 20°C, then providing the workpieces are for example made of steel, the measurement will still be substantially correct.

However, if workpieces are of a metal such as brass, which has a much higher coefficient of linear expansion, then allowance may have to be made for the change in temperature, using the relationship:

$$l_2 = l_1[1 + \alpha(T_2 - T_1)],$$

where T_1 is the datum temperature (normally 20°C), T_2 the existing temperature, l_1 the length at temperature T_1 and l_2 the length at temperature T_2. α is the *coefficient of linear expansion*, which is the change in unit length per one degree change in temperature (i.e. change per metre per °C or K, in SI units). α for steel is $(11 \times 10^{-6})K^{-1}$ and for brass $(20 \times 10^{-6})K^{-1}$.

The following table gives the coefficients of linear expansion for some common metals.

Metal	Coefficient of linear expansion
Aluminium	25×10^{-6}
Copper	17×10^{-6}
Mild steel	11×10^{-6}
60/40 brass	20×10^{-6}

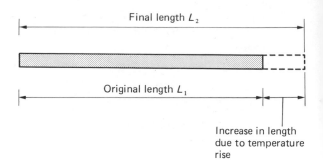

Metal rod

Standards room

Highly skilled inspectors are necessary to operate a standards room.

It must be temperature controlled at 20°C to avoid any risk of variations in equipment resulting from temperature changes. The standards room houses all types of very accurate measuring instruments: gauges, comparators, slip gauges, surface plates, optical instruments etc. These instruments are all manufactured to a higher degree of accuracy than the equipment used by craftsmen in engineering workshops.

Functions of a standards room
1   To ensure that workpieces for inspection are at the same temperature as the measuring equipment in the standards room.
2   To check the accuracy of workshop instruments for correct operation and accuracy of reading.
3   To check gauges, e.g. plug gauges and gap gauges, for wear.
4   To maintain the expensive and delicate equipment under the required carefully controlled conditions of use.

Temperature

The temperature of a metal or a liquid indicates its degree of 'hotness'.

To measure this one needs a defined scale, with at least two fixed points. On the Celsius scale the two fixed points are:
1   The melting point of ice (0°C)
2   The steam point of water (100°C)
Both these fixed points are taken at normal atmospheric pressure. Once these points have been established the Celsius scale is divided into one hundred equal graduations from 0° to 100°C. The scale is named after the Swedish astronomer Anders Celsius.

Expansion of solids
All solids increase in length when their temperatures are raised, i.e. *expand*, and when the temperature is lowered they become smaller, i.e. *contract* or shrink.

Steel bridge structures expand when subjected to hot weather conditions. A workpiece turned with heavy cuts will become hot and therefore expands.

This effect can be usefully applied to the manufacture of parts. For example, the tyre for a railway wheel is bored smaller than the outside diameter of the hub. The tyre is then heated so that it expands and can be fitted over the hub. When cooled, it shrinks onto the hub to give a tight fit.

Expansion in one direction only is called *linear expansion*. Each metal has its own coefficient of linear expansion. It is the length in mm that it will expand, for each 1 mm of the original length, for each 1°C temperature rise.

The increase in length (mm) =

the original length (mm) × coefficient of linear expansion mm/mm/°C × temperature rise °C

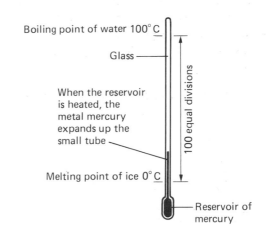

Celsius thermometer

Examples
1   The coefficient of linear expansion for a steel rod of length 200 mm is $10.9 \times 10^{-6}/°C$. If its temperature is raised from 20°C to 100°C, what will be the increase in its length?
Original length = 200 mm; coefficient of linear expansion = $10.9 \times 10^{-6}/°C$; temperature rise = $100° - 20°C = 80°C$; increase in length, i.e. expansion = ? mm.
Increase in length =
original length × coefficient of linear expansion × temperature rise

$$= 200 \times 10.9 \times 10^{-6} \times 80$$
$$= 0.1744 \text{ mm}$$

2 A shaft has a diameter of 160 mm. A steel collar is bored 0.1 mm smaller in diameter than the shaft. The shaft and collar are both at 20°C. To what temperature must the collar be heated so that its bore is 0.05 mm larger than the shaft? The coefficient of linear expansion of steel $= 11 \times 10^{-6}/°C$.

Increase in bore $= 0.1 + 0.05 = 0.15$ mm

Temperature rise $= T - 20°C$

Increase in bore =

$$\frac{\text{original}}{\text{bore size}} \times \frac{\text{coefficient of}}{\text{linear expansion}} \times \frac{\text{temperature}}{\text{rise}}$$

0.15 mm =

$$159.9 \times 11 \times 10^{-6} \times (T - 20°C)$$

$$\frac{0.15 \times 10^6}{159.9 \times 11} = T - 20°C$$

$$85.28 = T - 20$$

$$85.28 + 20 = T$$

$$105.28°C = T, \text{ temperature of the heated collar.}$$

Selective assembly

It is sometimes found that it is not economical to manufacture parts to the necessary degree of accuracy for their required functioning. Instead, they are made in an economic manner, measured to the required accuracy and are then graded or sorted into groups each of which contain parts of the same size to within close limits. They are then assembled with mating parts which have been similarly graded.

An example of this system is given in the mating of aluminium pistons in motor car cylinder bores. On a bore of 63 mm the best skirt clearance for a given type of piston is 0.12 mm on the diameter. If we assume that there is a tolerance of 0.02 mm on the bore diameter $(63.00^{+0.02}_{+0.00}$ mm) and the same on the skirt of the piston $(62.88^{+0.02}_{+0.00}$ mm), then the smallest piston in the largest bore would be $63.02 - 62.88 = 0.14$ mm clearance. The largest piston in the smallest bore would be $63.00 - 62.90 = 0.10$ mm clearance. By grading and marking the pistons as shown they may be selectively assembled to give the conditions required.

	A	B	C
Cylinder bore	63.00	63.01	63.02
Piston	62.88	62.89	62.90
Skirt clearance	0.12	0.12	0.12

Another example occurs in ball-bearing manufacture. The liner and outer rings and the balls are graded automatically for assembly.

Limits and fits

When a part has to be made and measured it is not possible to obtain an exact size. This can be accounted for by the range and accuracy of the measuring equipment available, the skill of the operator, the condition of the machine tool and its equipment and cutting tools. In trying to approach the exact size, two other factors are important, namely the time factor and the subsequent cost.

The required size of the part is referred to as the *nominal* size. The hole in the housing and the bush outside diameter is at a nominal size of 25.0 mm in the diagram.

Because the exact size cannot be obtained, designers must state the amount of deviation from the nominal size that they will tolerate. This is called the *tolerance*.

They must also state in which direction, relative to the nominal size, the tolerance must be positioned and so they state on the drawing the *limits of size* for that dimension. For the hole in the housing, the limits are 25.000 and 25.025, all the tolerance of 0.025 is on one side of the nominal size; i.e. it can be slightly greater, but not less than 25.000. It is a *unilateral tolerance*.

The bush is required to fit tightly into the housing. This type of fit is called an *interference fit*. The outside diameter of the bush must always be bigger than the hole in the housing. The shaft is required to run freely in the 16.0 mm nominal hole diameter in the bust. This type of fit is called a *clearance fit*.

An intermediate fit between the clearance fit and the interference fit is the *pushfit* or *transition fit*. This pushfit gives an accurate location and although easy to assemble would be too tight to run.

Item details

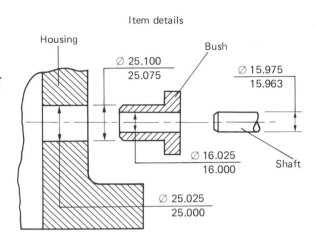

Assembly

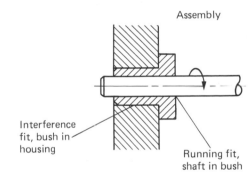

	Housing	Bush OD	Shaft OD	Bush ID
Maximum diameter	25.025	25.100	15.975	16.025
Minimum diameter	25.000	25.075	15.963	16.000
Tolerance	0.025	0.025	0.012	0.025
Limiting conditions	Max. interference = smallest hole ≙ largest bush diameter = 25.000 ≙ 25.100 = 0.100		Max. clearance = largest hole – smallest shaft = 16.025 – 15.963 = 0.062	
	Min. interference = smallest bush ∅ – largest hole ∅ = 25.075 – 25.025 = 0.050		Min. clearance = smallest hole – largest shaft = 16.000 – 15.975 = 0.025	

System of limits and fits

The diagrams for *clearance fit*, *interference fit* and *transition fit* show the conventional methods of illustrating principal terms used in a system of limits and fits.

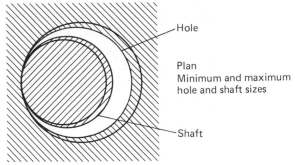

Hole

Plan
Minimum and maximum
hole and shaft sizes

Shaft

1   Basic size
    This is the same for both members of a fit. The limits of size are fixed relative to the basic size.
2   Maximum limit of size, *H*
    This is the greater of the two limits of size.
3   Minimum limit of size, *L*
    This is the smaller of the two limits of size.
4   Limits of size
    The maximum and minimum sizes.
5   Tolerance
    The tolerance is the difference between the maximum size and the minimum size, i.e. maximum size − minimum size.
6   Actual deviation
    This is the difference between a particular size and the basic size.

On the *clearance* fit diagram the lower deviation on the hole = minimum diameter hole − basic size.

The upper deviation on the shaft = basic size − maximum diameter shaft.

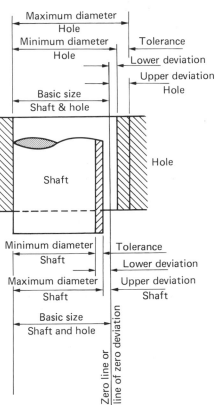

Clearance fit

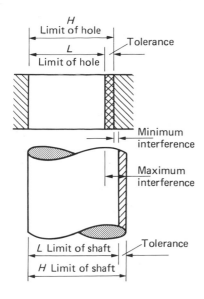

Interference fit

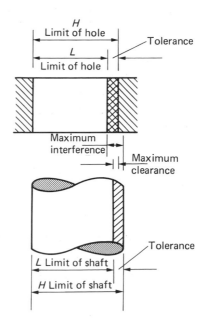

Transition fit

Selected ISO fits — hole basis (BS 4500A)

The ISO system provides a great many hole and shaft tolerances so as to cater for a very wide range of conditions. The system is based on a simple method of coding. A hole is designated by a *capital* letter, indicating the fundamental deviation, followed by a number which indicates a 'grade' (e.g. H7). Similarly, a shaft fundamental deviation is indicated by a small letter, followed by a grade number (e.g. g6).

A fit is designated by a combination of the two, e.g. H7–g6. So, if designers specify on a drawing ⌀ 20 H7–g6, they are asking for a basic diameter of 20 mm with a hole class H7 and a shaft class g6. The actual limits are given in the tables issued by the British Standards Institution (BS 4500 and 969).

Experience shows that the majority of fit conditions required for normal engineering products can be provided by a quite limited selection of tolerances and are as shown in the bar chart:
Selected hole tolerances:H7; H8; H9; H11
Selected shaft tolerances: c11; d10; e9; f7; g6; h6; k6; n6; p6; s6.

Because it is easier to manufacture and measure the shaft, it is desirable to be able to allocate the larger part of the tolerance available to the hole. Such a system of fits is said to be on a 'hole basis'.

The vertical heights of the bars are drawn to scale using the high and low tolerance values shown for *nominal sizes* 18 mm — 30 mm from the standard: BS 4500A. Different bar charts could be drawn for all the other nominal sizes shown.

Selected fits (hole basis)

From this table, which is derived from reading the bar chart in a vertical direction, suitable fits would be as follows: *Clearance fits* would be hole H11 and shaft c11, which would be stated as H11–c11, also H9–d10; H9–e9; H8–f7;H7–g6; H7–h6
Transition fit: H7–k6 and H7–n6
Interference fit: H7–p6 and H7–s6

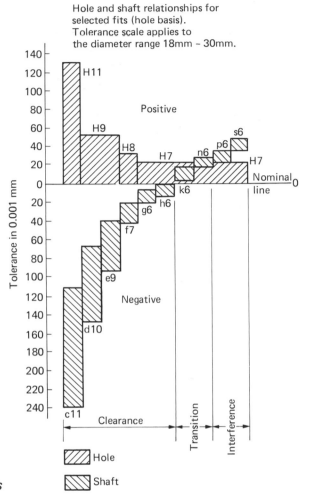

Hole and shaft relationships for selected fits (hole basis). Tolerance scale applies to the diameter range 18mm – 30mm.

Type of fit	Shaft tolerance	Hole tolerances			
		H7	H8	H9	H11
Clearance (slack running etc.)	c11				X
	d10			X	
	e9			X	
	f7		X		
	g6	X			
	h6	X			
Transition (push, slide etc.)	k6	X			
	n6	X			
Interference (force, drive etc.)	p6	X			
	s6	X			

Selected fits (hole basis)

ISO system of limits and fits

Data sheet 4500A — hole basis

Given that the basic size of a hole and shaft are 55 mm diameter and that it is an interference fit — hole/shaft, H7–p6, find:

1   The limits of size.
2   The tolerance on the shaft.
3   The tolerance on the hole.
4   The upper and lower deviation on the shaft.
5   The upper and lower deviation on the hole.
6   The minimum interference.
7   The maximum interference of the shaft in the hole.

From the Data Sheet 4500A the *nominal size* of 55 mm occurs in the columns shown *over 50 to 65*. Reading across the columns *interference fits* H7–p6 are shown.

1   The limits of size for the shaft $p6 = {}^{+51}_{+32}$
    $= \dfrac{55.051}{55.032}$ High limit
                           Low limit
    The limits of size for the hole $H7 = {}^{+30}_{0}$
    $= \dfrac{55.030}{55.000}$ High limit
                           Low limit

2   The tolerance on the shaft
    $= 55.051 - 55.032 = 0.019$ mm.

3   The tolerance on the hole
= 55.030 − 55.000 = 0.030 mm.
4   The upper deviation on the shaft
= maximum size − basic size
= 55.051 − 55.000 = 0.051 mm.
The lower deviation on the shaft
= minimum size − basic size
= 55.032 − 55.000 = 0.032 mm.
5   The upper deviation on the hole
= maximum size − basic size
= 35.030 − 55.000 = 0.031 mm.
The lower deviation on the hole
= minimum size − basic size
= 55.000 − 55.000 = 0.000 mm.
6   The minimum interference of shaft in the hole
= minimum shaft size − maximum hole size
= 55.032 − 55.030 = 0.002 mm.
7   The maximum interference of the shaft in the hole
= maximum shaft size − minimum hole size
= 55.051 − 55.000 = 0.051 mm.

BS: 4500B — shaft basis

In some circumstances, such as in the manufacture of a driving shaft, it may be necessary to accommodate a variety of accessories such as couplings, bearings, collars, etc. It is preferable to maintain a constant diameter for the permanent member, which is the shaft, and vary the bore of the accessories. A selection of shaft basis fits is provided in data sheet BS 4500B for use in applications of this kind.

Interference fits					
Tolerance		Tolerance		Nominal sizes	
H7	p6	H7	s6	Over	To
0.001 mm	0.001 mm	0.001 mm	0.001 mm	mm	mm
+10 / 0	+12 / +6	+10 / 0	+20 / +14	–	3
+12 / 0	+20 / +12	+12 / 0	+27 / +19	3	6
+15 / 0	+24 / +15	+15 / 0	+32 / +23	6	10
+18 / 0	+29 / +18	+18 / 0	+39 / +28	10	18
+21 / 0	+35 / +22	+21 / 0	+48 / +35	18	30
+25 / 0	+42 / +26	+25 / 0	+59 / +43	30	40
				40	50
+30 / 0	+51 / +32	+30 / 0	+72 / +53	50	65
		+30 / 0	+78 / +59	65	80
+35 / 0	+59 / +37	+35 / 0	+93 / +71	80	100
		+35 / 0	+101 / +79	100	120
+40 / 0	+68 / +43	+40 / 0	+117 / +92	120	140
		+40 / 0	+125 / +100	140	160
		+40 / 0	+133 / +108	160	180
+46 / 0	+79 / +50	+46 / 0	+151 / +122	180	200
		+46 / 0	+159 / +130	200	225
		+46 / 0	+169 / +140	225	250
+52 / 0	+88 / +56	+52 / 0	+190 / +158	250	280
		+52 / 0	+202 / +170	280	315
+57 / 0	+98 / +62	+57 / 0	+226 / +190	315	355
		+57 / 0	+244 / +208	355	400
+63 / 0	+108 / +68	+63 / 0	+272 / +232	400	450
		+63 / 0	+292 / +252	450	500

Selected ISO fits — hole basis

Data sheet 4500B — shaft basis
Given that the *basic size* of a shaft and hole is 90 mm diameter and that it is a *transition fit* shaft/hole h6–K7 find:

1 The limits of size.
2 The tolerance on the shaft.
3 The tolerance on the hole.
4 The upper and lower deviation on the shaft.
5 The upper and lower deviation on the hole.
6 The maximum interference.
7 The maximum clearance.

From the Data Sheet 4500B the *nominal size* of 90 mm occurs in the columns shown *over 80 to 100*. Reading across to the columns giving *transition fits* h6–K7 is shown.

1 Limits of size for the shaft $= 90^{0}_{-22}$

$= \dfrac{90.000}{89.978}$ High limit / Low limit

Limits of size for the hole $= 90^{+10}_{-25}$

$= \dfrac{90.010}{89.975}$ High limit / Low limit

2 Tolerance on the shaft
$= 90.000 - 89.978 = 0.022$ mm.

3 Tolerance on the hole
$= 90.010 - 89.975 = 0.035$ mm.

4 Upper deviation on the shaft
$=$ basic size $-$ maximum shaft size
$= 90.000 - 90.000 = 0.000$ mm.

Lower deviation on the shaft
$=$ basic size $-$ minimum shaft size
$90.000 - 89.978 = 0.022$ mm.

5 Upper deviation on the hole
$=$ basic size maximum hole size
$= 90.000 \quad 90.010 = 0.010$ mm.

Lower deviation on the hole
$=$ basic size $-$ minimum hole size
$= 90.000 - 89.975 = 0.025$ mm.

6 Maximum interference
$=$ maximum shaft size $-$ minimum hole size
$= 90.000 - 89.975 = 0.025$ mm.

7 Maximum clearance
$=$ Maximum hole size $-$ minimum shaft size
$= 90.010 - 89.978 = 0.032$ mm.

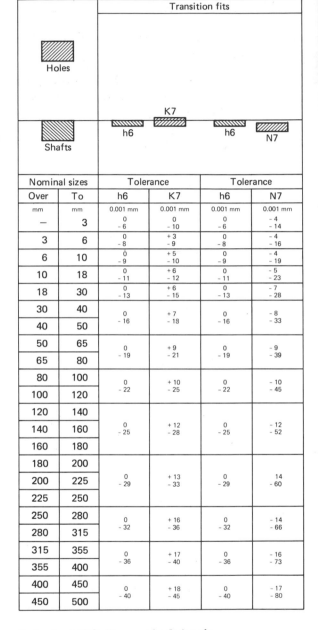

		Transition fits			
Holes					
			K7		
Shafts		h6		h6	N7
Nominal sizes		Tolerance		Tolerance	
Over	To	h6	K7	h6	N7
mm	mm	0.001 mm	0.001 mm	0.001 mm	0.001 mm
—	3	0 / −6	0 / −10	0 / −6	−4 / −14
3	6	0 / −8	+3 / −9	0 / −8	−4 / −16
6	10	0 / −9	+5 / −10	0 / −9	−4 / −19
10	18	0 / −11	+6 / −12	0 / −11	−5 / −23
18	30	0 / −13	+6 / −15	0 / −13	−7 / −28
30	40	0 / −16	+7 / −18	0 / −16	−8 / −33
40	50				
50	65	0 / −19	+9 / −21	0 / −19	−9 / −39
65	80				
80	100	0 / −22	+10 / −25	0 / −22	−10 / −45
100	120				
120	140	0 / −25	+12 / −28	0 / −25	−12 / −52
140	160				
160	180				
180	200	0 / −29	+13 / −33	0 / −29	14 / −60
200	225				
225	250				
250	280	0 / −32	+16 / −36	0 / −32	−14 / −66
280	315				
315	355	0 / −36	+17 / −40	0 / −36	−16 / −73
355	400				
400	450	0 / −40	+18 / −45	0 / −40	−17 / −80
450	500				

Selected ISO fits — shaft basis

Questions

1 The drawing shows the assembly of a shaft and its mating hole.

   With reference to the assembly give appropriate dimensions for each of the following
   (a) hole tolerance,
   (b) shaft tolerance,
   (c) minimum clearance,
   (d) maximum clearance
   (e) maximum metal condition of hole,
   (f) minimum metal condition of shaft.

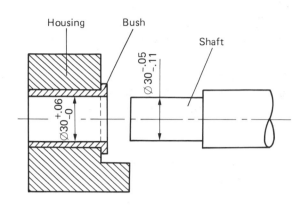

Assembly of a shaft and its mating hole

2 The drawing shows a shaft, bush and housing.
   (a) Copy and complete Table 1.

   (b) The bush (internal diameter) and shaft are manufactured to the dimensions shown. When the bush and shaft are fitted together give the values of:
       (i)   maximum possible clearance
       (ii) minimum possible clearance
   (c) A large number of the above components are manufactured. For the purpose of selective assembly the components are gauged and grouped as shown in Table 2.

   The components are paired, as shown in Table 3 to give the number of assemblies stated. Complete Table 3 for the maximum and minimum clearances for THE FOUR assemblies.
   (d) Under the system of selective assembly permissible in Table 3 give the values of:
       (i)   maximum clearance,
       (ii) minimum clearance.

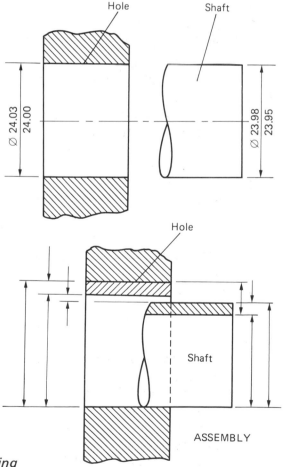

Shaft, bush and housing

TABLE 1

				LIMITS		Max. Metal Cond.	Min. Metal Cond.
				High	Low		
Item	Basic size	Class of fit	Tolerance				
Housing				40.025	40.00		
Bush (outside diameter)				40.042	40.026		

Unilateral Hole Basis   in accordance with BS 4500

TABLE 2

SHAFTS				BUSHES		
Group	Limits of size	No. off		Group	Limits of size	No. off
A	29.95/29.92	700		X	30.06/30.03	600
B	29.92/29.89	500		Y	30.03/30.00	600

TABLE 3

Selective Assembly	No. of Assemblies	Maximum Clearance	Minimum Clearance
A → X	600		
A → Y	100		
B → X	Unacceptable		
B → Y	500		

Gauging

If full advantage is to be obtained from a limit system it is essential to use *limit gauges* wherever possible. The checking of work can be done more positively and quickly using limit gauges as opposed to adjustable measuring instruments. Also, unskilled labour can be used. However, a disadvantage of using limit gauges is that they do not register the actual size of the component being checked. Wear of the gauge can also occur and this may place the size of the gauge outside the tolerance limits stated for the component.

Limit plug gauge
This type of gauge is used to check a machined hole. It is made from hardened and ground steel. The plug gauge has a long *GO* end which is made to the *low limit* and a shorter *NOT GO* end made to the *high limit*. If the GO end enters the hole and the NOT GO is unable to, then the machined hole is accepted. If the NOT GO end enters, then the hole is rejected. The lengths also identify the plugs and since the NOT GO end should not enter the hole being checked, a long gauging surface is not necessary.

Plain ring gauge
This type of gauge is used for inspecting or checking a shaft — a GO and NOT GO plain ring can be used. The bore of the GO ring will be made to the *high limit* on the shaft. The bore of the NOT GO ring is made to the *low limit* on the shaft.

Wear of gauges
However hard and wear resistant the gauge material is, it will eventually wear in the course of use. If it is made to the lower limit (for a hole), or upper limit (shaft), when new, with use it will soon be accepting components

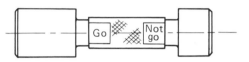

Limit plug gauge (solid type)

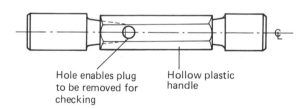

Hole enables plug to be removed for checking

Hollow plastic handle

Limit plug gauge

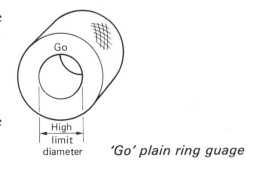

High limit diameter

'Go' plain ring guage

outside the limits for which it was made. This is compensated for by allowing a percentage (often 10 per cent) of the work tolerance for gauge wear.

BS 969:1953, gives recommended tolerances and their disposition with respect to the component tolerance zone for plain limit gauges such as plain plug, ring and gap gauges.

For example, if the GO ends of the working and inspection snap gauges for a shaft of $25.00^{+0.05}_{+0.00}$ mm were made 25.04 mm and 25.045 mm, they would wear to 25.045 mm and 25.05 mm, respectively, before it would become necessary to replace them. The inspection gauge is nearer the tolerance limit than the working gauge, so that this will ensure work that passes the working gauge will be accepted by the inspection gauge.

Precaution against wear is not so necessary for the NOT GO end of the gauge, since as it seldom passes over the work its wear is very small.

Limit caliper gauge and snap gauge

These gauges are used to check the outside diameter of shafts and sizes. The limit caliper gauge is used on work of large diameter. It is normally held in the fingers, but for much bigger sizes the gauge is hand held by the C part of the frame. The snap gauge is used for small diameter work.

Adjustable limit caliper gauge

This type of gauge is more expensive than the previous examples. When the long anvil is in position it is locked by screws. The gap between the GO anvil and the long anvil, i.e. the *high limit*, can be set by using a slip gauge combination between them. When the required feel has been obtained the GO anvil is then locked. The procedure is repeated using another slip gauge combination equal to the *low limit* between the NOT GO anvil and the fixed long anvil.

The advantages of this type of gauge are as follows:
1   Wear occurring on the anvils can be overcome by adjusting the anvils.
2   A range of different diameters can be inspected by using different slip gauge combinations.

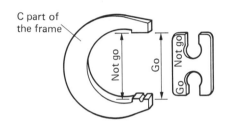

Limit caliper gauge and snap gauge

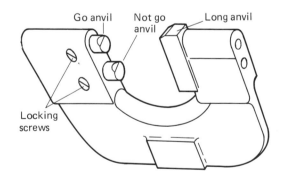

Adjustable limit caliper gauge

Plate depth gauge

This gauge is used to control the distance from the top face to the underside of a tee slot. It is shown checking the *high limit* (*H*) of the right-hand tee slot. In practice the gauge would then be withdrawn, reversed and the tee slot checked using the *low limit* side of the gauge. The same procedure would then be carried out for the left-hand tee slot.

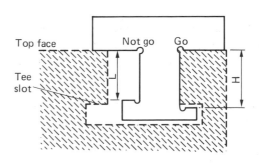

Plate depth gauge

Thread-pitch gauges

These gauges are made from flat steel plate with the contour of a thread machined on one edge of each gauge. A typical gauge has 14 thread gauges pivoted at one end of the body and 14 in the other end, plus one other gauge with an internal 60° vee form. The range of threads are from 0.25 mm pitch to 3.0 mm pitch.

Usually, the check is made by examining the component and gauge in contact and silhouetted before a light source.

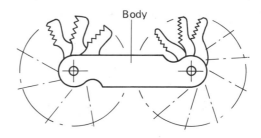

Thread — pitch gauges

Thread plug gauge

This gauge is used to check internal threads in a job. The longer GO head is made to the *low limit* of the thread. The shorter NOT GO head is made to the *high limits* of the thread.

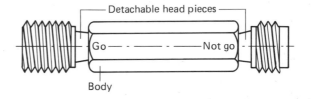

Thread plug gauge

Thread ring gauge

Thread ring gauges are used to check external threads on a shaft. A GO gauge is made to satisfy the *high limit* of the thread, the NOT GO satisfies the *low limit*.

Thread caliper gauge

The body, not shown, is similar to the limit caliper gauge. The locked anvils have a profile of a thread, ground as shown. A component that passes between the GO anvils, but not through the NOT GO anvils, would be accepted.

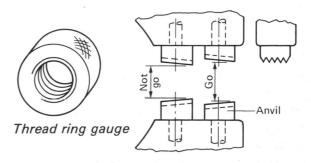

Thread ring gauge

Thread caliper gauge

Radius gauges

These gauges are made from flat steel-plate shaped with internal and external radii. A typical set has 9 gauges at each end of the holder. The gauges are free to rotate, so when one gauge is being used the remainder are rotated into the holder.

A typical set has a range of gauges from a radius of 2.75 mm, in steps of 0.25 mm, to 5.00 mm. When checking a radius on a job the necessary gauge is pressed and held at 90° to the surface and viewed against a light source.

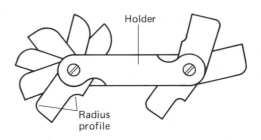

Radius gauges

Feeler gauges

Sets of thin pieces of steel held together in a holder are called feeler gauges. A range of thicknesses from 0.05 mm, in steps of 0.05 mm, to 1.00 mm is provided. Therefore, combinations may be arranged when checking narrow gaps, e.g. between the punch and die in tool making, flatness of a surface relative to a straight edge, gaps in sparking plugs.

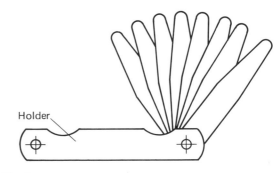

Feeler gauges

Pin gauge

The pin gauge is a plain bar of steel with conical ends. It is used for checking large bores where a plug gauge would be heavy to use, clumsy and expensive to make. A NOT GO and a GO pin gauge are necessary when checking bores.

Pin gauge

Advantages and disadvantages of limit gauging systems

Advantages
1   Limit gauges for controlling the size of components can be used by unskilled labour.
2   Inspection is rapid.
3   Gauges are not easily damaged.
4   They have a long life.

Disadvantages
1   Inspection with slip gauges must be carried out in order to be aware of possible wear of the gauge.
2   When components are rejected by the gauge there is no indication of the size of the component.

Taper plug gauge and taper ring gauge

Taper gauges are mostly designed to control a toleranced diameter at one end of the taper on the work, and also to exercise some control over the rate of the taper.

Method of checking a taper on a workpiece
1   Coat the tapered surface with a suitable marking agent, such as prussian blue.

2   Assemble the gauge to the workpiece.
3   Rock and turn the gauge slightly.
4   Withdraw the gauge.

If the gauge is found to have a uniform coating of blue all over its surface then the taper of the workpiece is correct.

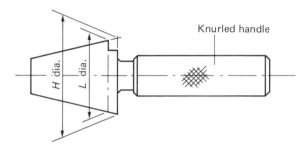

Taper plug gauge with gauging steps

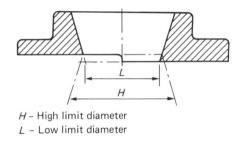

H – High limit diameter
L – Low limit diameter

Taper ring gauge with gauging steps

Thread measuring machine

The most important measurement of a screw thread is the *effective diameter*, for if this is not correct then the screw will be unsatisfactory. In the diagram, the line through A and B on the thread flanks is parallel to the axis of the screw and AB equals half the pitch.

To measure a thread using a hand micrometer, 3 wires of known diameter are placed as shown. This overcomes the possibility of the micrometer tilting sideways and is called the *3-wire system*. When the screw is held between centres, as shown on the thread measuring machine, then the *2-wire system* is used with a *floating micrometer*.

The machine consists of a base, a lower slide and a cross-slide. The cross-slide carrying the micrometer can move in the directions as shown. The cross-slide has two brackets, one of which carries a large micrometer drum and

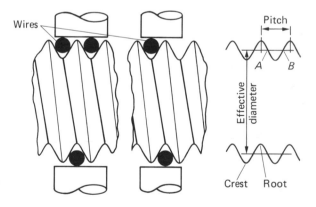

Three-wire and two-wire methods of thread measurement

the other a *fiducial indicator*. This is a spring-loaded device which registers the pressure on the measuring anvil opposite to the micrometer spindle. When the correct pressure is applied, a pointer which moves across a short scale is brought to a central zero position.

With the suspended wires in place the top thread diameter can be measured.

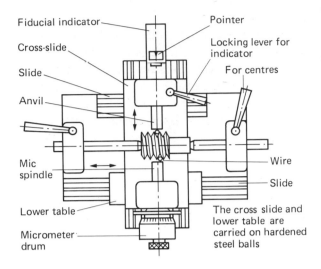

Thread diameter measuring machine

Measuring instruments

Micrometer depth gauge
A micrometer depth gauge is shown in the illustration. Interchangeable spindles of varying lengths increase the usefulness of this depth gauge.

The sequence of operations to measure the depth of a machined slot are as follows:
1   With the spindle withdrawn sufficiently so that there is no contact with the slot bottom, press the cross-piece into contact with face A.
2   Rotate the thimble until the spindle makes slight contact with the slot bottom.
3   Rotate the ratchet to obtain the correct pressure.
4   Take the micrometer reading.
5   In calculating the actual depth of the slot, allowance must be made for the length of spindle.

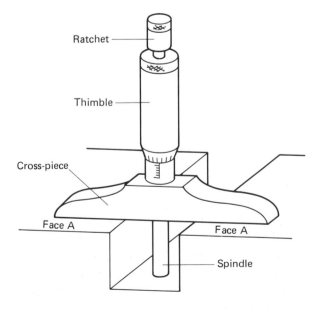

Micrometer depth gauge

Inside micrometers

The measurement of bores may be made using the inside micrometer. A greater degree of skill is required as compared with using an outside micrometer. When using the instrument, it is necessary to 'rock' in an axial plane about one end. A series of extension pieces are available to give a range from 50 mm to 300 mm in length.

Other uses include measuring on aircraft, bridges, large size jigs and fixtures. Supports must be placed to overcome the sagging effect.

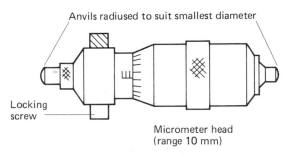

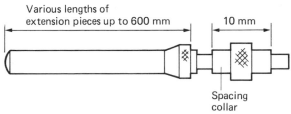

Inside micrometers

Telescopic pin gauge

To operate, the spring-loaded plunger is pushed into its housing and locked in position by turning the knurled head locking screw. It is then placed into the bore and the locking screw is released. The gauge is then in the position as shown and the plunger is locked by tightening the screw. It is then rocked about point A to check on the correct 'feel'. The gauge is withdrawn and measured by using an external micrometer.

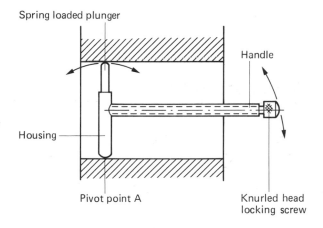

Telescopic pin gauge

Moore and Wright 2000 electronic digital micrometer

This is the first ever hand-held electronic digital micrometer that is completely self-contained. It is of robust construction — the solid state electronics are protected by stainless steel and a tough acetal copolymer casing. The instrument is powered by its own rechargeable power pack.

The micrometer has the following features:
1 Capacity range 0–25 mm.
2 Illuminated five-figure digital read-out.
3 Accuracy is to ±2 microns (0.002 mm).
4 The unique constant force spindle closure ensures consistency from one reading to the next and from one operator to another.

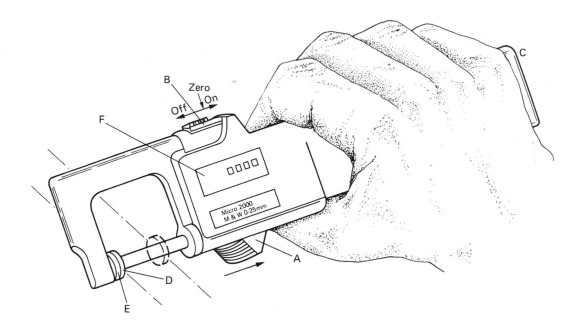

5   The digital display is automatically set to zero immediately the unit is switched on.

6   At the touch of a button, instant zero set is obtained against a reference standard and therefore makes the instrument self-calibrating.

7   The direct comparison feature enables dimensional variations between like components to be accurately measured and indicated in the read-out display as a plus or minus variation.

A Spindle slide control
B On/off switch incorporating set zero facility
C Handle
D Spindle anvil
E Fixed anvil to jaw frame
F Display window

Moore & Wright, hand electronic digital micrometer

The helix angle of a thread

A *screw thread* can be defined as an inclined line wrapped round a cylinder.

The diameter D of the cylinder or shaft is usually taken as the mean or average diameter of the top and root diameters of the thread.

When a nut is placed on the thread and rotated through one revolution then the axial distance travelled through is the *lead*, L, of the thread.

For a *single-start* thread, lead L = pitch × 1
For a *two-start* thread, lead L = pitch × 2
For a *three-start* thread, lead L = pitch × 3
From the right angled triangle

$$\tan \alpha = \frac{\text{lead}}{\text{circumference}}$$

$$\tan \alpha = \frac{L}{^{22}/_7 \times D}$$

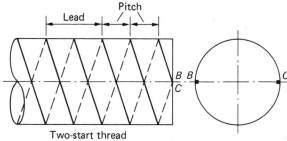

Single-start thread

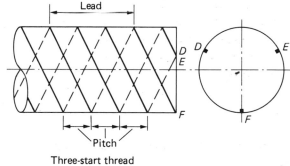

Two-start thread

Three-start thread

Diagrammatic representation of single and multi-start threads

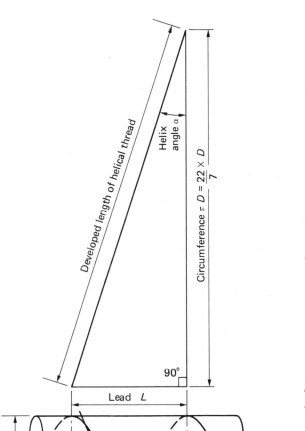

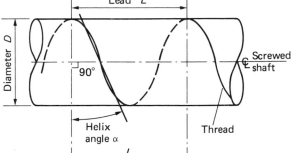

Helix angle of a thread

Example

Find the helix angle for a square thread of 38 mm outside diameter, 6 mm pitch and three-start thread.

Mean diameter D

$$= \frac{\text{top diameter} + \text{root diameter}}{2}$$

$$= \frac{38 + 32}{2} = \frac{70}{2}$$

$$\therefore D = 35 \text{ mm}$$

Lead L = pitch × 3 = 6 mm × 3 = 18 mm

$$\text{Tan } \alpha = \frac{L}{{}^{22}/_{7} \times D} = \frac{18 \text{ mm}}{{}^{22}/_{7} \times 35 \text{ mm}}$$

$$= \frac{18}{110} = 0.1636$$

If tan α = 0.1636, then helix angle α = 9°17′

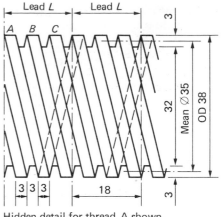

Hidden detail for thread A shown.
Separate threads B and C in outline.

Square thread (3 start, 6 mm pitch)

The vernier

The principle of the vernier was invented by the French mathematician Pierre Vernier in 1631. The vernier scale is the name given to the small sliding scale which moves over a fixed scale. In the workshop, vernier scales (and therefore vernier readings) are found on height gauges, inside and outside caliper gauges, depth gauges and protractors.

For the caliper gauge the *fixed scale* has dimensions marked off in 1 cm units. The vernier *sliding scale* has 10 marked divisions which total 9 cm in length. Therefore, each division on the vernier scale = $\frac{1}{10}$ × 9 = 0.9 cm. The difference in length between one fixed scale division and one vernier division = 1.0 cm − 0.9 cm = 0.1 cm.

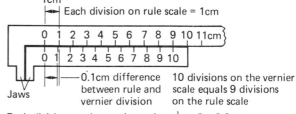

Each division on the vernier scale = $\frac{1}{10}$ × 9 = 0.9cm

Example
In the illustrated example the distance between the two jaws X is obtained as follows:

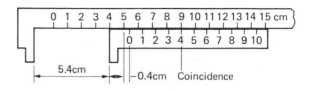

The mark 0 on the vernier scale is between 5
and 6 on the main scale. Therefore the
distance is at least 5 cm. The line on the
vernier that is coincidental with a line on the
main scale is the 4. This means that the 0 on
the vernier scale is $4 \times 0.1 = 0.4$ cm beyond
the 5 cm main scale mark.
Therefore, the distance X $= 5.0 + 0.4 = 5.4$
cm.
This type of instrument is accurate to 0.1 cm,
which is 1mm.

The type of vernier scale which has 25
divisions equal in length to 12 mm (24
divisions) on the fixed scale is the type most
commonly used in a machine shop.
One division on the fixed scale $= \frac{12}{24} = 0.5$
mm. One division on the vernier
scale $= \frac{12}{25} = 0.48$ mm. Therefore, the
difference in length between the
divisions $= 0.5 - 0.48 = 0.02$ mm. The instrument is therefore accurate to
0.02 mm $= \frac{1}{50}$ of a millimetre.

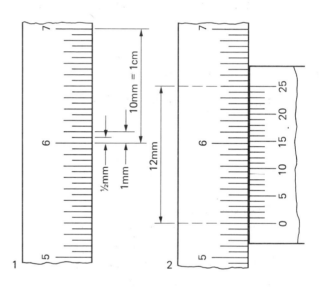

Principle of the metric vernier

In the illustrated metric example the 0 on the
vernier scale is between 15.0 and 15.1 cm (150
to 151 mm). The line on the vernier that is
coincidental with a line on the main scale is the
16. This means that the 0 on the vernier scale
is $16 \times 0.02 = 0.32$ mm beyond the 150 mm
main scale mark. The reading is therefore
$150 + 0.32 = 150.32$ mm.

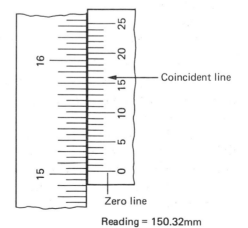

Reading = 150.32mm

Example of metric vernier reading

The vernier protractor

This instrument is used for the accurate measurement of angles, such as the taper on a tapered plug gauge, the angle of the slope of a sine bar, or the angle of a vee block. It is also used when marking-out angles on sheet metal and blocks of metal.

The sliding blade is locked by the screw and when the large nut is slackened the blade rotates with the vernier scale and its disc. When the required angle is obtained, the nut is tightened. The blade is part of the main scale showing degrees. The vernier scale is divided so that 12 divisions equal 23° on the main scale. Therefore, each vernier division equals $23/12° = 1^{11}/12° = 1°55'$ of angle, which is 5 minutes less than the 2° division on the main scale.

Example

To read the vernier protractor in (a) the vernier 0 is noted relative to the 0 on the main scale. The angle is between 25° and 26°. Finding the vernier line to the left of the vernier 0 that coincides with a main scale line gives us the minutes to add on to 25°. The coincidence is at the 25 minute line. The angle of the protractor is 25° 25 minutes.

Find the angle of the protractor in example (b). For (c) and (d) the points of coincidence are indicated by an arrow. State the angular readings.

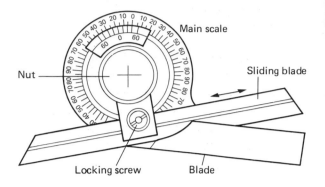

Vernier protractor

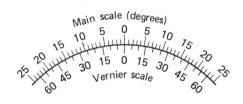

(a)

(b)

(c)

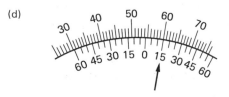

(d)

Dial indicators

Lever-type dial indicator

This instrument is suitable for making measurments in restricted positions. It is often used in situations where the plunger-type of dial gauge is unsuitable. It lends itself to being carried on a vernier height gauge or a scribing block. On some types the stylus lever can be set in a number of different positions.

The *bias lever* has two positions of operation which enables the dial gauge operator to register on either the top or bottom side of the ball contact. It can be used in clocking the centres of bores, checking for teeth wear on gears etc.

A lever-type dial indicator

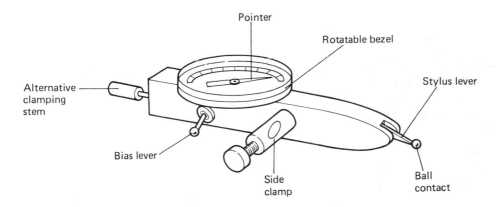

Plunger-type dial indicator

In this instrument a plunger moves up and down, passing through the indicator and out at the top. The plunger has a rack cut into it which meshes with a pinion. Any movement of the plunger is transmitted through a gear system which causes the pointer to rotate. The movement or deflection is read off the calibrated dial. The indicator can be carried by a vernier height gauge or scribing block when, for example, checking machine tool alignment or concentricity of bushes and shafts.

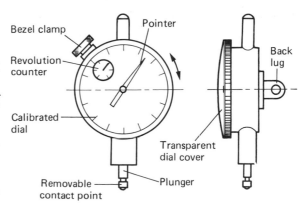

A plunger-type dial test indicator

Examples

The upward movement of the plunger-type dial test indicator causes the rack teeth on the stem to drive the rack pinion and the gear wheel in a clockwise direction. The pinion and the gear wheel are keyed on the same shaft. In turn, the gear wheel meshing with the 20-teeth pinion causes it to rotate in an anticlockwise direction.

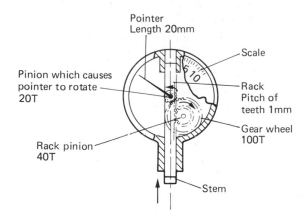

For the mechanism illustrated, calculate the following:

1 The angle through which the pointer moves when the plunger is moved upwards by 1.0 mm.
2 The distance that the arrow-head point moves.
3 The magnification obtained by this mechanism, i.e. the ratio of the distance found in (2) to the plunger movement of 1.0 mm.

A lever-type dial indicator is shown. Movement of the stylus A against the job causes the lever at B to push against the helix. This causes the spindle to rotate and move the pointer over the scale.

1 If stylus A moves 1 mm, how far does the tip of lever B move?
2 If the tip of lever B moves 1.2 mm, by how many revolutions will the spindle rotate?
3 The magnification of this instrument depends on three factors. What are they?
4 With reference to the values given on the figure, what is the magnification of the instrument?

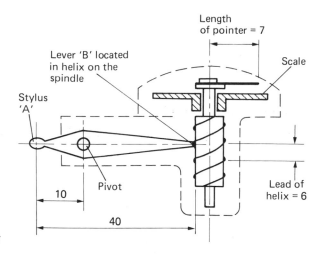

A lever-type dial indicator

The dial gauge as a comparator
The following guidelines should be followed when using a dial gauge as a comparator.

1 The plunger on the dial gauge must be set vertically to the base in its two directions.
2 By releasing the lever on the arm the dial gauge and the arm can then be adjusted upwards or downwards.

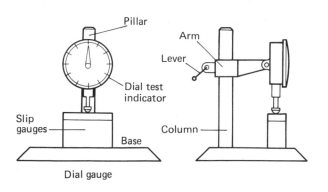

Dial gauge

3   A set of slip gauges for a definite overall
    length is then placed on the base.
4   The plunger is then lowered to make
    contact with the top of the slip gauges.
    When the pointer is at the 12 o'clock
    postion the lever is locked.
5   Rotate the graduated dial so that the
    position 0 lines up with the pointer.
6   By removing the slip gauges, components
    can now be passed between the base and
    the plunger. When the pointer registers on
    the clockwise side the component is *bigger*
    than the slip gauges. When the pointer
    registers on the anticlockwise side it is
    smaller than the slip gauges.

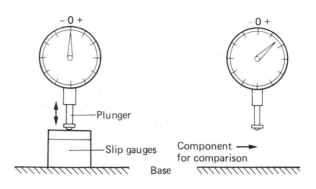

This set-up of a dial gauge, column, arm, base
and slip gauges forms an assembly called a
comparator. It compares the size of components with a fixed length or datum.

Note:
A micrometer is complete in itself. It does not
refer to any other datum and the size given is
final.

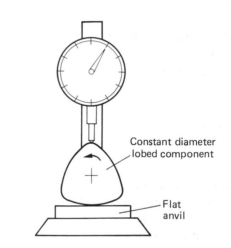

Testing for out-of-roundness
A constant-diameter lobed component will
appear to be circular when checked on a flat
anvil. The use of a comparator or micrometer
will not detect out-of-roundness. However, if
the component is rotated in a vee block any
out-of-roundness will immediately show up as
the component rides up and down.

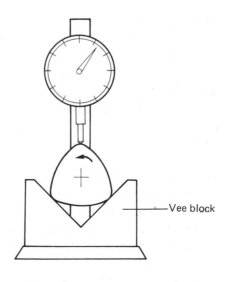

Testing for out of roundness

Uses of the dial test indicator

The indicator can be used in the following situations.

1 Testing for the concentricity of the outer diameter of a bush, relative to its inside diameter. The bush is located on a close fitting mandrel carried between centres, or held in a vee block. If there is no deflection of the pointer when the bush is rotated, then the outer diameter is concentric to the inside diameter, i.e. the thickness of the bush is constant.
2 The lathe — setting work in a 4-jaw chuck.
3 The slotting machine — setting work on centre with the turntable.
4 The milling machine — setting the jaw vice parallel to the arbor.

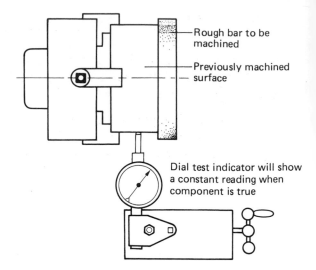

he lathe — truing up with DTI

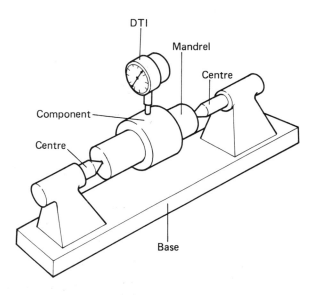

Testing for concentricity

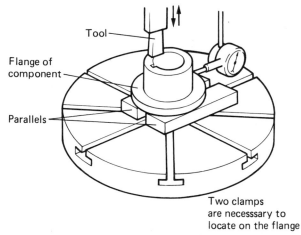

Setting up the slotting machine

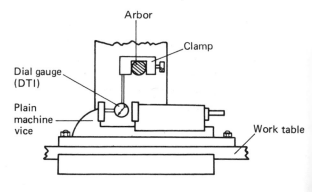

Milling machine

Cosine error

When using a dial gauge it is vital that the axis of the plunger is at 90° to the work surface in the two vertical planes.

When the dial gauge plunger is inclined at an angle of θ, contact with the work surface is at B. The correct contact should be at C, when the plunger is at right-angles to the work surface.

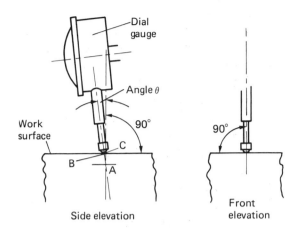

Side elevation

Front elevation

From the enlarged scale drawing of the right-angled triangle ABC, AB = actual reading of the dial gauge.
AC = true reading required,

then cosine θ = $\dfrac{AC}{AB}$.

AB × cosine θ = AC.
Actual reading × cosine θ = true reading.

The multiplying factor, cosine θ, which converts the actual reading to a true one, is referred to as *cosine error*.

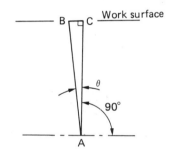

The Sigma comparator

In this instrument the amplification of the movement of the plunger is obtained by a series of levers. The upward movement of the plunger causes the lower lever to rotate anti-clockwise. It pulls down the link, acting on the leverage and on the top link. This causes anticlockwise movement of the pointer. The Sigma comparator is an example of a mechanical type of measuring instrument.

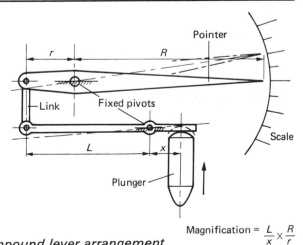

Magnification = $\dfrac{L}{x} \times \dfrac{R}{r}$

Compound lever arrangement

The important features for a comparator are:
1   The scales must be large and easy to read.
2   It must be robust, well made and hard
    wearing.
3   It should have a wide range of use.
4   Rapid adjustment.
5   The plunger should exert a constant
    pressure on the work being inspected.
6   The plunger must be able to be lifted clear
    by a trigger, so that a component can be set
    on the table. Releasing the trigger causes
    the plunger to register.
7   The finger should be connected to a 'dead
    beat' mechanism. This causes the finger to
    settle quickly and not oscillate.
8   Over-travel of the finger on the scale must
    not cause damage to the comparator. The
    lapped table on the Sigma comparator is
    reversible and this feature enables the life
    of the surface to be prolonged without
    relapping. The numerous shallow slots in
    the table are to overcome the 'adhesion' of
    a flat component, when being inspected.

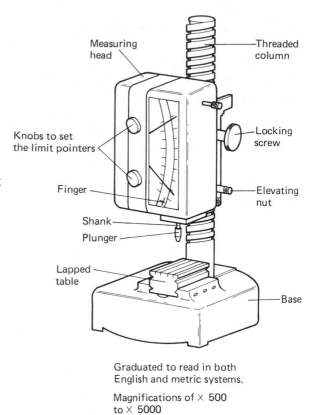

Graduated to read in both
English and metric systems.

Magnifications of × 500
to × 5000

Sigma comparator

Optical projector

A convenient and effective method of checking
the profile and dimensions of small shapes is to
magnify their profile by means of lenses and
transmitted light. The enlarged image can
then be compared with an accurate layout
made to the scale of the enlargement. Sizes
may be checked by direct measurement on the
enlarged shadow, and subsequent division by
the multiplication factor.

The magnifications available usually vary from
10 to 50, and in some cases 100. A choice of
say, × 10, × 30 and × 50 can be obtained on
the same apparatus by fitting different lenses.

Projection methods of examination are well

adapted to the examination of form tools,
profile gauges, press tools, gear teeth, screw
threads etc.

Designs vary, but essential features are a
condenser or collimator for projecting a
parallel beam of light from the source onto the
object, which is located between the condenser
and the projection lens. After passing through
the lens the light may shine directly onto a
receiving screen or be reflected onto it by one
or more mirrors.

The drawing shows the principle of the
Vickers contour projector. Light from the
lamp-box passes through the condenser, picks

up the object to be projected and then passes through the lens. It is then deflected by the roof prism onto the mirror, which again deflects it onto the projection screen. On this instrument, the mirror and the light passing to it are enclosed in a case. The micrometer heads allow movement of the stage upon which the projected object is carried so that minute movements may be made for the purpose of comparison on the screen. The micrometer adjustment swings the stage at an angle. This adjustment is necessary when screw heads are being examined, as the light must pass through the thread along its helix angle.

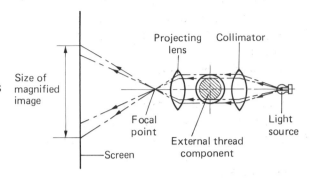

Principle of operation of the optical projector

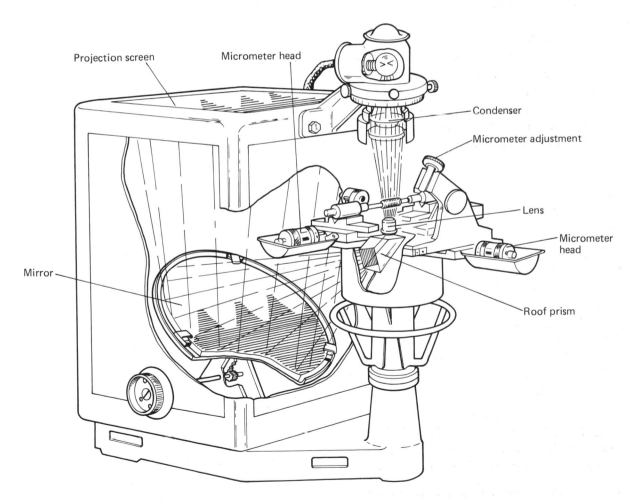

Vickers contour projector

Angle slip gauges

In the same way that end standards of length may be built up by wringing together slip gauges, angles may be built up by wringing together angle gauges. The upper and lower faces of each angle block are lapped accurately flat and at a certain specified angle to each other. A typical set is illustrated, including a square plate.

Angle gauges may be wrung together, in either of two ways. This will produce an angle between the two unwrung faces which is either the *sum*, or the *difference* between the angles of the two gauges.

The illustration shows angle gauges of 41° and 27° which have been wrung together in two different ways. In the first example they have been wrung to produce the sum of their angles:

$$41° + 27° = 68°$$

The second example shows how the same two gauges can be wrung to give the difference between the angles:

$$41° - 27° = 14°$$

This property is made use of in building up a series of gauges to produce the required angle. With the set of gauges shown it is possible to build up any angle from 3 seconds of arc upwards, in steps of 3 seconds of arc.

The illustrations show how angle gauges can be used to check a 120° vee gauge. In this example a square plate is used. Angles A,B,C and D of the plate each equal 90°. Therefore, by using gauges of 27° and 3° together with the plate, a combined angle of 120° can be obtained:

$$90° + 27° + 3° = 120°$$

The 120° angle of the vee gauge can now be checked by using the set-up shown.

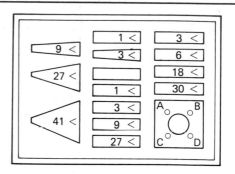

Degrees	Minutes	Seconds
1	1	3
3	3	6
9	9	18
27	27	30
41		

Set of angle gauges

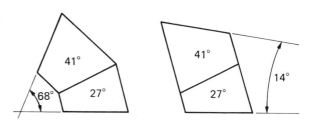

Two methods of combining angle gauges

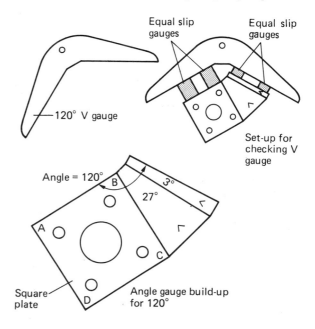

The sine bar

The sine bar is a precision instrument used for work involving angular measurement. It consists of a bar carrying a suitable pair of rollers or plugs which have a known exact distance between their centres. The gauge is used in conjunction with slip gauges. With roller A on the datum, the angle α is set up by raising B to the correct height, using whatever slip gauges are necessary.

For the sine bar to be accurate it should be made to the following specifications:
1   The rollers or plugs should be the same diameter and parallel.
2   The centre distance between the rollers must be exact. 100 mm or 200 mm is the usual centre distance.
3   The centre line AB of the rollers must be parallel with the top edge of the bar.
4   Adjacent faces must be square with each other.

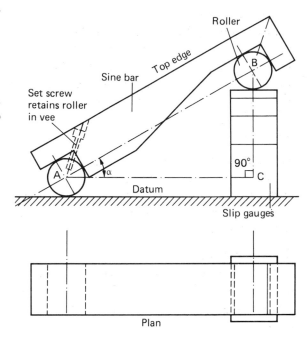

Calculation for sine bar setting
In the right-angled triangle ABC

$$\text{Sin BAC} = \frac{BC}{AB}$$

BC = height of slip gauges
AB = centre distance of rollers
BAC = angle of slope, called alpha α

then $\sin \alpha = \dfrac{\text{height of slip gauges}}{\text{centre distance of rollers}}$

Sin $\alpha \times$ centre distance of rollers
    = height of slip gauges.

Example
If centre distance of sine bar AB = 100 mm and angle α = 23.2° calculate the slip gauge height BC.

Solution
Angle α = 23.2°, sin α = 0.3939

$\sin \alpha = \dfrac{\text{slip gauge height}}{\text{centre distance of sine bar}}$

$\therefore 0.3939 = \dfrac{\text{slip gauge height}}{100}$

$\therefore$ Slip gauge height = 0.3939 $\times$ 100
                = 39.39 mm

Sine table

Sine tables are a development of the sine bar principle and are set in a similar manner. The sine bar is suitable only for relatively small work of light weight. The sine table has a larger working surface and is much more robust than the sine bar and is therefore suitable for larger, heavier work.

A further development is the compound sine table in which two sine tables are mounted on a common base with their axes of tilt set at right angles to each other. The compound angle to be set is resolved into its individual angles in two planes at right angles to each other, and each table is set accordingly.

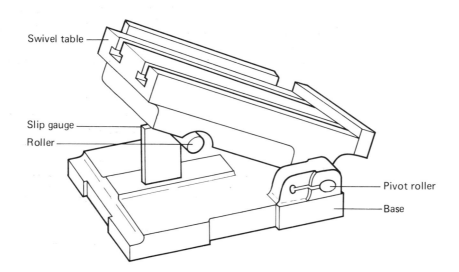

Sine table

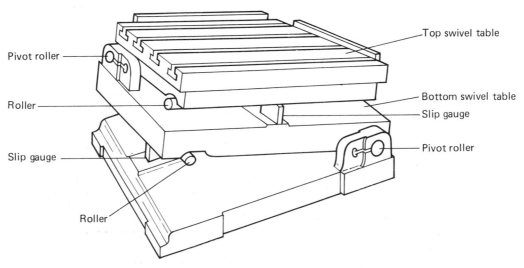

Compound sine table

Method of checking a tapered plug gauge

As shown in the drawing, the slip gauge pile is increased until a constant reading is recorded when a dial test indicator is run along the edge XX. The edge XX is then parallel to the datum surface.

The angle α of the sine bar = the included angle of the tapered plug gauge.

Question

The above method was used to check a batch of five tapered components. The engineering drawing specified an included angle of 30 ± ¹⁄₁₀°.

The table shows the height of slip gauges for each component. Indicate whether a component has passed or failed.

Complete also the other table for HIGH and LOW values.

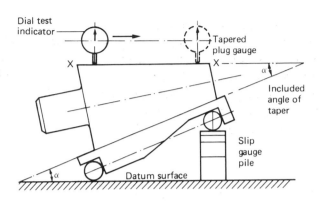

Method of checking a tapered plug gauge

High and low values

High limit	Angle α	
Low limit	Angle α	
Slip gauge height high		mm
Slip gauge height low		mm

Height of slip gauges for each component

Component	Slip gauge height (mm)	Sine bar centre (mm)	Pass	Fail
1	99.70	200		
2	100.30	200		
3	99.44	200		
4	100.38	200		
5	100.00	200		

Spirit levels

Spirit levels are accepted as tools for use in precision engineering. They provide a quick and accurate means of checking surfaces for:
1 Flatness, e.g. cast iron surface plates and tables, machine tool tables and straight edges.
2 Alignment, e.g. spindles of machine tools relative to their working surfaces.

Flat base level
This type of level has an unrelieved flat base of steel, hardened and lapped. The base length is usually from about 100 mm to 200 mm. The advantage of the lapped base is that the length can be varied at will by wringing two slip gauges on to the base at the desired distance apart.

A flat base level

Spirit level with vee grooves in the base
The body is usually made of cast iron or steel and has a flat bearing surface at each end. A longitudinal 120° vee groove is cut in the bearing surfaces for use on cylindrical surfaces. Base lengths can vary from 250 mm to 500 mm.

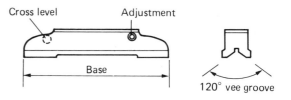

A spirit level; vee grooves in base

Square block level
The square block level is usually made of cast iron and is about 200 mm square. The four bearing surfaces are flat and two adjacent sides could have 120° vee grooves as shown. The *cross level* is necessary when the level is used on a cylindrical surface. This type of level is very useful for checking the alignment of machine tools.

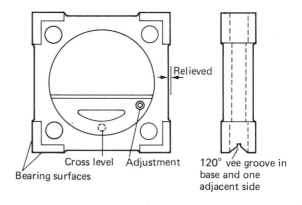

A square block level

Adjustment

The adjustment control enables one to set the vial level, i.e. the bubble is perfectly symmetrical, as shown on the scale dimensions, and therefore the base is perfectly horizontal.

Levels are usually marked with nominal sensitivity such as 20 seconds of arc/2.5 mm, 10 seconds of arc/2.5 mm etc. Alternatively, this angle may be expressed as the equivalent length of arc at the end of a 250 mm radius or base length. Then, one second of arc = 0.0012 mm in 250 mm.

Sensitivity is defined as: *that angle of tilt which causes the bubble in the vial to move through one scale division.*

The spirit level

The spirit level consists of a glass vial, the inside top surface of which is formed into a radius. The vial can have a ground surface or consist of a glass tube which has been bent into an arc of a circle. The sealed vial contains spirit and an air bubble. The vial is secured into the spirit level base.

Theory

The arc CAD represents the inner radius of the vial. O is the centre of the radius R. When the base of the level L is horizontal the bubble is at A. If the base is tilted to the new position OB_1, point A will move to A_1, but the bubble will remain vertically above O.

Angle BOB_1 = Angle AOA_1

In mathematics, the angle θ radians

$$= \frac{\text{length of arc}}{\text{radius}}$$

then θ radians $= \dfrac{AA_1}{R}$

also θ radians $= \dfrac{BB_1}{L}$

therefore, $\dfrac{BB_1}{L} = \dfrac{AA_1}{R}$ and $BB_1 = \dfrac{L \times AA_1}{R}$

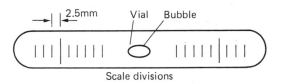

Scale divisions

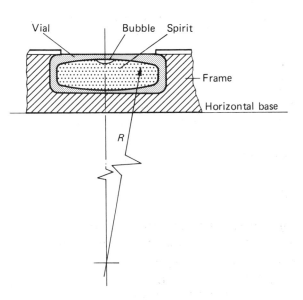

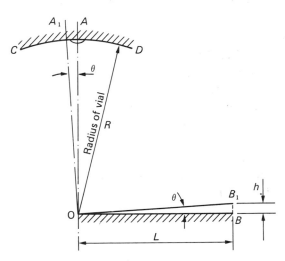

Relationship between angle of tilt θ, movement of bubble AA_1, radius of vial R, height h of one end of the base above the other end and length of base L.

In practice, because the vertical height h is so very small then we can take it that $h = $ arc BB_1

then $h = \dfrac{L \times AA_1}{R}$

so, h

$= \dfrac{\text{length of base} \times \text{distance bubble moves}}{\text{radius of vial}}$

If the *angle of tilt* is required in degrees, then

since θ in radians $= \dfrac{\text{movement of bubble}}{R}$

As 1 radian $= 57.3$ degrees, then:

θ in degrees $= \dfrac{57.3 \times \text{movement of bubble}}{R}$

Examples

1   A spirit level is 250 mm long and it is found that when one end is raised 0.02 mm above the other, the bubble moves 1.50 mm along the dial. Calculate the radius of the vial.

Length of base $L = 250$ mm
$h = 0.02$ mm
Movement of bubble $AA_1 = 1.50$ mm
$h = \dfrac{L \times \text{distance bubble moves}}{R}$
$h \times R = L \times \text{distance bubble moves}$
Radius of vial $R = ?$ mm

$R = \dfrac{L \times \text{distance bubble moves}}{h}$

$R \text{ mm} = \dfrac{250 \text{ mm} \times 1.50 \text{ mm}}{0.02 \text{ mm}}$

$R = 18\,750$ mm

Answer: Radius of Vial $= 18.750$ m.

2   The base of a spirit level is 400 mm long and the radius of the vial is 25 m.
Find:
(a)   The height of one end of the base above the other end, and
(b)   the angle of tilt in radians and degrees when the bubble moves 3 mm.
$L = 400$ mm; $R = 25 \times 1000$ mm;
$h = ?$ mm
Angle of tilt $= ?$;   Distance bubble moves $AA_1 = 3$ mm

Solution

(a) $h = \dfrac{L \times \text{distance bubble moves}}{R}$

$= \dfrac{400 \text{ mm} \times 3 \text{ mm}}{25 \times 1000 \text{ mm}} = \dfrac{1200}{25\,000} \text{ mm}$

$= 0.048$ mm

(b)   Angle of tilt in radians

$= \dfrac{\text{distance bubble moves}}{R}$

$= \dfrac{3 \text{ mm}}{25 \times 1000 \text{ mm}}$

Angle of tilt in degrees

$= \dfrac{57.3 \times \text{distance bubble moves}}{R}$

$= \dfrac{57.3 \times 3}{25 \times 1000}$

Angle of tilt in minutes

$= \dfrac{57.3 \times 3 \times 60}{25 \times 1000} = 0.413$ minutes

The dividing head

The dividing head is a piece of equipment that can be used on machines such as milling, grinding and drilling machines. The function of a dividing head is to hold work and to rotate it a part of a turn in order to carry out a machining operation.

Application of a simple dividing head

In the example illustrated it is necessary to mill 8 equal and equi-spaced slots across the cylindrical workpiece. This can be done using a dividing head, the simplest form of which embodies an index plate, with either a toothed edge or a circle of equi-spaced holes into which a taper plunger fits. The one shown is a wheel with 64 teeth. Thus, with the plunger locking the workpiece in the first position, the first hole is cut. Then, the *indexing gear* is rotated through 8 teeth positions and the plunger is set in this position. The procedure is repeated.

The number of slots to be milled

$$= \frac{\text{the number of teeth in the indexing gear}}{\text{the number of teeth positions to be moved through by the plunger}}$$

$$8 = \frac{64}{8}$$

If 4 slots are required in the blanks then,

$$4 = \frac{64}{16}$$

The plunger has to engage in every 16 tooth positions. Indexing gears with a different number of teeth can be substituted in place of the 64 tooth gear as shown.

Usually, indexing gears and plates are chosen so that the number of teeth or holes has many factors. A good example is 48, which would permit the cutting of 48, 24, 16, 12, 8, 4, 3 or 2 slots.

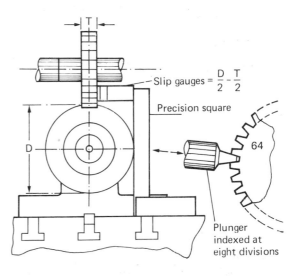

Setting work to centre and method of indexing

Principle of the dividing head

This type of mechanism, which is enclosed in a housing (not shown), is able to cater for all indexing problems. It has a crank handle which rotates the single start worm shaft which in turn drives a 40T worm wheel. One complete turn of the handle displaces one tooth of the worm wheel. Then the worm wheel, whose shaft carries the work, rotates through $\frac{1}{40}$ of $360° = 9°$. Two turns of the handle will rotate the work through $9° \times 2 = 18°$ and so on.

An *index plate* can be fixed to the housing — the worm shaft is free to rotate through it. This plate has a series of hole circles. Holes on a pitch circle diameter are equally spaced. The plunger type handle on the crank has a pin which is located in one of the holes. Assume that the plunger is positioned in a hole in a PCD containing 20 equally spaced holes in the index plate. By withdrawing the plunger pin and rotating it into the next hole, the crank has turned through $\frac{1}{20}$ of a turn. The work will move through

$$\frac{1}{40} \times \frac{1}{20} = \frac{1}{800} \text{ of a revolution}$$

$$= \frac{360°}{800} = 0.45°$$

If n divisions are required on the work then the

$$\text{crank turns} = \frac{40}{n}$$

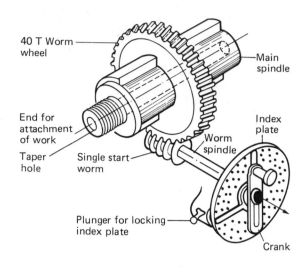

Diagrammatic sketch showing principle of dividing head

The simple dividing head milling assembly

This assembly can be used to cut teeth in a cutter blank. The cutter blank is securely held on a mandrel set between centres. The drive from the dividing head to the cutter blank is by means of a catch plate and carrier.

1 18 teeth are required to be cut in the blank by using an index plate with an 18 hole circle. With the plunger pin located in one of the 18 holes the first cut A is made. From the formula:

$$\text{Crank turns} = \frac{40}{n},$$

where n = number of teeth to be cut

$$= \frac{40}{18} = 2\frac{4}{18}$$

i.e. 2 complete turns and 4 holes in an 18 hole circle.

For the position B the plunger is now rotated 2 complete turns and 4 hole positions from position A. For the position C again 2 complete turns and 4 hole positions from position B are required. This is repeated until position D is reached, when the blank will have 18 equally spaced milled teeth.

2 Seven slots have to be milled in a circular plate. Three indexing plates are available. The selection being as follows:

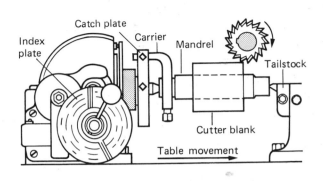

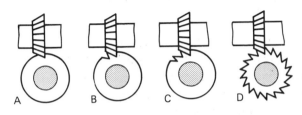

Dividing head milling assembly

	Hole circles
Plate No. 1	15 16 17 18 19 20
Plate No. 2	21 23 27 29 31 33
Plate No. 3	37 39 41 43 47 49

By inspecting the hole circles, Plate No. 2 with 21 holes and Plate No. 3 with 49 holes could be used. 21 and 49 are both divisible by 7, giving whole numbers of 3 and 7. By using the 49 hole circle, then each slot would be milled when the plunger has moved through 7 holes.

3   Milling a bevel cutter blank

It is required to mill 10 equal and equi-spaced slots in a cutter blank. The included angle is to be 35 degrees. An index plate with 48 holes is to be used.

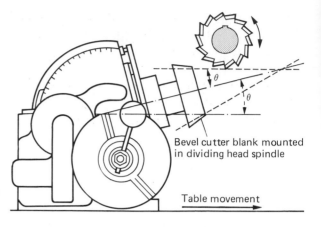

Bevel cutter blank mounted in dividing head spindle

Table movement

The method used is to secure the blank in the dividing head and raise the axis of the blank through an angle of θ, which is half of the included angle of 35°, i.e. $\dfrac{35}{2} = 17.5$ degrees. With the plunger located in one of the 48 holes in the index plate and the cutter set on centre, the first cut is made. From the formula, crank turns

$$= \frac{40}{n} = \frac{40}{10} = 4.$$

By rotating the crank 4 complete turns, and again locating the plunger in a hole, the second slot can now be cut and so on, until the 10 slots have been cut.

Milling a bevel cutter blank

The rotary table

If a vertical-spindle milling machine is equipped with a rotary table it can be used for an extremely wide variety of jobs. The rotary table is bolted onto the machine table and is usually located by tenons in the centre tee slot. It has tee slots cut in its own upper surface so that work can be bolted to it. A taper hole is accurately positioned at its centre so that, with the aid of a short mandrel, work can be accurately positioned over the centre of the table.

The rotary table can also be used on other machines, e.g. milling, slotting, vertical boring and drilling. The mechanism, which is similar to a driving head, has a handle which rotates a single-start worm engaged with a worm wheel.

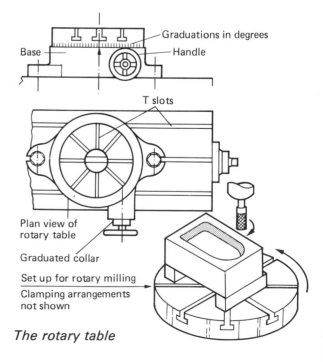

Graduations in degrees

Base

Handle

T slots

Plan view of rotary table

Graduated collar

Set up for rotary milling

Clamping arrangements not shown

The rotary table

On the Parkinson Rotary Table 1 revolution of the handle rotates the table by 4°. Therefore, it has a reduction of $\dfrac{360°}{4°} = \dfrac{90}{1}$. Therefore, 90 turns of the handle are needed to rotate the table once. However, on the Victoria Rotary table 1 revolution of the handle rotates the table by 4½°.

Therefore its reduction

$$= \frac{360°}{4½°} = 360 \times \frac{2}{9} = \frac{80}{1}$$

An angular vernier scale located on the base enables one to accurately note the angle turned through. In place of the graduated collar, index plates and a crank similar to the dividing head, can be used. It then means that any number of divisions or angular spacings is now possible.

The illustration shows a set-up for drilling six equi-spaced holes on a pitch circle diameter. The rotary table centre is set a distance equal to half the pitch circle diameter of the holes to be drilled. By rotating the table through 60° each hole is drilled in turn.

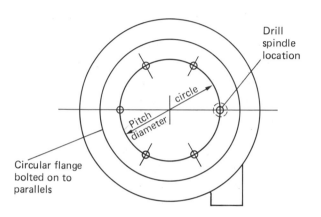

Set-up for drilling of 6 holes

Examples

1   Calculate suitable indexing to cut the following on a dividing head:
   (a)   6 splines on a shaft,
   (b)   15 teeth on a gear blank,
   (c)   48 graduations on a collar.
   The dividing head ratio is 40:1 and two indexing plates are available with hole circles of 15, 16, 17, 18, 19, 20 holes and 21, 23, 27, 29, 31 and 33 holes.

Solution

(a)   For 6 divisions : Indexing

$$= \frac{40}{\text{number of divisions}}$$

$$= \frac{40}{6} = 6\frac{4}{6} = 6\frac{2}{3} = 6\frac{2 \times 7}{3 \times 7}$$

$$= 6\frac{14}{21}$$

= 6 whole turns and 14 holes in a 21 circle.

(b)   For 15 divisions : Indexing

$$= \frac{40}{15} = 2\frac{10}{15}$$

= 2 whole turns and 10 holes in a 15 circle.

(c)   For 48 divisions : Indexing

$$= \frac{40}{48} = \frac{5}{6} = \frac{5 \times 3}{6 \times 3} = \frac{15}{18}$$

= 15 holes in an 18 circle.

2   Calculate the indexing for the following angles on a workpiece:
(a)   42°   (b)   15°30'   (c)   29°30'
The dividing head ratio is 40:1 and index plates are as in the previous example.

Since 1 turn of the crank rotates the spindle $\frac{1}{40}$ turn, then the work rotates $\frac{1}{40} \times 360° = 9°$. Therefore, turns of crank to give any angle.

$$= \frac{\text{angle required}}{9}$$

Solution

(a)   42° Indexing

$$= \frac{42}{9} = 4\frac{6}{9} \text{ turns of crank}$$

$$= 4\frac{6 \times 3}{9 \times 3} = 4\frac{18}{27}$$

$$= 4 \text{ whole turns and 18 holes in a 27 circle.}$$

(b)   15°30' Indexing $= \frac{15\frac{1}{2}}{9} = 1\frac{6\frac{1}{2}}{9}$

$$= 1\frac{6\frac{1}{2} \times 2}{9 \times 2} = 1\frac{13}{18}$$

$$= 1 \text{ whole turn and 13 holes in an 18 circle.}$$

(c)   29°30' Indexing $= \frac{29\frac{1}{2}}{9} = 3\frac{2\frac{1}{2}}{9}$

$$= 3\frac{2\frac{1}{2} \times 2}{9 \times 2} = 3\frac{5}{18}$$

$$= 3 \text{ complete turns and 5 holes in an 18 circle.}$$

Geometry

Intersecting straight lines
When two straight lines intersect at a point O then the opposite angles are equal: angles A and B.

Two straight lines XX and X_1X_1 are parallel to each other. When a straight line YY cuts the parallel lines then all angles indicated as C are equal. All angles indicated as D are also equal.

Pythagoras' theorem
On any right-angled triangle ABC, a square area can be constructed on each side, i.e. at AB, BC and AC, as illustrated. It is found that: the square, AB × AB = the square, BC × BC + the square, AC × AC.

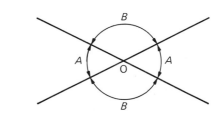

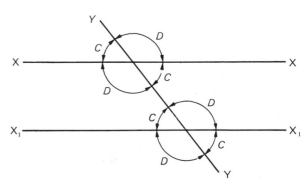

Intersecting straight lines

Pythagoras' theorem states that '*in a right-angled triangle*, *the square on the hypotenuse equals the sum of the squares on the other two sides*'.

Then $AB^2 = BC^2 + AC^2$

The hypotenuse of a right-angled triangle is the side opposite the right angle, i.e. the longest side.

Example

In a right-angled triangle the hypotenuse $AB = 5$ and $BC = 4$, what is the length AC?

$$AB^2 = BC^2 + AC^2$$
$$5^2 = 4^2 + AC^2$$
$$25 = 16 + AC^2$$
$$25 - 16 = AC^2$$
$$9 = AC^2$$

By taking the square root of both sides,

$$AC = 3$$

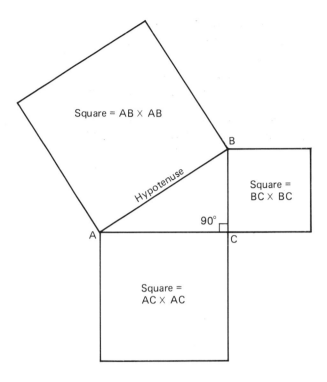

Pythagoras' theorem

Angles

1   An *angle* is an amount of turning.
2   In the circle, when the radius OA turns about the centre O, and returns to its starting position, then OA will have turned through an angle of 360 degrees.
3   Dividing the circle into four equal quadrants, it follows that each

angle at the centre $= \dfrac{360°}{4} = 90°$,

and is called a *right angle*.

The drawings show examples of angles in each of the four quadrants of a circle.

Angle θ_1 is in the first quadrant. This is called an *acute angle*. An acute angle is any angle which is less than $90°$.

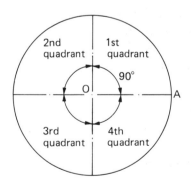

The circle

Angle θ_2 is in the second quadrant and is an *obtuse angle*. An obtuse angle is any angle between 90° and 180°.

Angle θ_3 is in the third quadrant — between 180° and 270°. The fourth angle, θ_4 is in the fourth quadrant and therefore has a value between 270° and 360°.

4 One degree is further divided into 60 minutes and the minute is divided into 60 seconds.

Then   1 degree = 60 minutes
            1 minute = 60 seconds
or stated as   1° = 60′
                1′ = 60″

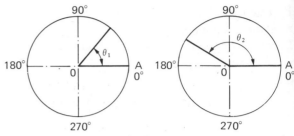

First quadrant — acute angle   Second quadrant — obtuse angle

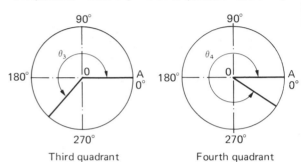

Third quadrant   Fourth quadrant

Angles in the four quadrants of a circle

Properties of a circle
AB = diameter, d.
Radius OA = radius OB = r.
Segment area = area DEC
Sector area = area ODEC

$$= \frac{\theta°}{360°} \times \text{area of the circle}$$

$$= \frac{\theta°}{360°} \times 3.142 \times r^2$$

CD = chord, and CF = FD, because a perpendicular from the apex of the isosceles triangle OCD bisects the base CD.

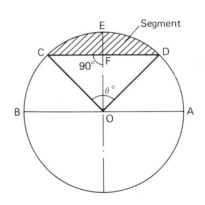

Properties of a circle

Worked example
A circle of 10 mm radius has a sector angle θ of 90°.
Calculate the area of the sector.

$$\text{Area of sector} = \frac{90°}{360°} \times 3.142 \times 10^2$$

$$= 78.55 \text{ mm}^2.$$

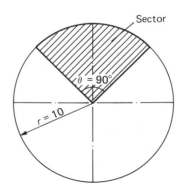

Triangles

1 All the angles of a triangle added together equal 180°.
2 In an *equilateral* triangle:
  (a) All the sides are equal in length.
  (b) All the angles equal each other.

    Therefore each angle is $\dfrac{180°}{3} = 60°$.

3 In an *isosceles* triangle:
  (a) Two angles are equal, $\hat{DFE} = \hat{DEF}$.
  (b) Two sides are equal, $DF = DE$.
  (c) The perpendicular from the apex, DG to baseline FE, bisects this base line, so that $FG = GE$.
  (d) $\hat{FDG} = \hat{EDG}$.
4 For any triangle the area of a triangle
  = half the base × perpendicular height of the triangle.
  = ½ × base × *h*.

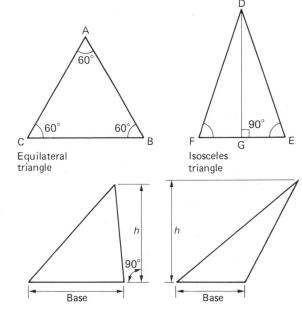

Triangles

Tangents to a circle

From A, two *tangents* AB and AC touch the circle at D and E respectively. By joining O to D and O to E, two *congruent* triangles are formed: triangles AOD and AOE.
$OE = OD$, $AE = AD$, $\hat{OAE} = \hat{OAD}$, $\hat{ODA}$ and $\hat{OEA}$ are right angles.

Intersecting chords

Chords AB and DE intersect at C. Then
$AC \times CB = DC \times CE$.

Practical application
In engineering this relationship of intersecting chords has a practical application. The width of a flat W cut at a given depth h on a circular bar, then $AC = CB = \frac{1}{2}W$

From $AC \times CB = DC \times CE$

$$\frac{1}{2}W \times \frac{1}{2}W = h \times (D - h)$$
$$\frac{1}{4}W^2 = Dh - h^2$$
$$W^2 = 4(Dh - h^2)$$
$$W = \sqrt{[4(Dh - h^2)]}$$

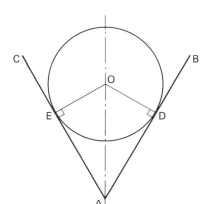

Tangents to a circle

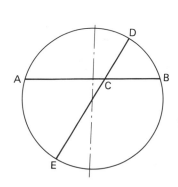

Intersecting chords

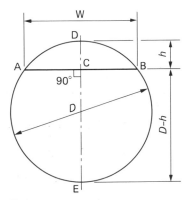

Calculating the width of a milled flat

Sines, cosines and tangents

The sine of the angle BAC equals the side BC divided by the side AB.

Then, sin BAC $= \dfrac{BC}{AB}$

1 Sin BAC $= \dfrac{30}{60} = 0.5$

From a table of *natural sines* the angle stated for sin 0.5 is 30°. Other examples are given in the table. Calculate the answers for **5** and **6** to complete the table.

Cosine of angles
The cosine of the angle BAC equals the side AC divided by the side AB.

Then, cos BAC $= \dfrac{AC}{AB}$

1 Cos BAC $= \dfrac{50}{60} = 0.8333$

From a table of *natural cosines* the angle stated for cos 0.8333 is 35° 35'. Complete the table.

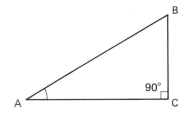

	AC	AB	Ratio $\frac{AC}{AB}$	Angle BAC
1	30	60	$\frac{30}{60} = 0.5$	30°
2	50	70	— =	
3	60	80	— =	
4	60	100	— =	
5	70	95	— =	
6	75	150	— =	
			Cosine of the angle BAC	

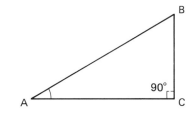

	BC	AB	Ratio $\frac{BC}{AB}$	Angle BAC
1	50	60	$\frac{50}{60} = 0.8333$	35° 35'
2	40	60	$\frac{40}{60} = 0.6666$	41.8°
3	45	65	$\frac{45}{65} = 0.6923$	43.8°
4	55	70	$\frac{55}{70} = 0.7857$	51.8°
5	65	75	=	
6	70	75	=	
			Sine of the angle BAC	

Tangent of angles
The tangent of the angle BAC equals the side BC divided by the side AC.

Then, tan BAC $= \dfrac{BC}{AC}$

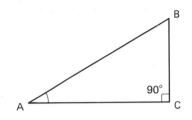

1   Tan BAC $= \dfrac{30}{60} = 0.5$

	BC	AC	Ratio $\dfrac{BA}{AC}$	Angle BAC
1	30	60	$\dfrac{30}{60}$ = 0.5	26° 34′
2	40	55	— =	
3	60	50	— =	
4	80	40	— =	
5	90	40	— =	
6	100	35	— =	
			Tangent of the angle BAC	

From a table of *natural tangents* the angle stated for tan 0.5 is 26° 34′. Complete the table.

Questions

1   The illustrations show intersecting straight lines. State all the angles.
2   The illustration shows the intersection of parallel straight lines. State all the angles.
3   Calculate the hypotenuses of the four right-angled triangles.

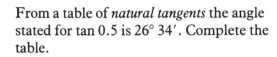

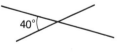

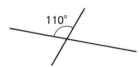

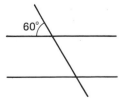

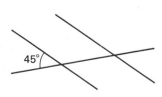

4 Calculate the areas of the triangles in
Question 3.

5 Calculate the lengths of the sides marked
x for the three triangles illustrated.

6 Calculate the areas of the following
equilateral triangles, given that they have
side lengths of: (a) 60 mm (b) 80 mm (c)
100 mm (d) 200 mm (e) 250 mm. The
middle example of Question 5 provides
the clue needed for this question.

7 Complete the table for the *isosceles*
triangle illustrated.

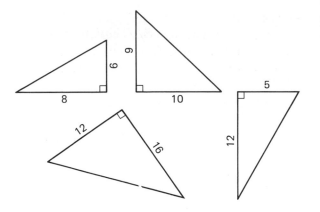

AB	BC	Area	Angle ABC	Angle BAC
60	40			
85	50			
100	60			

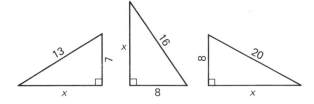

8 A precision roller rests in a vee block.
Calculate the distance *h* (the height of the
vee block).

9 The top of the Ø 34 roller is level with the
top of the vee. What is the width of the
vee?

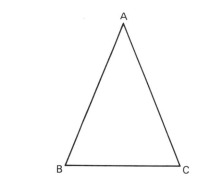

Isosceles triangle

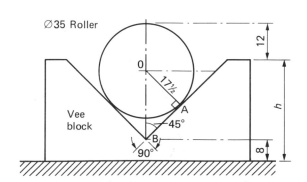

Surface plate

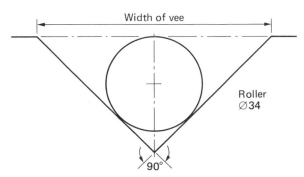

10 What is the distance h from the top of the vee block to the top of the roller?
If another roller of $\varnothing$ 44 is placed in the vee instead of the $\varnothing$ 34 roller what would be the new value of h?

11 Calculate the distances L and x for the roller in a dovetail.

12 Calculate the distance H on the $\varnothing$ 84 shaft and the width of the flat.

13 Calculate the width of the flat W and the height of the segment h.

14 Given that the height milled off the bar is 6 mm, what is the width of the flat W?

15 When two circles touch, the point of contact is on the line joining the two centres. Three rollers are touching each other. Calculate the height H.

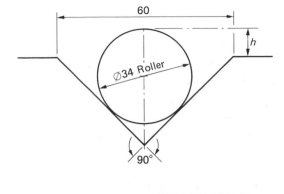

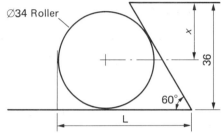

Roller in a dovetail

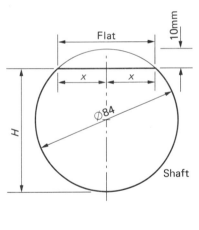

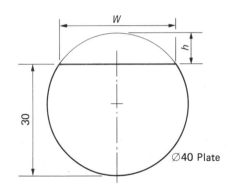

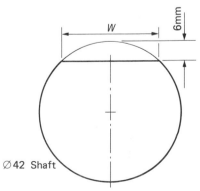

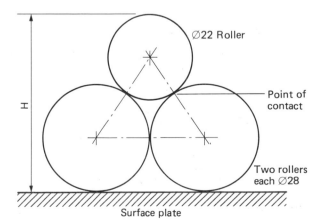

16 Two rollers are located in a machined channel. What is the length W?
17 Find the width *x* of the template.
   Note: remember that when two circles touch at a point, the point and the centres of the two circles are in the same straight line.
18 A 30 radiused template rests vertically on a surface plate. Two ∅ 13 precision rollers are placed as shown. What is the length L over the rollers?
19 Given that AB is 40 mm, what is the area of the removed segment ABC?
20 Calculate the area of the radiused template.

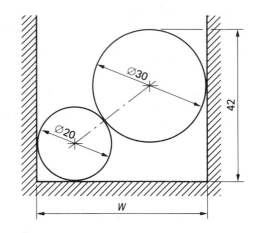

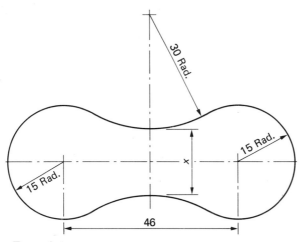

Template

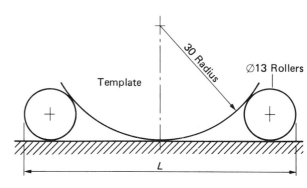

Radiused template

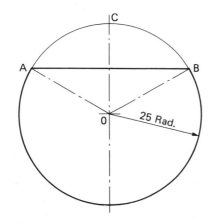

Disc

Radiused template

Co-ordinate positioning on machine tools and marking-out on the surface plate

The drawing shows a template with machined edges OX and OY at 90° to each other. For the dimensions and angles given the 3-hole centres E, F and G have to be marked-out using a vernier height gauge, angle plate and surface plate.

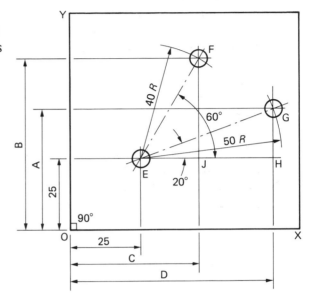

Procedure

1   With the edge OX horizontal, the vertical distances to each of the holes is required. Distance A and B have to be calculated.
2   With the edge OY horizontal, the vertical distances C and D have to be calculated.

Calculations

In the right-angled triangle EGH:

$\sin 20° = \dfrac{GH}{50}$

$\therefore GH = \sin 20 \times 50$

$\quad = 0.3420 \times 50$

$\quad = 17.10 \text{ mm}$

$\cos 20° = \dfrac{EH}{50}$

$\therefore EH = \cos 20 \times 50$

$\quad = 0.9397 \times 50$

$\quad = 46.98 \text{ mm}$

Then A $= 25 + GH = 25 + 17.10$

$\quad\quad\quad\quad\quad\quad = 42.10 \text{ mm}$

$\quad D = 25 + EH = 25 + 46.98$

$\quad\quad\quad\quad\quad\quad = 71.98 \text{ mm}$

In the right-angled triangle EFJ:

$\sin 60° = \dfrac{FJ}{40}$

$\therefore FJ = \sin 60 \times 40$

$\quad = 0.866 \times 40$

$\quad = 34.64 \text{ mm}$

$\cos 60° = \dfrac{EJ}{40}$

$\therefore EJ = \cos 60 \times 40$

$\quad = 0.5 \times 40$

$\quad = 20.00 \text{ mm}$

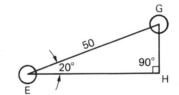

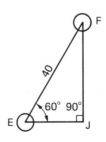

Then B $= 25 + FJ = 25 + 34.64$

$\quad\quad\quad\quad\quad\quad = 59.64 \text{ mm}$

$\quad C = 25 + EJ = 25 + 20 = 45 \text{ mm}$

Hole	Co-ordinate dimensions			
E		25		25
F	C	45.00	B	59.64
G	D	71.98	A	42.10

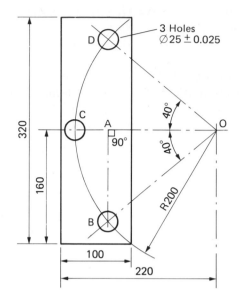

Problem

Three holes have to be bored using a jig boring machine in the 320 × 100 mm plate illustrated. The three hole co-ordinates have to be calculated.

Calculations

In the right angled triangle OAB,

$$\sin 40 = \frac{AB}{200}$$

$$\therefore AB = \sin 40 \times 200$$
$$= 0.6428 \times 200$$
$$= 128.56 \text{ mm}$$

$$\cos 40 = \frac{AO}{200}$$

$$\therefore AO = \cos 40 \times 200$$
$$= 0.766 \times 200$$
$$= 153.20 \text{ mm}$$

$$Y = 160 - AB = 160 - 128.56$$
$$= 31.44 \text{ mm}$$
$$Y_1 = 160 + 128.56$$
$$= 288.56 \text{ mm}$$
$$X = 220 - 200$$
$$= 20.00 \text{ mm}$$
$$X_1 = 220 - AO = 220 - 153.20$$
$$= 66.80 \text{ mm}$$

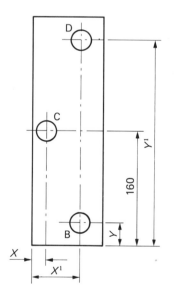

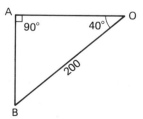

Hole co-ordinate drawing

Table of results

Hole	Co-ordinate dimensions			
B	X_1	66.8	Y	31.44
C	X	20.0		160
D	X_1	66.8	Y_1	288.56

Questions

1   TEMPLATE
The co-ordinate dimensions for the three holes A, B and C are given.
Calculate:
(a)   the centre distance between holes A and C,
(b)   the angle CAB.

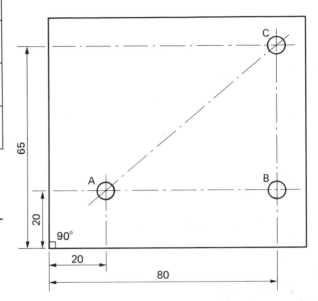

Template

2   SINGLE DOVETAIL SLIDE
Calculate the missing figures for the three different dovetail slides and enter them in the table.

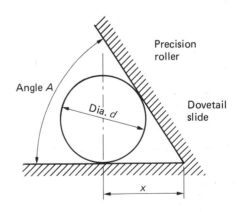

	Angle A	Dia. d	Dimension x
1		30 mm	36.21 mm
2	60°	40 mm	
3	50°		26.8 mm

Single dovetail slide

3   DOUBLE DOVETAIL SLIDE

Calculate the distance L between the two precision 20 mm diameter rollers set in the 45° dovetails.

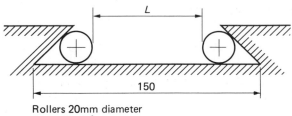

Rollers 20mm diameter
Dovetails 45°

4   DRILL TEMPLATE

Polar co-ordinates for the hole positions shown are given in the table. Complete the table, giving the X and Y co-ordinates for each individual hole.

Note: YBAE represents the Y co-ordinates for holes B, A and E.

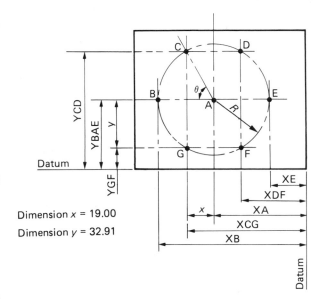

Dimension x = 19.00
Dimension y = 32.91

5   JIG PLATE

Five ∅ 10 holes are to be drilled on centres 1, 2, 3, 4 and 5 as shown. Calculate the hole co-ordinate dimensions for each hole.

Note: (a)   the line to the centre of hole 1 from the centre of the pitch circle diameter is parallel to OY;

   (b)   the five holes are equispaced on the PCD.

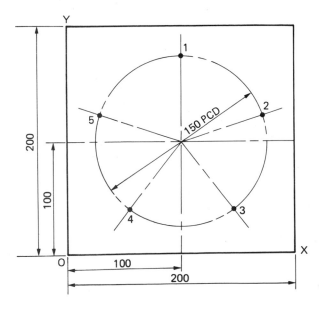

Hole Ref.	Dia.	Co-ordinate dimensions			
		Polar		Cartesian	
		Radius R	Angle θ	X	Y
A	25	0	0°	67	48
B	12	38	0°		
C	12	38	60°		
D	12	38	120°		
E	12	38	180°		
F	12	38	240°		
G	12	38	300°		

Drill template

Jig plate

Straight edges: BS 5204

Steel straight edges of rectangular section

Straight edges are principally used to check flat surfaces, to align a number of articles or to rule accurate straight lines. When a straight edge is used on edge and supported at two points it will deflect under its own mass.

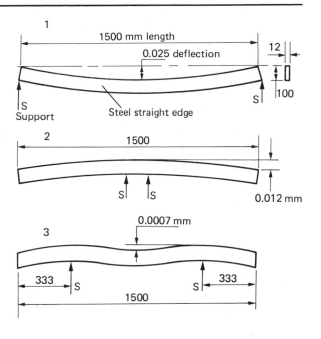

1. When a 1500 mm long straight edge, with a cross section of 12 mm wide × 100 mm deep, has supports at its ends, it will deflect or sag by 0.025 mm in the middle.
2. Placing the supports near the middle will cause the ends to sag by 0.012 mm.
3. Placing the supports at points ⅖ × length from either end has the effect of obtaining the minimum deflection of 0.0007 mm.

    ⅖ × 1500 mm = 333 mm.

    Sizes of straight edges range from 300 mm to 2000 mm in length and sections from 5 mm × 30 mm to 13 mm × 125 mm.

Cast iron bow-shaped straight edges

Sizes are from a length of 300 mm and depth of 80 mm to a length of 8000 mm and depth of 800 mm.

Due to the width of their working surface, bow-shaped straight edges are used for 'bedding-in' — for example, lathe beds.

Prussian blue is first of all smeared over the bed and then the working surface is lowered onto the bed. The straight edge is moved in a small circle and then lifted off. The high spots will appear bright, and will then need to be scraped.

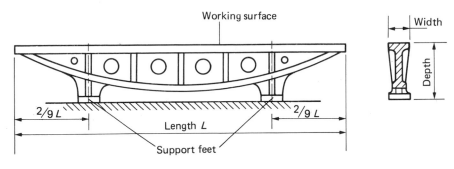

Bow shaped straight edge — material: cast iron

Cast iron I-section straight edge

Sizes range from a length of 300 mm × 75 mm depth to 5000 mm × 350 mm. Above 1500 mm in length this cast iron I-section takes over from the steel straight edge although its uses are the same.

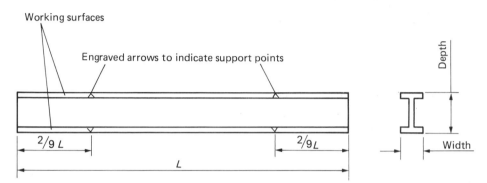

Cast iron I-section straight edge

Questions

1 Complete the table for the various given lengths of steel straight edges in mm.

2 The horizontal slide on a bed of a lathe was tested for flatness using slip gauges and a steel straight edge. The straight edge of length 1000 mm was supported by two slip gauges (L and R) at the correct support positions. Slip gauge readings were taken at positions 2, 3, 4 and 5. The results are as shown. Complete the table (a) assuming that the bed slide was perfectly flat and (b) draw a graph of slip gauge positions against actual slip gauge dimensions.

Slip gauge position	1	2	3	4	5	6
Actual slip gauge dimension	11.01	11.035	11.045	11.073	11.094	11.11
Dimension for a flat surface	11.01					11.11

Length of straight edge	300	500	1000	1500	2000
Distance of each support from the ends					
Support centre distance					

3 Work holding

Objectives

(a) The student will appreciate the necessity to locate a piece of work, so that when it is machined it will be firmly and efficiently held.

(b) The student will be able to decide on the most efficient method to locate and hold a piece of work.

(c) The student will understand the need for, and the method used, to balance an 'out-of-balance' force on a rotating workpiece.

(d) The student should be able to understand the principles and the applications of mechanical, hydraulic, pneumatic and electromagnetic holding and locating set-ups.

Six degrees of freedom

When machining, the work must be held firmly to prevent movement. The six possible directions of movement are called the *six degrees of freedom* and are illustrated in the diagram.

1 Vertical movement.
2 Horizontal movement.
3 Horizontal movement at right-angles to 2.
4 Twisting about the horizontal axis.
5 Twisting about the horizontal axis at right-angles to 4.
6 Twisting about the vertical axis.

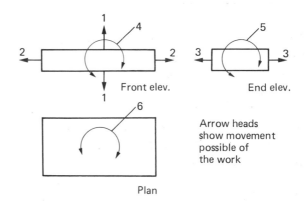

Prevention of movement

The methods used to prevent movement are:
1 Solid stop.
2 Frictional resistance.

Solid stop

The figure shows the work being fed onto a milling cutter. The force of the cutter teeth pushing the work against the *solid stop*, which is the vice jaw, prevents movement.

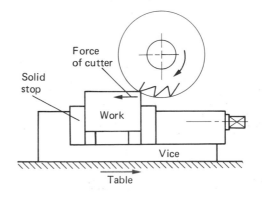

Frictional resistance

The work is held in the vice, which has been turned through 90° from the set-up for the solid stop. The force of the cutter when machining tends to slide the work out of the vice. However, the *frictional resistance* of the jaws onto the work acts in the opposite direction.

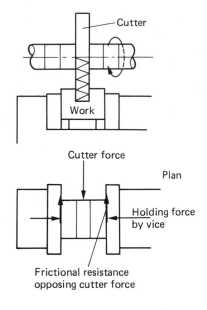

Force

A force is that which moves, or tends to move, the object to which it is applied. Thus, if a cutting tool is applied to a workpiece, it exerts a force which will tend to move the workpiece. In order that this shall not happen, the workpiece is clamped onto the machine bed. The clamp increases the *frictional resistance* between the workpiece and the bed surface, so that the 'pushing' force exerted by the tool is insufficient to overcome this friction; and the work therefore remains rigid.

Clamps are normally bolted onto the machine surface using T-bolts. Tightening the nut on the bolt involves a *torsional* or twisting force, provided by a spanner. It is common experience that if one has two spanners, one long and one short, one can, by *exerting the same force*, tighten the nut more with the longer spanner than with the shorter one.

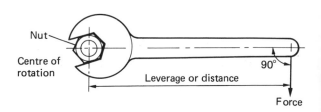

Spanner

Thus in this case, what matters is not just force but *torque*, which is (force × distance). *Force × distance* is also called the *moment* of the force. When several forces act on a body they will tend to move it. If it is pivoted at a point, the movement will be a 'twisting' one around the point. For the body to remain at rest, two conditions must be satisfied:

1 The resultant (or sum) of the forces must be zero.
2 The sum of the moments tending to cause clockwise motion must equal the sum of the moments tending to cause anticlockwise motion.

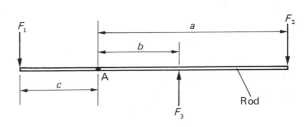

Thus, assume a rod of negligible weight is pivoted at point A. Forces F_1, F_2, F_3 are applied as shown, at distances c, a and b respectively from A.

For the rod to remain at rest: the *resultant* forces must be zero; that is, the downward forces must equal the upward forces;

$$\therefore F_1 + F_2 = F_3$$

Force F_2 will tend to turn the rod clockwise about A. Its clockwise moment about A is ($F_2 \times a$). Both F_1 and F_3 will tend to turn the rod anticlockwise about A. Their moments about A are respectively ($F_1 \times c$) and ($F_3 \times b$). So, for equilibrium:

$$(F_2 \times a) = (F_1 \times c) + (F_3 \times b)$$

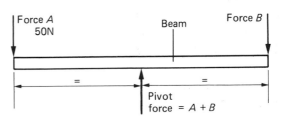

Parallel forces on a beam
In the first example, for the beam to be at rest then force A + force B = 100 N. Force A = 50 N, therefore force B = 50 N.

Force A must be greater than force B when the pivot support is moved nearer to A, see the second example.

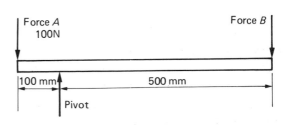

Take moments about the pivot:

Clockwise moments = anticlockwise moments

$$100 \text{ N} \times 100 \text{ mm} \quad \text{Force } B \times 500 \text{ mm}$$
$$10\,000 = \text{Force } B \times 500$$
$$\frac{10\,000}{500} = \text{Force } B$$
$$20 \text{ N} = \text{Force } B$$

Note: when taking moments, all distances must be measured at right-angles to the line of action of the force. Thus, in the diagram, whilst the anticlockwise moment about X is

$(F_1 \times a)$, the clockwise moment is *not* $(F_2 \times b)$, but $(F_2 \times c)$, where c is the perpendicular distance from X to the line of action of F_2.

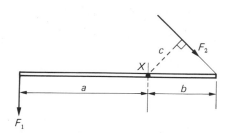

Clamping

If the work does not have parallel sides or has rough sides, is too big or is an unsuitable shape for holding in a vice, then clamps are used.

Tee slots are needed and are found on a great number of machine tools. The work is prevented from moving by frictional resistance between the underside of the clamp on the work and the table surface and the underside of the work.

For an efficient clamping set-up the following are necessary:
1 All mating surfaces should be clean and clear of swarf, dirt, oil, etc.
2 The packing piece should be the same height as the work.
3 The clamp should be larger in section at the bolt hole in order to resist permanent bending of the clamp due to the 'pulling down' of the nut.
4 All the area C of the clamp should be in contact with the job. No daylight should be seen when looking along the surface of the job.
5 The distance A must be much less than B. This results in a much bigger amount of the downward force due to tightening the nut to act on the work.

Holding work for drilling
Use of parallel strips
With the workpiece set up on parallel strips the drill can cut through the work without damaging the table.

Use of vee blocks and step block
The workpiece can now be drilled so that the drilled hole is on the vertical centre line of the work cross-section.

Use of an angle plate
The work is held by an angle plate, which is bolted to the drill table, and a C-clamp. The work could also be held with another C-clamp on the other end of the angle bracket.

Screw lever clamp
These clamps are constructed of thick gauge steel-plate, with screw handles and pivot pins. They could be used in the above set-up in place of C-clamps. The screw handles and the lever system produce a very large clamping force.

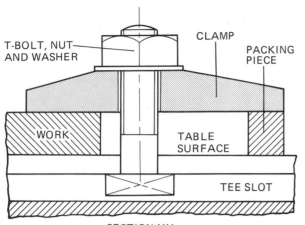

SECTION XX

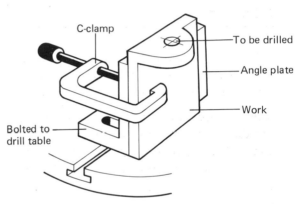

Use of vee blocks and step block

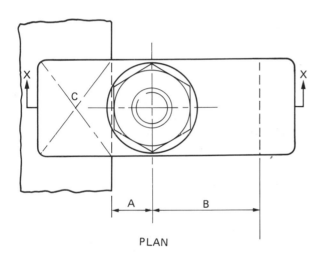

PLAN

Clamping of work to a machine table

Use of angle plate

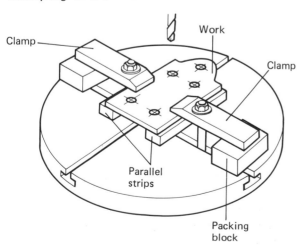

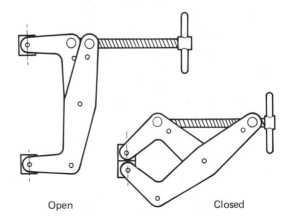

Open   Closed

Screw lever clamp

Holding work for drilling — use of parallel strips

Collet chucks

A collet is a type of chuck. It is tightened by being drawn into a tapered socket in the spindle nose by a draw tube which bears against the back end of the spindle.

They are used on centre lathes, vertical milling machines, jig borers, grinding machines and capstan and turret lathes.

Collet chucks have the following features:
1   They can be designed and made to suit various cross-sections of bar stocks.
2   Cross-sections of bar can be round, square or hexagonal.
3   They can be used for second operation works on small diameter components.
4   A collet is made of steel, having three or four equally spaced slots running for the greater part of its length.
5   The nose of the collet has an external taper which engages with a similar taper on the nose of the spindle.
6   The bore is made to suit the bar stock.
7   Following heat treatment, all necessary surfaces are ground to a great degree of accuracy.
8   When the bar stock or component is located in the collet, a force is applied to the taper on the nose of the collet. Due to the slots in the collet, the nose closes and grips the bar stock or component.

Types of collet chuck in use:
1   Draw-back collet
2   Push-out collet
3   Dead length collet
4   Master collets using inserts
5   Loose pads

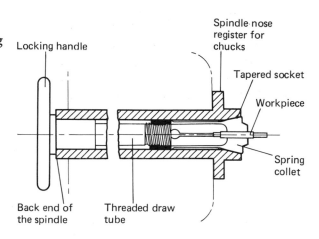

Collet chuck assembly

Draw-back collet

The procedure is to screw the nose cap tightly into the spindle and slide in the collet. The thrust tube is then fed in from the other end of the spindle and it is screwed onto the draw-back collet. The bar is then fed through the spindle and the collet until the correct length projects beyond the collet face. Turning the thrust tube pulls the collet into the nose cap and the collet closes. The main disadvantage of this collet is that the bar moves back slightly when the jaws grip.

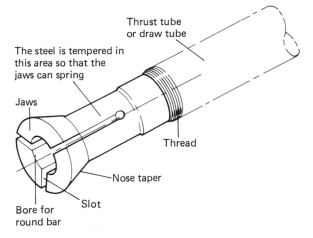

Draw-back collet

Push-out collet

With the nose cap removed the required collet is placed in the spindle bore. The nose cap is then screwed onto the spindle and locked. The bar is fed through the machine spindle thrust tube and collet up to the set length bar stop. To close the collet the thrust tube is pushed as indicated. The taper on the nose of the collet slides in contact with its mating taper on the nose cap, causing the collet to grip the bar. Closing the collet causes the bar to be pushed forward hard against the bar stop.

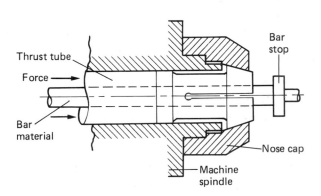

Push-out collet set-up

Dead length collet

This collet operates in a similar way to a push-out collet, except that the thrust tube pushes a sleeve onto the collet jaws. The main advantage is that there is no axial movement on the component; therefore, it is used a great deal for second operation on a component where exact location is important.

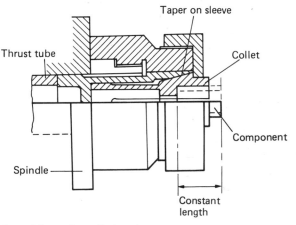

Dead length collet set-up

Master collets using inserts

These collets can be the draw-back or push-out types with replaceable jaws. For a particular type of collet various sets of inserts can be accurately located and held by locking screws. For example, the inserts can be for (a) a range of diameters, or (b) a range of hexagonal sizes.

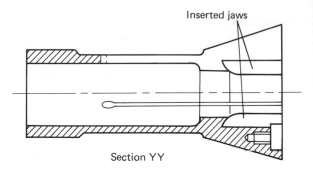

Section YY

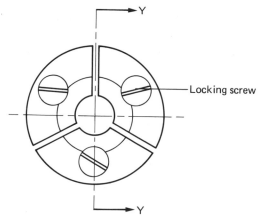

Master collet using inserts

Loose pads

This type of collet is used for holding black bar, the cross-section of which is not a perfect circle. The four pads 'nest' inside the collet and are held there by the expansion force in the springs. In practice, as the collet jaws close, the pads are able to align themselves independently of each other.

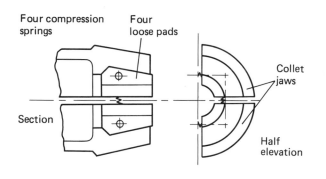

Collet with loose pads

Swing eye-bolt and knurled nut clamp

A box jig is a piece of equipment which is box-like in construction and has a removable lid. It is used, for example, to locate a channel component inside the box. By closing the lid and clamping it down a hole can be drilled using the bush.

The advantages of a box jig are:
1   The hole centre is automatically located for drilling.
2   The box can be used by unskilled labour.
3   The time taken is much less than by marking-out and drilling in the normal way.

To unload the box jig, the knurled nut is slackened off so that the eye-bolt swings clockwise off the latch plate. The latch plate is then rotated anticlockwise about its hinge pin, to give access to the component in the box.

Cam clamp
An alternative to the above arrangement is the cam clamp. It has the advantage of quick operation. A turnbuckle is used to obtain the correct clamping action on the component. One part of the eye-bolt is a right-hand thread whilst the other is left-hand.

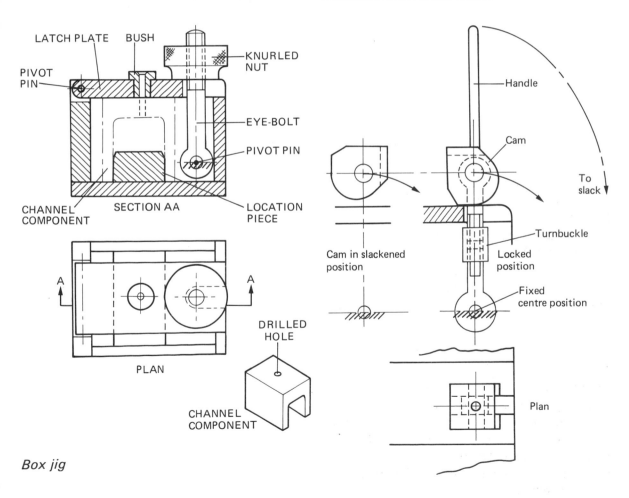

Box jig

Quick acting toggle clamps

These clamps are constructed of thick-gauge sheet metal, pins, studs and pressure pads. An easily applied hand force on the handle produces a very big clamping force.

The diagram shows the clamp in a slightly raised position. Clockwise movement of the handle will raise the stud higher.

To clamp a job the handle is moved to its vertical position and immediately pivot B passes through the line between pivots A and C maximum load is on the work and the linkages lock.

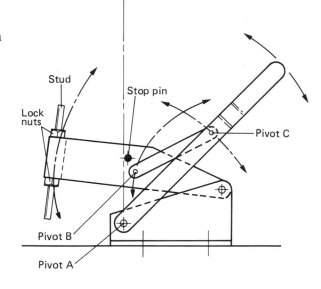

The clamp with the plunger in its maximum off position is also shown. Moving the handle anticlockwise causes the plunger to move to the left. When pivot pin B passes below line AC maximum load is applied on the work and the linkages lock.

The diagram shows the clamp in its locked position. Lifting the handle releases the clamp and the stud moves clockwise as shown.

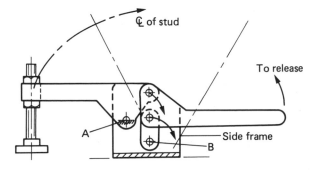

A and B are pivot pins located in the 2 side frames

Elevation with one side frame removed

Questions

1 What advantage has the T-head bolt over the square-head bolt?
2 What are the advantages and disadvantages of using a step block when clamping work?
3 What components would you clamp using the pin or the U-clamp?
4 Different lengths of stud can be screwed into a tapped head. What is the advantage of this method when compared with using the square-head bolt?
5 The drawings show various clamping set-ups. State whether each set-up is a correct or incorrect method of clamping.

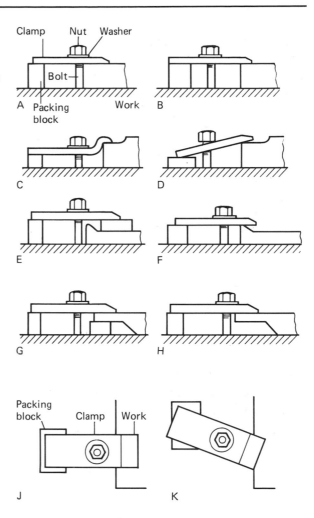

Right and wrong clamping

Pneumatic (air) chucks

The drawing shows a pneumatic toggle chuck. The toggle linkage provides a radial clamping force at the jaw. The push rod operates the toggle by pneumatic pressure. Pneumatic chucks have the following features:

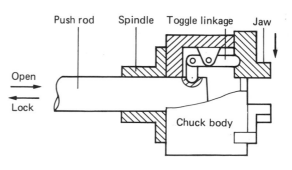

Pneumatic toggle chuck

1 Used for production work.
2 Compressed air provides the clamping force.
3 The push rod obtains its force due to compressed air acting on a piston in a cylinder.
4 Easy to load the work.
5 Easy to unload.
6 Fast in operation.
7 Saves time.
8 Position of jaws can be varied mechanically.
9 For accurate work holding, some machining of the jaws may be necessary — hence the use of soft jaws.
10 If the supply of compressed air fails, then the work is still held in complete safety due to the mechanical locking of the toggle linkages.

Diaphragm chucks

The drawings show the operation of a diaphragm chuck.
1 When the push rod is retracted the diaphragm (a large spring washer) causes the jaws to grip the work.
2 The movement of the push rod distorts the diaphragm spring which opens the jaws to release the work.

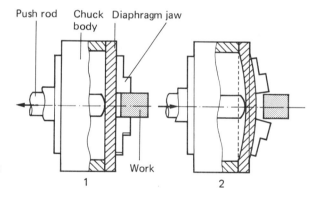

From the above 1 to 9 apply.

The diaphragm automatically returns to its flat state and locks the work mechanically. Failure of the compressed air results in the work still being held in safety.

Simple lever clamp and toggle clamp

(a) To clamp work 1 to 7 and 10 in the above apply.
(b) Adjustment due to different thicknesses of work can be made using the clamp adjusting screw.

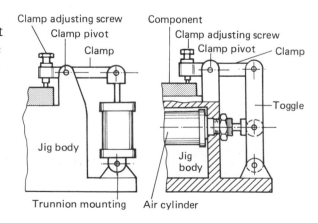

Simple lever clamp and toggle clamp

Power jacks

A number of correctly positioned power jacks enables one to clamp components or sub-assemblies very quickly and efficiently. Further processes can then be carried out on them. Power jacks are used to clamp work in jigs for welding, riveting, forming, drilling and milling, as well as machining processes for 'one off' components.

Swing clamp

With the jack bolted down, the clamp can be operated pneumatically (air supply) or hydraulically (oil supply). Pressure is fed through the pressure connection point by a pressure pipe to act on a piston. The piston pushes the rod and the arm rocks about the pivot to apply a clamping force on the adjustable head, so clamping the work.

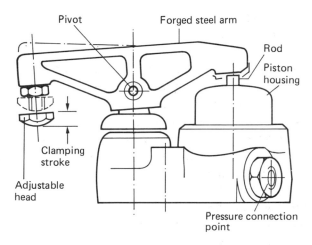

Advantages
1 No manual operation.
2 Fully automatic.
3 Saves time.
4 Very useful and effective on production work.
5 Can be mounted so that clamping is horizontal.
6 A number of clamps can be used to act at the same time.

Air operated machine vice

An air line connected to port A passes in air under pressure, which then acts on the full piston area. To release the work a valve handle in the pressure line is moved to admit air under pressure into port B. Air pressure now acts on the rod area of the piston. Air in the cylinder is exhausted out via port A.

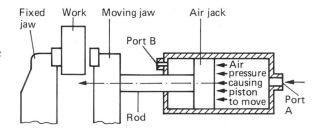

Hydraulically operated shaper machine
Shaping machines operated by a hydraulic ram
have the advantage that both their cutting
speeds and feeds are infinitely variable. High
range models have cutting speeds of up to 40
m per minute. The ram is connected directly
to the piston of a hydraulic cylinder. The
length and position of the stroke is set by dogs
attached to the ram. A further advantage of the
hydraulic shaper is that the cutting speed can
be kept reasonably constant throughout the
stroke, thus giving a better finish and avoiding
ripple marks which can be difficult to avoid
with gear drive machines — particularly for
long strokes. Hydraulic shapers are expensive
and are therefore used in the tool room and for
jobs which require a good finish.

The drawing shows the operation of a shaper
machine. The pump delivers oil under pressure through the slide valve to the full diameter
of the piston, thus moving the ram to the
right. Oil, not under pressure, is returned to
the tank. When the slide valve is moved to the
right, see dotted position on drawing, oil
under pressure operates on the rod area of the
piston. This action moves the ram to the left.
Thus the position of the ram can be controlled
by operation of the slide valve. The dotted
arrows show the oil paths when the slide valve
is moved to the right-hand position.

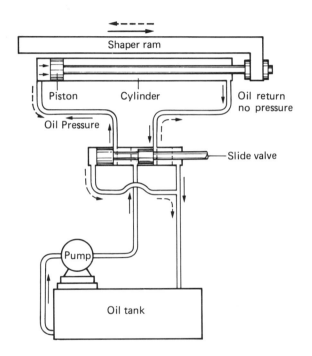

Question

Hydraulically operated work-holding device
The diagram shows an arrangement similar to
the hydraulically operated machine table, but
this time operating a work holding device. The
movable jaw is required to move in the
direction of arrow W.

Show the direction of oil flow between parts A, B, C, D, E, F and G by copying and then completing the drawing.

Note: the position of the control valve bobbin is not necessarily correct.

Assuming that losses within the system are negligible calculate, using the principle of moments, the clamping force exerted at the movable jaw when the oil pressure at the piston gives a total force of 100 N.

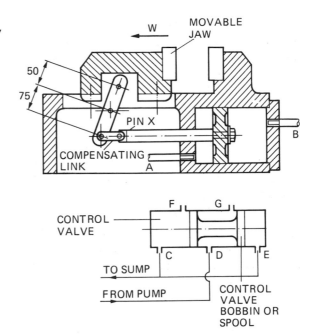

Bar magnet

If a bar magnet is allowed to swing freely in a horizontal plane it will take up a position such that one end points towards the Earth's magnetic north pole. This end is usually marked with the letter N and the other S.

If a thin sheet of cardboard is placed on the magnet and sprinkled with iron filings, the filings will arrange themselves into a pattern when the card is tapped. The lines are similar to the ones illustrated. They are called lines of magnetic *field* or *flux*. The region around the magnet is called the magnetic field. The direction of the magnetic field is convention-ally regarded as being from the north magnetic pole to the south magnetic pole.

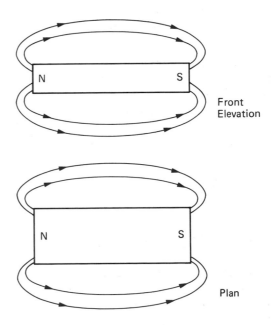

Similarly, if iron filings are placed on a piece of card through which passes a wire carrying an electric current a magnetic field is produced and the filings show a pattern. The lines of flux are circular.

When a current passes through a *circular loop* of wire the magnetic field is as shown.

With a long coil of small diameter the distribution of the magnetic field established when current flows in the coil is somewhat similar to that obtained with a bar magnet. By placing a core made of iron inside the coil a *solenoid* is produced. With the current flowing, the core becomes *magnetised* and when the current is switched off it is demagnetised. In industry this property is used in operating mechanisms, e.g. car starter motor, brake systems on machines and cranes used to lift ferrous metals.

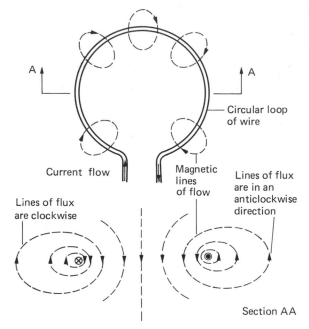

x Denotes current flowing away from the reader

● Denotes current flowing towards the reader

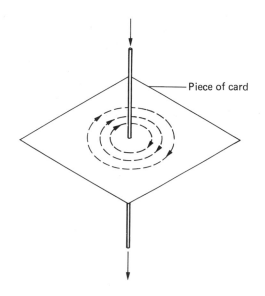

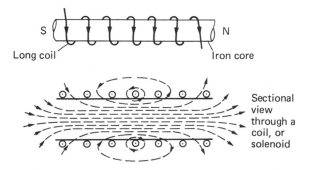

Three types of electromagnet

Horseshoe magnet
One useful form of solenoid consists of a U-shaped yoke of iron, with a coil wound around its 'limbs' as shown. With the current flowing in the direction shown, the electromagnet behaves as though N and S poles existed as indicated. If the direction of the current is reversed then the polarity of the magnet is also reversed.

The strength of attraction of the magnet, for the separate piece of iron or steel depends on the
1 Size of current
2 Number of turns
3 Metal of the limbs
4 Cross-sectional area of the limbs

For a divided magnetic path the single coil is wound on the central limb.

By suitable designing of the coils and yokes, and by using fairly high currents, very strong magnetic forces can be generated. These forces can be sufficient, for example, to hold work-pieces firmly on machines. Electromagnets are used for lifting metals, and for magnetic chucks on surface grinding machines.

Electromagnetic chuck
This must be supplied from a direct current (DC) supply. It can be circular or rectangular surface shape, up to a size of about 2 metres.

While such chucks are very useful, they have the disadvantage of requiring an electrical supply, which permanent magnet chucks do not.

The permanent magnet chuck
Special alloy steels used for permanent magnets have the property of taking a high state of magnetism and retaining it for a long time.

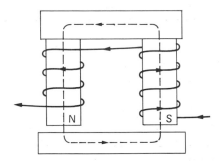
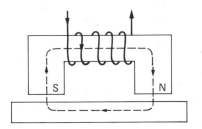
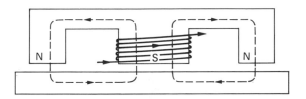

Three types of electro-magnets

They can be used in permanent magnet chucks. Because such a chuck is self-contained, it is portable and can be set up on any machine if required. There is no limit to its size.

The working face of a permanent magnet chuck is made of non-metallic alloy in which steel inserts are fitted to line up with the pole faces of the magnet. Movement of the handle causes the magnets to move sideways so that in the 'ON' position the pole pieces are in line with the inserts and the magnetic flux passes through the work. In the 'OFF' position the inserts are each in contact with the two poles of the magnets and the flux is effectively shorted out. Therefore, no flux passes through the work and so it can be removed.

Demagnetisation

Metals that have been on a magnetic chuck do retain some magnetism. To remove the magnetism they are placed on an electromagnet energised by an alternating current (AC).

Magnetic base

This is a frequently used and useful piece of equipment in the machine shop. The base and sides of the ends are ground to an accurate finish. The base is shown with the button in the 'out' position and it is then magnetised. By pressing the button in, demagnetisation occurs and the base can be removed.

This unit can be readily located on any ferrous surface and provides a rigid support to the pillar. A dial test indicator can be clamped to the pillar, or clear perspex safety guards.

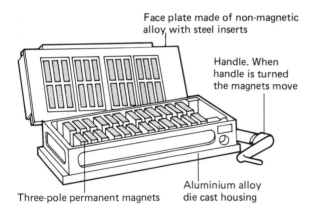

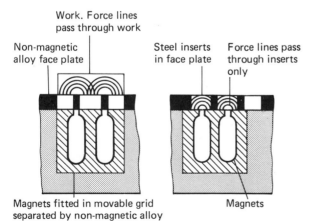

The permanent magnet chuck

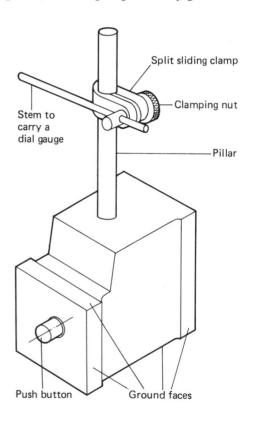

Magnetic base

Out of balance forces

Lathework

1 When an operation such as turning or boring on a lathe is being carried out on a mass of work, whose centre of mass or centre of gravity is not on the axis of the spindle, then the lathe is subjected to *out of balance forces*.
2 The forces or loads on the headstock fluctuate with every revolution.
3 Hammering of the bearings results. Vibrations are set up in the machine and damage and a threat to safety could result.
4 Holes in the work would be elliptical.
5 Surface finish would be very poor. Vibration of the turning tool or boring tool would produce patterns.
6 Excessive, annoying noise would be set up by the tools.

Note: By running the lathe as slow as the operation permits, the effect of the *centrifugal* force is reduced.

Static balancing

This is a method of balancing which is used when the work is *static*, i.e. at rest.

1 If the workpiece has a mass m, and its centre of gravity is at a distance r from the centre of rotation, then another mass M must be bolted on the same diameter.

Clearly, for balance, taking moments about 0:

$$(m \times r) = (M \times R)$$

But in practice, experience usually determines what size M shall be and how far from 0 it should be positioned. Then adjustments are made until smooth running is achieved.

2 If the workpiece shape is such that procedure **1** cannot be carried out, then two masses m_1 and m_2 can be used to achieve balance.

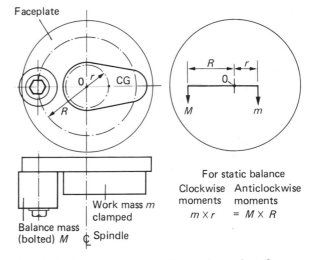

For static balance

Clockwise moments	Anticlockwise moments
$m \times r$	$= M \times R$

Static balancing — hole to be bored at 0

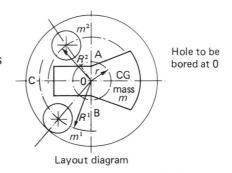

Layout diagram

Static balancing of three masses

Retaining nuts

Machines are always subjected to vibration due to:

1 Out of balance forces
2 Engagement and disengagement of gears
3 Movement of belts
4 Shock loads and loading on moving parts
5 Explosions in engines, caused by very great pressures exerted for a short time on pistons in cylinders
6 Oil pressures in pipe lines
7 Oscillatory mechanisms

Nuts which are used to secure parts such as gears, ball and roller bearings, clutches, lead screws, handles etc. have to secure them on their shafts. They are called *retaining nuts*.

To withstand vibrations which could result in the nut slackening off a selection of methods are used to lock the nut. These are illustrated.

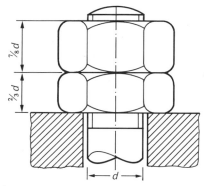

Lock nuts

Lock nuts
The thin nut is tightened up, then the thick nut is tightened against the thin nut, a spanner on each acting against the other.

Sawn nut
A saw cut is made on one side of the nut. If the nut is then struck by a hammer blow the slot will close up. This causes part of the thread to be deformed and lock the nut onto the thread.

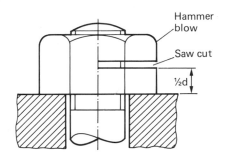

Sawn nuts

Plain nut and taper pin
When tightened up, a hole is drilled through the nut and bolt. A pin is then pushed through and the split is opened out to hold it in position.

Simmonds nut
The nylon insert locks on to the thread as shown in the diagram.

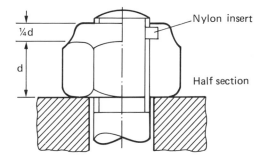

Simmonds nut

Keys and keyways

Keys are pieces of steel which are used to provide a temporary fastening. They are inserted between two parts to prevent a relative turning movement, as would be the case with a wheel and shaft. The grooves cut in the shaft or mating part are called *keyways*.

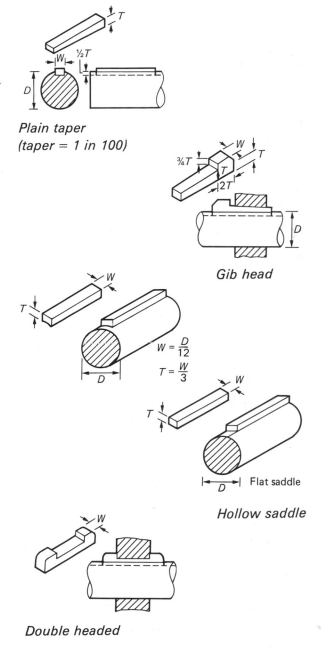

Plain taper
(taper = 1 in 100)

Gib head

Plain taper key
This type may be either square or rectangular in section and is sunk into the shaft for half its thickness. Plain taper keys are normally used where the fixing is more or less permanent.

Gib head key
It is specially designed so that it can be easily extracted and is useful where parts have to be separated occasionally for repairs.

Saddle keys: hollow saddle and flat saddle
They are only suitable for very light loads since they rely on the friction between the shaft and key. The flat saddle key transmits greater power than the hollow saddle key.

Double headed key
The heads prevent any axial movement in the hub.

Dovetailed key
The dovetailed portion fits into the hub and the lower part into a groove in the shaft.

$$W = \frac{D}{12}$$

$$T = \frac{W}{3}$$

Flat saddle

Hollow saddle

Double headed

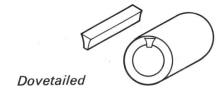

Dovetailed

Round or pin key

This type is only suitable for low-power transmission.

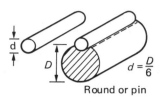

Round or pin

Woodruff key

It is a segment of a disc fitting into a corresponding slot cut in the shaft. This form of key is used for gear wheel drives and machine tools.

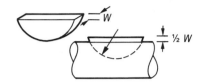

Woodruff

Feather key

It has parallel top and bottom faces. This type allows a pulley to move freely in an axial direction but at the same time prevents it turning without the shaft.

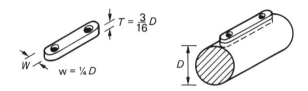

Feather key

Splined shafts

These consist of shafts which have one or more grooves, called *splines*, cut along their length. The shafts are named after the number of splines: single-spline shaft, four-splined shaft etc. The sliding piece, which may be a hub, wheel, lever or gear wheel, allows for free axial movement as well as a positive drive to be obtained.

Spline shafts are commonly found in the gear boxes of machine tools and motor vehicles.

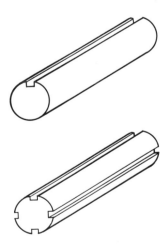

Single and four splined shafts

Tenons and drawbolts

Tenons are precision made steel blocks complete with a counterbored hole. The tenons locate accurately in machined slots in the machine spindle of a horizontal milling machine. They are then secured by socket-head cap screws.

When the arbor is assembled into the machine spindle the two recesses in the flange fit over the tenons. The *draw-in bolt* is slid into the hole in the spindle. The bolt's thread engages with the tapped hole in the tapered end of the arbor. Using the lock nut the arbor is then positioned tightly in the tapered hole in the spindle.

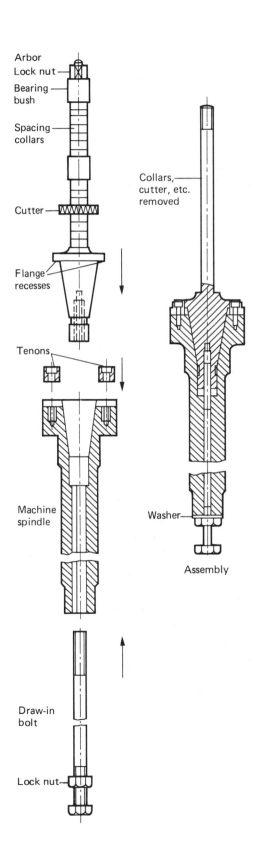

Arbor
Lock nut
Bearing bush
Spacing collars
Cutter
Flange recesses
Tenons
Machine spindle
Draw-in bolt
Lock nut

Collars, cutter, etc. removed
Washer
Assembly

Dowels

Dowels are pins, usually cylindrical in shape, which correctly position two parts relative to each other by passing through suitably located holes.

The functions and characteristics of dowels can be summarised in the following way:
1   They are accurately ground, both cylindrically and parallel.
2   Often made from silver steel, which is supplied in lengths of high-carbon 0.9% steel. There is no silver in the metal. It has a highly polished mirror surface, due to centreless grinding, which has caused it to be called 'silver'.
3   A push fit in assembled parts.
4   Dowels should be spaced as far as possible to give the greatest accuracy in re-assembling parts in-line.
5   Two in number.
6   Used with socket-head cap screws, studs or bolts which clamp the parts together, temporary fastening system.
7   Removed with a pin punch.

Examples of the effective use of dowels can be seen in the pierce and blank tool and a shaper steady.

Pierce and blank tool

This tool is used to produce washers. It consists of three main parts: the stripper plate, die plate and bolster. The stripper plate has clearance holes for the screws and punches. The die plate has clearance hole for the screws and accurate die shape whilst the bolster has tapped holes for screws and clearance for blanks.

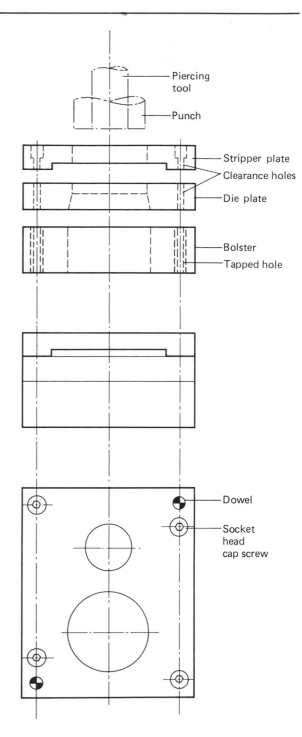

Pierce and blank tool

The three parts are accurately lined up and
held tightly by the cap screws. Finally, two
dowel holes are drilled and reamed through
the assembly. The dowels are then pushed into
place.

When the die has to be surface-ground the tool
can be taken apart and re-assembled accurately
due to the dowels.

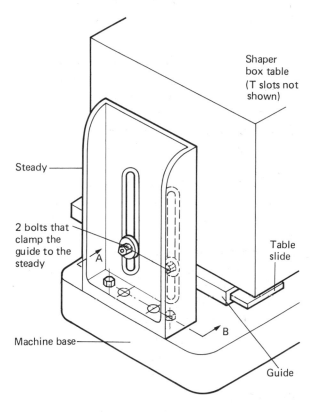

Shaper steady
Two dowels are fitted into the steady and
machine base to guarantee alignment of the
horizontal guide for the table. Two bolts are
used to clamp the steady to the base.

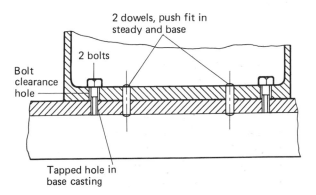

Shaper steady

Location of components

When working on press tools, router machines, drill jigs, welding jigs, inspection fixtures, etc. it is necessary to position or locate the components before further machining processes can be carried out.

The taper on a pin serves as a lead into a hole in thin components. The component is lowered and located onto the bottom of the head.

For very large holes, the head is milled to form two flats. It is then easier to locate and remove the component.

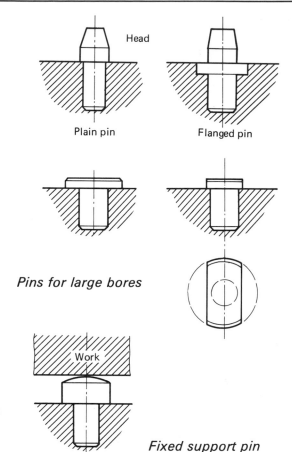

Plain pin   Flanged pin

Pins for large bores

Fixed support pin

1 A fixed *support pin* or pins are used to locate components which have a rough surface.
2 A number of these pins may be set to form a shape in an inspection fixture. The component is located against the side of the heads.

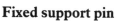

Fixed support pin

Bottle jacks

Bottle jacks and adjustable supports are used when a component which is to be machined requires support against deflection.

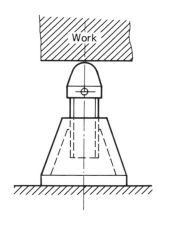

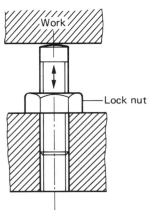

Bottle jack   *Adjustable supports*

Jigs and fixtures

Jigs
A jig is a device which holds a component during a machining operation. It also provides guides for cutting tools, so that a desired feature can be accurately machined into the correct position on a large number of successive components.

It is not usual to clamp a jig to a table.

Fixtures
A fixture is a component-holding device which is clamped to a table. There are no tool guides. Fixtures are used mainly for milling, but also for grinding, turning and broaching to a lesser extent. Skill is required to set the cutter relative to the fixture.

Design principles
1 Loading and unloading procedure to be quick, easy and safe.
2 Efficient method of clamping the component.
3 The mass of the jig and fixture should be kept as low as possible, but still be rigid in construction.
4 No sharp corners.
5 Hard wearing surfaces on guides and locating faces.
6 Adequate room for swarf.
7 Cost.

Advantages of using a jig or fixture
1 Eliminates marking-out each component.
2 All machined surfaces will be accurately placed.
3 Interchangeability of components.
4 High production.
5 They can accommodate odd shaped components.
6 Semi-skilled or unskilled operators can be used.

Tee-bolt milling fixture

A large number of machined *cheese-headed bolts* are required to have their heads machined by milling, so that T-holding-down bolts are produced.

Particulars of the milling fixture to be used
The *fabricated base* has all the faces marked and machined. The two *slides* retain the *vee locating piece* and permit the *sliding piece* to move in the horizontal direction only. A *clamp* and *stud* with a washer complete the fixture.

The setting-up procedure is as follows:
1 The fixture is accurately set, with its centre line at right-angles to the arbor axis, on a horizontal milling machine and bolted down.
2 With two side and face milling cutters, set to the distance W (the finished size for the bolt head), the setting piece on the fixture base is set symmetrically, between the cutters, with feeler gauges.

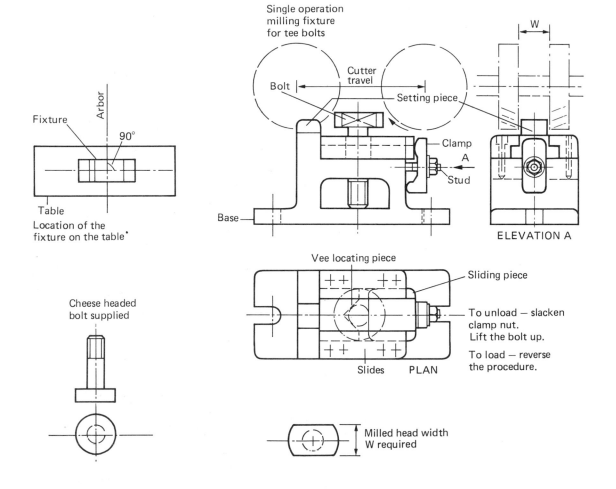

Location of the fixture on the table

Single operation milling fixture for tee bolts

ELEVATION A

Cheese headed bolt supplied

Vee locating piece

PLAN

Milled head width W required

In order to machine the head of the bolt supplied, the bolt is placed as shown, with its threaded end on the top side of the base. The clamp is then tightened up, and the sliding piece and the vee locating piece, act as a vice on the bolt shank.

The cut is *then* taken as shown and the table is returned to its starting position. The finished bolt is released by loosening the clamping bolt.

Drill jig
A large number of *plain bearings* are required to have a hole drilled as shown. This hole will be used for oil lubrication.

Particulars of the drill jig
The 'housing' of the jig is made of plates. These are the base, vertical plates A and B and the top plate C. All these parts are assembled together by countersunk socket-head cap screws, and mating parts are dowelled together. The drill bush is a press-fit into the top plate C, and its centre is set accurately, to the distance L, from the inner face of plate B. The shouldered *locating spigot* locates in the plate A, and is further held by the nut. The large 'C' *washer* and *lock nut* complete the assembly.

In order to drill the bearing, the 'C' washer is removed, and the bush is fed onto the locating spigot. By replacing the 'C' washer and tightening the lock nut, the bearing is locked onto the datum face of plate A. Following the drilling, the lock nut is slackened, the 'C' washer removed, and the drilled plain bearing is removed.

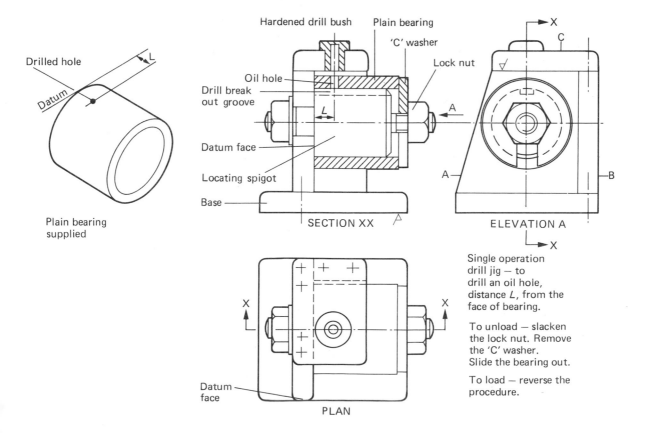

Drilled hole

L

Datum

Plain bearing supplied

Hardened drill bush   Plain bearing

'C' washer

Oil hole

Drill break out groove

Lock nut

Datum face

Locating spigot

Base

L

SECTION XX

A

A

A

B

C

ELEVATION A

X

X

Datum face

PLAN

X

X

Single operation drill jig — to drill an oil hole, distance *L*, from the face of bearing.

To unload — slacken the lock nut. Remove the 'C' washer. Slide the bearing out.

To load — reverse the procedure.

4 Machine tools

Objectives

(a) The student should be able to name the basic structural requirements for a number of different machine tools.

(b) The student will be able to recognise and appreciate the need for different transmission systems.

(c) The student will be familiar with BS symbols for hydraulic components, and the operation of components.

(d) The student should be able to recognise the types of bearings and their uses.

Machine tools

The basic requirements of any machine tool are:

1 It must generate the required shape for which it has been designed.

2 The shape so generated must be within the dimensional tolerances specified.

3 The surface finish must lie within prescribed limits, although this factor is also largely controlled by the quality of the tooling and tool setting.

4 Metal must be removed at an economic rate.

5 The machine must be safe and convenient to operate and set up.

6 Maintenance must be minimal but easy to carry out.

The basic construction of machine tools have the following features: a *basic structure* which supports a *power source*; *slideways* and *lead screws*; and a work-table (surface datum) or *an axis* (line datum) for work setting.

In the case of the *box column drilling machine* the basic structure is the cast iron box column, and the power source is the electric motor with its *transmission system* to the spindle and *feed*

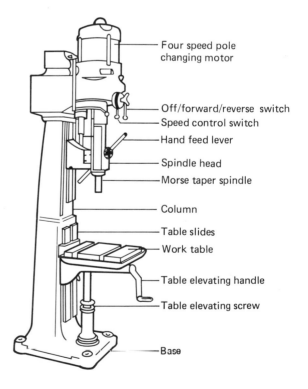

Four speed pole changing motor

Off/forward/reverse switch
Speed control switch
Hand feed lever
Spindle head
Morse taper spindle
Column
Table slides
Work table
Table elevating handle
Table elevating screw
Base

Box column drilling machine

mechanism. The basic structure also has slide-ways which control the table and the spindle head movements. The table elevating screw is a lead screw which moves the table on the table slides.

For a lathe, the basic structure is the *base* onto which is located the *bed*. The power source is an electric motor normally situated just above floor level, with its transmission system of belts and gears, located in the *headstock*. The headstock locates onto a machined face on the bed. The centre of the headstock bearing is the axis (line datum) for work setting. The bed has the slideways to carry the saddle, holding the cutting tool; this is fed along the bed by the feed shaft for turning operations or alternatively by the lead screw for screwcutting operations.

The feed shaft and the lead screw are part of the transmission system from the headstock.

Fabricated box structures

A *Startrite bandsawing machine* is an example of a fabricated box structure manufactured from thin plate steel and welded on assembly. It has the advantages that it can be easily manufac-tured by cutting the plates on an oxy-acetylene profile cutting machine, and then welding them in fixtures. All surfaces inside and outside can then be finished by painting and spraying. All the processes can be carried out by unskilled labour.

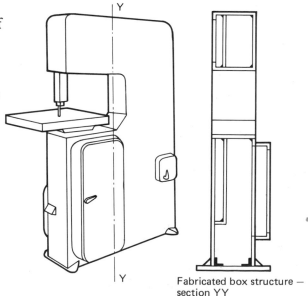

Fabricated box structure — section YY

Startrite bandsawing machine

Another fabricated box structure for a machine tool is the one shown for a lathe. Vertical plates are welded to the thick base plate and then the shelving is welded into place. The fabricated tray, with bases for the headstock and for the foot of the longitudinal slideways already welded in place, then completes the fabricated box structure. The hole 'cut-outs' provide access for the motor drive coolant pump, entry for cables and storage of lathe accessories. The fitting of doors, grill etc. completes the structure.

The splash guard is made of thin sheet and beaded on its top edge.

All surfaces are then finished by spraying or painting.

The structures possess great strength, rigidity and stability.

Harrison 12" swing lathe — box structure fabricated base

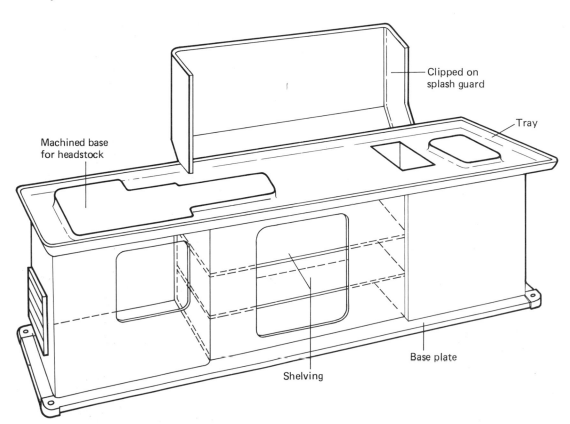

A lathe bed

It must be designed and manufactured so that for its weight it must have great stiffness and absorb vibrations when the machine is being worked. It must also have holes in the section for the passage of shafts and pipes, areas to secure vital parts, e.g. coolant pump, electric control box, motor, switches etc. and generous guide surfaces for mating parts to slide along.

The bed of a lathe, when cutting work, is subjected to the twisting action of the torque applied to the work by the headstock and bending of the bed due to the downward force of the job on the tool.

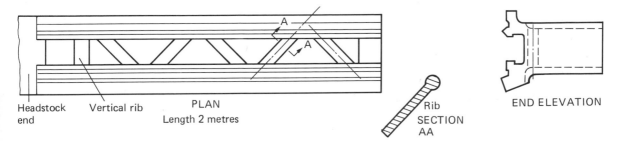

Headstock end   Vertical rib   PLAN   Length 2 metres   Rib SECTION AA   END ELEVATION

Lang lathe bed

Correct installation of the machine tool on the floor of the shop is very important.

A common type of basic structure is the box structure, an example of which is the vertical column for a drilling machine.

The box structure used in machine tools has very great strength and is sometimes further strengthened by gusset plates or webs. Holes are normally cast for access to assemble parts, such as balance weights, shafts, screws, pumps, motors etc., to build up the complete machine tool.

Grinding machine bed

This machine bed has a deep box section of great rigidity to oppose distortion. This quality of rigidity is very important to produce work of high precision.

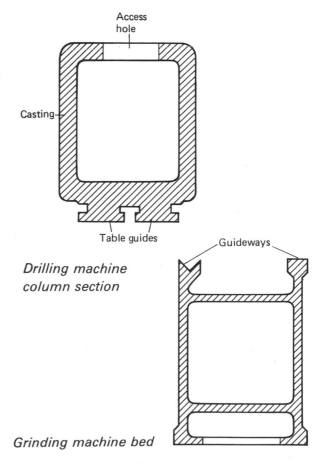

Access hole

Casting

Table guides

Drilling machine column section

Guideways

Grinding machine bed

Materials of construction

The basic structure is usually an iron casting which has good vibration damping properties. It is machined and then ground or hand scraped.

The sliding surfaces are 'chilled' when the bed is cast in order to obtain a close-grained hard-wearing surface.

Castings for the tailstock and headstock are similarly 'chilled', so offering a hard surface to withstand the knocks that they are subjected to in day-to-day use.

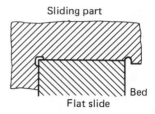

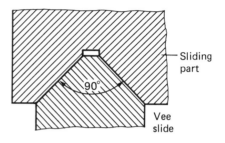

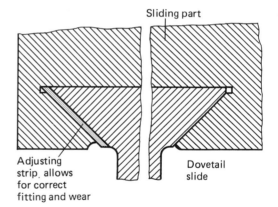

Slideways

1   They are machined and scraped.
2   They locate, align and guide machine parts, e.g. tailstock and saddle.

The sliding part and slideway must:
1   Allow for lubrication.
2   Allow for adjustment for wear.
3   Facilitate assembly.
4   Be designed to exclude swarf from the mating surfaces.

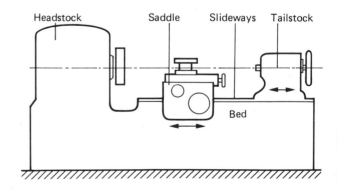

Lathe

Friction

When you slide a piece of material along a dry surface a resistance is felt. The rougher the surfaces in contact, the greater the resistance.

The resistance is called *friction*. In engineering it is important to have a low frictional resistance in bearings and slides, while in clutches and belt drives a high frictional resistance is required.

The block of mass m rests on a rough surface, exerting a downward force mg which is exactly counter-balanced by the normal reaction force $N = mg$. If a force P is applied as shown and gradually increased then, whilst at first the block will not move, at a particular value of P it will. Thus as P increases, so does the frictional force F; for if F was not equal to P, there would be movement. At the value of P when movement just takes place $P = F = \mu N$, called the coefficient of friction, depends upon the nature of the two materials in contact. Since, in this case, $N = mg$, we may write $P = \mu\, mg$, so that $\mu = P/mg$. But the more general result, $\mu = N/mg$ should be borne in mind, because N is not always equal to mg. It would not be, for example, if the block were held by a magnetic chuck exerting a downward pull F_m. In such a case $N = (mg + F_m)$ and $P = \mu\,(mg + F_m)$.

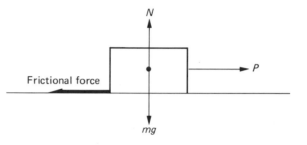

Angle of friction
If a block of mild steel is placed at the end B of a length of mild steel flat bar and then end B is raised, at a certain angle ϕ (phi) the block will move down at slow uniform velocity. From trig. tables:

Tangent of angle ϕ = coefficient of friction μ.

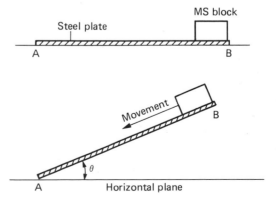

Experiment

To obtain the coefficient of friction for mild steel sliding on mild steel using the horizontal plane.

Method

The mass of the block is noted and weights are added to P until slow uniform motion of the block is obtained on the plane. The block is again set back to its original position and a further mass is added so making the total block mass greater. Again P is built up to slide the block. This method is repeated, in each case adding to the block mass.

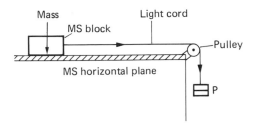

P	$P1$	$P2$	$P3$	$P4$	Kg
m	$m1$	$m2$	$m3$	$m4$	Kg

Because P = weights in Kg × g force on block = mass in Kg × g due to gravity then a type of 'force' graph '$P - m$' can be drawn in Kg units.

Plotting the graph a straight line is obtained.

From a selected triangle ABC the slope is:

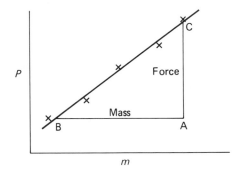

$$\frac{\text{AC}}{\text{AB}} = \frac{\text{force } P}{\text{mass } m} = \mu \quad \text{the coefficient of friction of steel on steel}$$

The result should be about 0.2 for clean smooth steel surfaces. Repeat with the surfaces lubricated. The result should now be about 0.03.

Control of linear movement

Adjustable stops on machine tools

When it is necessary to regulate the travel of a table, *adjustable stops* are used.

For a *milling machine*, a *dead stop cam bracket* can be clamped by a tee bolt, on the front vertical face of the table. As the bracket and table, under power, come near to the plunger the rounded head of the plunger follows the *running trip* face. It is depressed, so that at position A it operates an electrical limit switch in a circuit. This stops the table. In other machines the plunger knocks out and releases a dog clutch to stop the table.

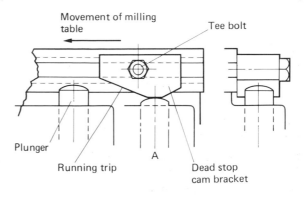

Adjustable stop milling machine

For a *cylindrical grinder*, accurate reciprocating movement of the table is required. Two *adjustable stops* are required, one as shown and one of opposite hand located to the left (not shown). With the table moving to the left, the *swinging striker plate* hits the *pin* on the *hydraulic circuit actuating lever*. It moves the pin to position B, so turning shaft C. The turning of shaft C alters the pressure flow of the hydraulic fluid from one side of the actuating piston to the other side of the piston. The result is that at position B the table is brought to stop, and the fluid pressure then moves the table to the right. The table is then stopped by the other stop bracket pushing pin B to the position as shown. The fluid is again reversed in the circuit and the table moves to the left.

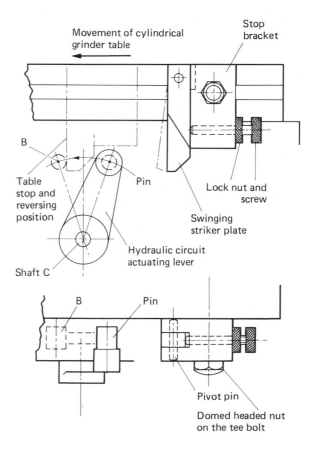

Adjustable stop cylindrical grinder

Lubrication

The following features contribute to the safe and economic lubrication of machine tools.

1 Plates on machines clearly showing the grades of lubricant, quantities and intervals required. The machine name, type and model should also be clearly visible.
2 Lubrication, either automatic or required at not less than 200 hour intervals and reservoirs large enough for that period.
3 Suitable method of lubrication to minimise or prevent metal-to-metal contact at all times.
4 Sufficient lubricant capacity to prevent overheating and thermal distortion of machine tool structures. When necessary, coolers fitted or reservoirs placed outside machine.
5 Reservoirs placed so that lubricant checking and replenishing are possible without machine shutdown or hazard.
6 Visual means of checking oil levels in reservoirs, visible to oilers when they fill them.
7 Lubrication points in one central position, accessible without removing guards or covers or interfering with machine settings.
8 Adequate sealing to prevent contamination and provision for removal of contaminants collected by the lubricant in use, e.g. fit filters.
9 Drain points large enough for rapid emptying and fitted with suitable shut-off valves. They should be far enough from the floor to get a container under them.

Electric motor mountings and adjustment

Vee and flat belts, after a length of service, become stretched and therefore slack in operation. In order to 'take up' this slackness and obtain the correct tension in the belts, two methods are shown to move the motor and its pulleys away from the driven pulleys on the machine.

Cylindrical grinder
The adjusting screw is retained from axial movement by the two collars on either side of the plate.

Method
Rotating the right-hand screw clockwise causes the sliding motor base to move towards the screw head, so tightening the vee belts.

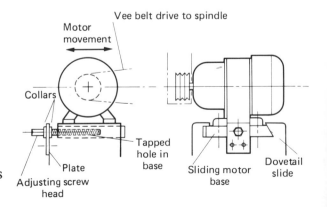

Cylindrical grinder

Horizontal milling machine

When the isolating switch is moved to its OFF position the rear inspection door of the machine can be opened and the belt adjustment mechanism is as shown. The platform can swivel about the pivot.

Method

To adjust the belt tension the platform has to move downwards. The adjusting nut on the eyebolt is slackened and the eye bolt nut tightened. When the inspection door is closed and locked the isolator switch is moved to its ON position.

Motor Variable Speed Unit Set

The electric motor is mounted on a pair of rails.

Method

To inspect or replace the coupling the motor's tee bolts can be undone and the motor can then slide away from the variable speed unit.

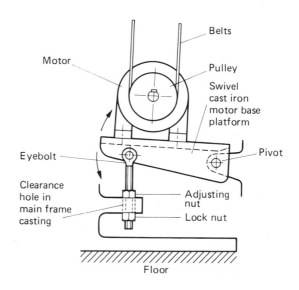

Belt adjustment mechanism — horizontal milling machine

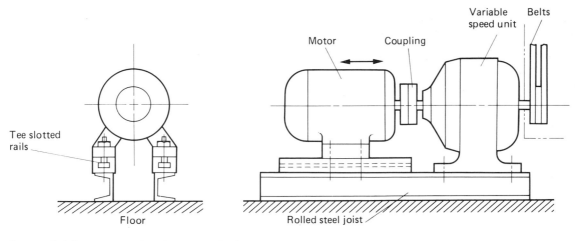

motor variable — speed unit set — lathe

Isolating switch box

The box is made of cast iron and is normally screwed onto a vertical face on the machine tool.

The power supply leads into one side of the box from the mains supply, through the box and then out at the other side. It then goes to the *'stop-start' push-button control box*. The wing nut locks the cover to the box.

By operating the switch handle downwards, the power supply is isolated from the machine tool. It is only when the switch is in this position that the cover is able to rotate on its hinge pin and expose the interior of the box.

The U-shaped contacts are clamped to its insulated shaft. These are not shown on the diagram.

For safety reasons, the switch handle cannot now be turned to the ON position due to the interference of the cover. When the cover is turned to close the box and the wing nut tightened, the handle is moved upwards to the ON position. The strong spring operated mechanism then pulls the handle and U contacts into their copper terminals. The circuits are then completed from wires A to A_1, B to B_1 and C to C_1.

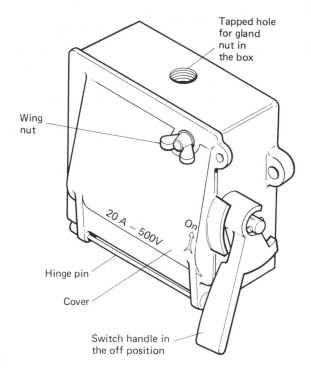

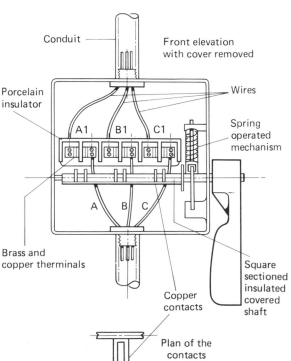

Isolating switch box

Question

Mechanical hacksaw machine
1   Investigate the machine, sketch two views
    of the crank-con rod mechanism and state
    the stroke.
2   Sketch the guide and slides section XX.
3   What direction must the teeth point?
4   As a result of the tension on the blade by
    tightening the wing nut, what is happening
    to the centre line shown?
5   How is the frame held up so that metal
    stock can be locked in the vice?
6   Why does the machine stop operating
    when the metal has been cut?

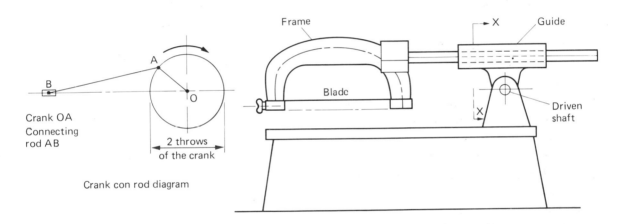

Mechanical hacksaw

Checking the alignment of machine tools

Pedestal drilling machine
1   *Object*: to check the table squareness to the
    axis of the spindle.
    Method: With the table and internal
    spindle taper thoroughly clean, the test
    mandrel and clock gauge are set as shown.
    Rotate the spindle and record readings at
    positions 1, 2, 3, 4, 5, 6, 7 and 8. Plot the
    graph 'position number — clock reading'.

2 *Object*: to check the run-out of the internal taper in the spindle.
Method: with the clock gauge located on the spindle, set to zero, rotate the mandrel by hand and note reading at each 90° position. Plot 'run-out — clock reading'.

3 *Object*: to check the squareness of the spindle in the two vertical planes relative to the table.
Method: set the dial gauge to zero at the top of the blade and feed downward for a certain length. With the engineer's square next set at 90° to first position; repeat the method.

Lathe

1 *Object*: to check parallelism between centres relative to the slides on the bed.
Method: with the test mandrel held between centres, the clock gauge held in the tool post, move the carriage by hand. Repeat, checking at 90° to the first position.

2 *Object*: to check squareness of the face plate to axis of headstock spindle.
Method: clock gauge located and set to zero, rotate face plate by hand; note reading at each 45° position.
Draw a graph.

3 *Object*: to check run out of (a) collet and (b) 3-jaw chuck.
Method: in turn, rotate the mandrel.

4 *Object*: to check parallelism of tailstock barrel in horizontal and vertical planes to the guides.
Method: with the barrel extended and the clock gauge secured to the tool post, note the clock readings for the length of the barrel. Repeat the procedure with the clock gauge set in the horizontal plane.

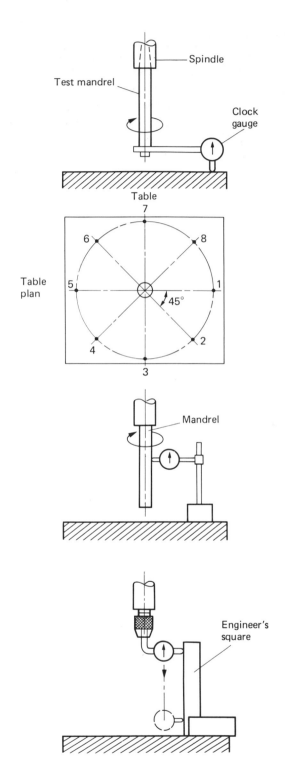

Squareness of spindle

Shaper machine

1 *Object*: to check the table parallelism with the stroke of the ram.
  Method: with clock located at position 1 set to zero and travel ram by hand and return. Move table to position 2; repeat procedure. Similarly for position 3. Draw graphs on the three dimensional layout.

2 *Object*: to check movement of clapper box at right angles to surface of table.
  Method: with clock gauge held in place of the tool, feed gauge downwards on edge of blade of the engineer's square.

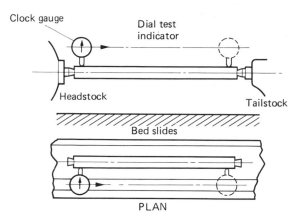

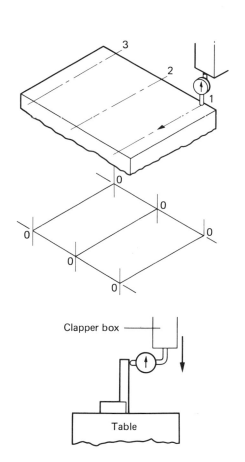

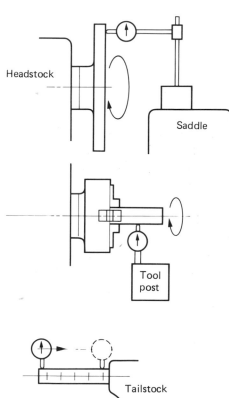

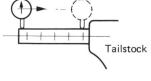

Belts and pulleys

Where the centre distance between two rotating shafts is very great then power can be transmitted by using pulleys and belts.

Simple flat belt pulley system
The belt can be made of a length of material suitably joined or moulded. It is called an endless belt.

Belt materials are leather, rubber, cotton and moulded fabric and rubber. To be efficient in transmitting power:
1   The belt must be a good tight fit on the pulleys.
2   It must have high frictional properties between the belt and pulley.
3   It must have the greatest possible contact length between the belt and pulley; the angle at the centre of the pulley is called the *angle of lap*.
4   The ratio of pulley diameters should not exceed 5 or 6.

If pulley A the *driver* pulley rotates one revolution, then a length of belt equal to the circumference of pulley A has passed over this pulley. Therefore, this same length has pulled off *driven* pulley B, so rotating it. B being bigger than A, it follows that B has rotated a part of a revolution only.

Then we can say:

$$\frac{\text{Revolutions of A}}{\text{Revolutions of B}} \times \frac{\text{Circumference of A}}{\text{Circumference of B}} =$$

$$\text{revs A} \times \pi \text{ dia. A} = \text{revs B} \times \pi \text{ dia. B}$$
$$\text{revs A} \times \text{dia. A} = \text{revs B} \times \text{dia. B}$$
$$\text{OR rev/min A} \times \text{dia. A} = \text{rev/min B} \times \text{dia. B}$$

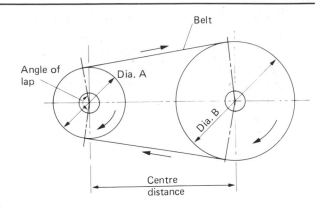

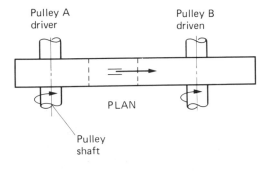

Flat belt pulley system

Example
If pulley A has a dia. of 100 mm, rotates at 330 rev/min and drives a pulley B of 220 mm by means of a belt, what is the dia. of B?

Solution
$$\text{rev/min A} \times \text{dia. A} = \text{rev/min B} \times \text{dia. B}$$
$$330 \times 100 = 220 \times \text{dia. B}$$
$$\frac{330 \times 100}{220} = \text{dia. B}$$
$$150 \text{ mm} = \text{dia. B}$$

Stepped pulleys or speed cone

When a series of speeds is required pulleys are used.

The motor cones all rotate at the same speed.

Moving the belt to the different diameters on the motor cone and onto the corresponding ones on the driven shaft, a series of three different speeds is obtained.

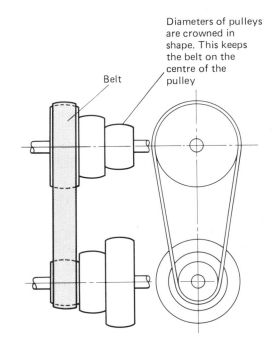

Diameters of pulleys are crowned in shape. This keeps the belt on the centre of the pulley

Belt

Three-speed cone pulley system

Vee belts

Vee belts are endless belts having a cross-section as shown in the shaded parts of the diagram, thus fitting into the vee-shaped pulley profile. The majority of vee belts used in machine tools are a woven fabric and rubber moulded endless construction.

Owing to the wedging action on the sides of the belt:
1 Slip does not occur as can happen with flat belts.
2 It can transmit much greater power compared with flat belts.

Clearance must always occur under the belt and bottom of the groove. The formulae for calculating the speed of the vee pulleys is the same as for flat pulleys.

The mean diameter of the belt on the pulley is used.

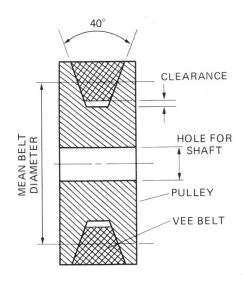

40°

CLEARANCE

HOLE FOR SHAFT

PULLEY

VEE BELT

MEAN BELT DIAMETER

Cross-section of a vee pulley and belt

Example

A vee-belt drive is as shown.

Calculate the mean belt diameter for pulley B.

Mean belt dia. of pulley A = 95−10 = 85 mm.

$$\text{rev/min A} \times \text{mean dia. A} = \text{rev/min B}$$
$$\times \text{mean dia. B}$$

$$200 \times 85 = 68 \times \text{mean dia. B}$$

$$\frac{200 \times 85}{68} = \text{mean dia. B}$$

$$250 \text{ mm} = \text{mean dia. B}$$

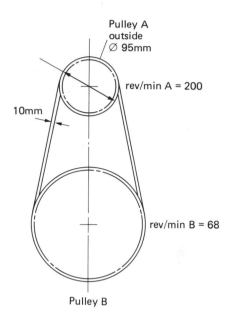

Pulley A outside
Ø 95mm

10mm

rev/min A = 200

rev/min B = 68

Pulley B

Colchester Chip Master lathe

Belt drive arrangement

Removing the guard on the headstock end of the lathe, the layout is as shown.

By measurement:
Mean diameter of A =   70 mm
Mean diameter of B = 110 mm
Mean diameter of C =   75 mm
Mean diameter of D = 130 mm

With a rev counter instrument two speeds, 1500 and 4000 rev/min, were recorded for pulley A.

Calculate:
1   The two pulley speeds for pulley D.
2   The lead screw is a single start square thread 6 mm pitch. What are the two rates of saddle travel along the bed?

Note:
One revolution of the lead screw, and the saddle moves a distance equal to the pitch, which is 6 mm.

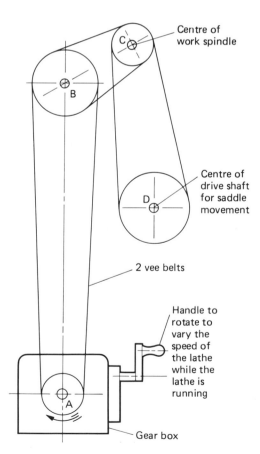

Centre of work spindle

C

B

Centre of drive shaft for saddle movement

D

2 vee belts

Handle to rotate to vary the speed of the lathe while the lathe is running

A

Gear box

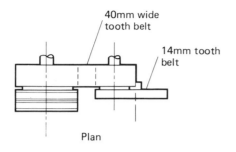

Plan

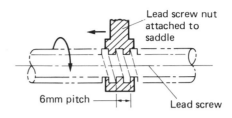

Progress No. 2G bench drill

Hoover Motor, 1425 rev/min, horse power ¾,
5 speed range.

Rev/min	Driver pulley	Mean dia. mm	Driven pulley	Mean dia. mm	Rev/min	Speed number
	A	85	F	170		1
	B	100	G	150		2
	C	125	H	125		3
	D	150	J	100		4
	E	170	K	85		5

Rev/min of A × mean dia. A = rev/min of F × mean dia. F

Calculate rev/min of F and similarly, speeds for G, H, J and K, which are the drill speeds. Draw the graph 'speed number — rev/min driven'.

Jones & Shipman grinding machine

Motor speed: 1440 rev/min.

Vee pulley	Mean dia. mm	Rev/min
A	80	
B	90	
C	165	
D	125	
E	115	
F	55	

Flat pulley	Dia. mm	Rev/min
G	150	
H	40	

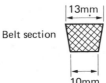

Belt section

13mm

10mm

Fill in the tables.

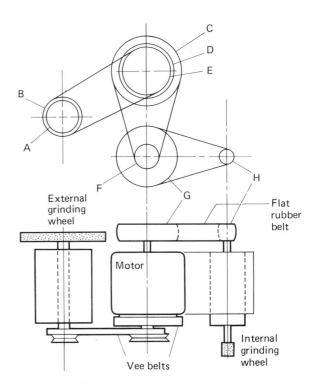

C
D
E
B
A
F
G
H
External grinding wheel
Flat rubber belt
Motor
Internal grinding wheel
Vee belts

The motor speed and mean diameters of the pulleys for a *bandsaw machine* were as follows:

Drivers mean dia. mm	Drivers rev/min	Driven mean dia. mm	Driven rev/min	Speed No.
50	750	240		1
60		230		2
90		220		3
120		180		4
160		150		5

Motor Speed   750 rev/min

Rev/min of A × dia. A = rev/min of F × dia. F

Rev/min of A × 240 = 750 × 50

$$\text{rev/min of A} = \frac{750 \times 50}{240}$$

$$= 156.25 \text{ rev/min}$$

Similarly:

Rev/min of B × dia. B = rev/min of G × dia. G
G

1   Calculate all the speeds.
2   Complete the table.
3   Draw a graph of 'speed number against driven rev/min'.

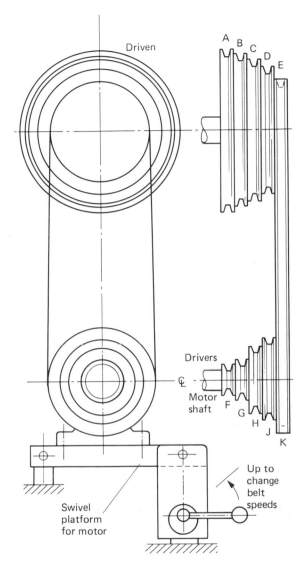

Startrite bandsaw, variable vee belt system

Clutches

Two shafts in line may be connected by a *coupling* so that one will drive the other. These rigid shaft couplings can be cast or forged and when in operation the bolts are subjected to shearing stress.

In machines, frequent disconnection of one shaft to the other is required by the coupling. This type of coupling is called a *clutch*.

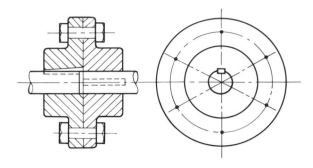

6 equally spaced fitted bolts

Tapered keys driven from the inside faces of the flange

Flange coupling

The *dog clutch* is shown in its engaged position; both shafts are rotating. A mechanism locates in the slot and to disengage the drive the left-hand coupling travels to the position shown, the teeth come apart and the rotation of one of the shafts stops. The left-hand coupling is a sliding fit on its shaft. The right-hand coupling is rigidly keyed to its shaft.

Friction clutch

Friction clutches transmit motion from a driver shaft to a driven one by couplings having flat surfaces which press one on the other. Friction transmits the motion. Engagement is gradual and slipping takes place but as engagement proceeds and the speed of the driven shaft builds up to that of the driver then slipping ceases.

An example of a friction clutch is the *plate clutch*.

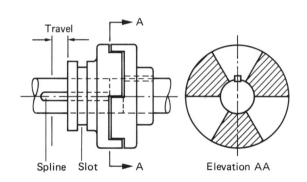

Dog clutch

Plate clutch

Friction material is riveted to a steel plate which is free to move on the shaft. The pressure plate travels axially by means of a spline. To engage the clutch, a crank mechanism is used. One end located in the slot moves the pressure plate towards the flywheel. The friction disc is sandwiched between the flywheel and the pressure plate; the spring exerting pressure to obtain the rotation of the driven shaft.

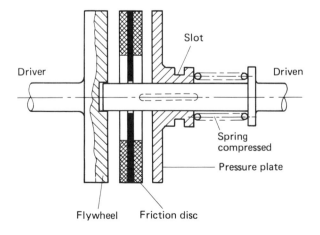

Plate clutch — disengaged position

Cone clutch

The driven plate is shaped like the frustum of a cone, and its sloping area is lined with friction materials. The driver plate is internally shaped to receive the driven plate, as shown.

To engage the clutch, a mechanism acting in the slot releases the compressed spring, causing the cone to slide along the shaft. When the friction material on the cone makes contact with the internal taper on the flywheel the cone and its driven shaft rotate..

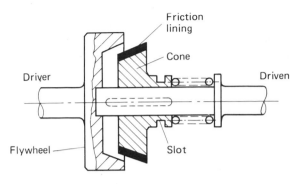

Cone clutch — disengaged position

Spline shafts

In a multispeed gearbox it is necessary for gears to move axially and to rotate on their shafts.

Spline shafts are used and have one or more splines of the same shape, and the sliding gears are similarly matched.

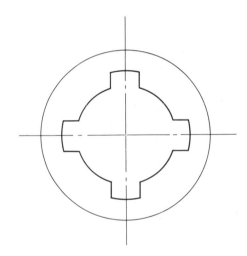

Four-spline sliding hub, wheel, gear or lever

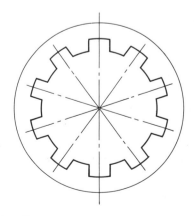

Ten spline item

Control of linear movement

Rack and pinion mechanism
The gear wheel, called a pinion, rotates on a shaft in bearings and engages with similar teeth arranged in a straight row. On a lathe bed the rack is 'fixed' on the underside of the front slides. The pinion, keyed on a shaft, is part of the saddle and rotating a handle causes the pinion to run along the rack so taking the saddle with it. Power feed can also be applied to the pinion.

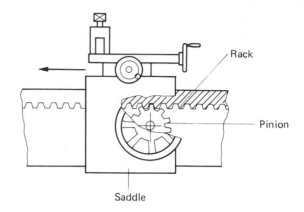

Rack and pinion mechanism — lathe

Some examples are as follows:
1 In a clock gauge the plunger has a rack cut in it. The teeth engage with a pinion, which is part of a train of gears, which rotates the pointer.
2 The hand feed on a drilling machine.
3 Hand movement of a lathe saddle.

Nut and screw mechanism
(a) Rotating the handwheel rotates the screw, and the nut moves along in an axial direction.
(b) Rotating the tommy bar with the nut fixed causes the tommy bar and screw to move in an axial direction.

Some examples are:
1 Table movements for machine tools.
2 Barrel movement for a tailstock.
3 Engaging nut on a lead screw.

$$VR = \frac{2 \times \pi \times \text{leverage}}{\text{pitch}}$$

$$= \frac{2 \times {}^{22}/_{7} \times 0.2\text{ m}}{10/1000\text{ m}}$$

$$= 2 \times \frac{22}{7} \times 0{\cdot}2 \times \frac{1000}{10} = 125{\cdot}68$$

$$\text{Efficiency} = \frac{MA}{VR} \times 100$$

$$36 = \frac{\dfrac{8750\text{ N}}{\text{Effort N}}}{125.65} \times 100$$

Example
A screw jack having a thread of 10 mm pitch, single start, is used to raise a load of 8750 N. If the efficiency of the screwjack at this loading is 36%, calculate the effort that must be applied at a leverage of 0·2 m and the mechanical advantage.

$$36 = \frac{8750}{\text{Effort}} \times \frac{100}{125.68}$$

$$\text{Effort} = \frac{8750}{36} \times \frac{100}{125.68} = 193.5\text{ N}$$

$$MA = \frac{8750\text{ N}}{193.5\text{ N}} = 45.2$$

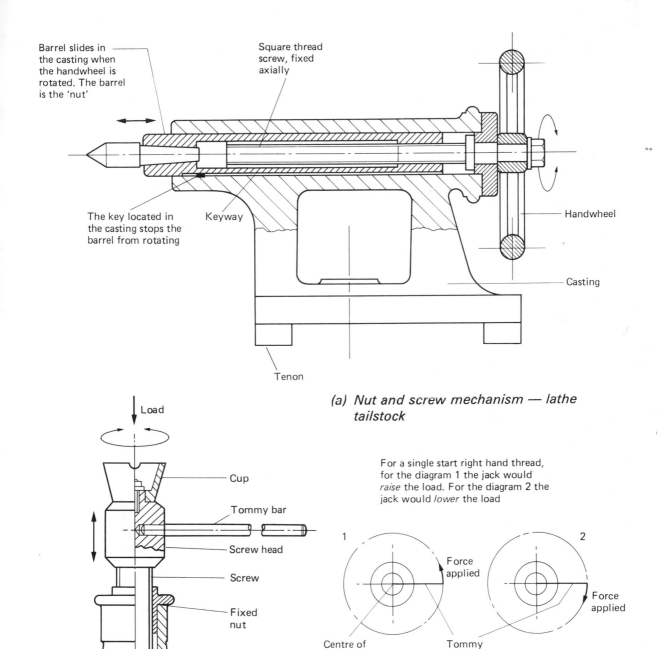

Barrel slides in the casting when the handwheel is rotated. The barrel is the 'nut'

Square thread screw, fixed axially

The key located in the casting stops the barrel from rotating

Keyway

Handwheel

Casting

Tenon

(a) Nut and screw mechanism — lathe tailstock

Load

Cup

Tommy bar

Screw head

Screw

Fixed nut

Casting

For a single start right hand thread, for the diagram 1 the jack would *raise* the load. For the diagram 2 the jack would *lower* the load

1

2

Force applied

Force applied

Centre of rotation

Tommy bar

Plan of the screw jack to a small scale

(b) Nut and screw mechanism — screw jack

Questions

1 A screw jack has a thread of 8 mm pitch. What is the load that can be raised by an effort of 350 N applied at a leverage of 0.16 m if the efficiency is 43%?

2 A screw jack has a 10 mm pitch thread and the effort is applied at a radius of 0.15 m. If the load of 5000 N is raised by an effort of 300 N, calculate the efficiency of the screw jack.

3 *Nut and screw*
Particulars of machines are as follows:
   1 Adcock & Shipley milling machine
   2 Bench vice
   3 Harrison lathe
   4 Lang lathe

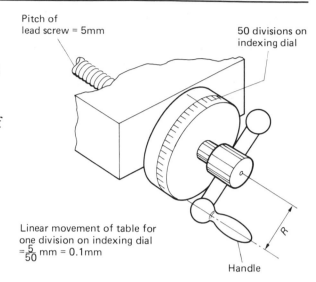

Pitch of lead screw = 5mm

50 divisions on indexing dial

Linear movement of table for one division on indexing dial
$= \frac{5}{50}$ mm = 0.1mm

Handle

Nut and screw

Complete both tables

	Lead screw pitch	Handle radius R	Divisions on drum	Movement ratio $\dfrac{\text{effort's distance}}{\text{Load's distance}}$
1	5 mm	80 mm	250	
2	6 mm	27 mm		
3	4 mm	35 mm	200	
4	6 mm	65 mm	300	

$$\text{Movement ratio} = \frac{\text{1 rev of handle}}{\text{Lead screw pitch}}$$

$$\text{For } 1 = \frac{2 \times 22 \times 80}{7 \times 5} = \frac{100 \cdot 6}{1}$$

	Linear movement of table for 1 division on dial
1	
2	
3	
4	

4 *Mandrel press*
When an effort was applied to the handle, for one revolution, the distance moved by the spindle was measured and found to be 12 cm. What is the machine's movement ratio?

5 *Rack and pinion mechanism*
How far would the centre line of the pinion move to the left for one revolution of the pinion?

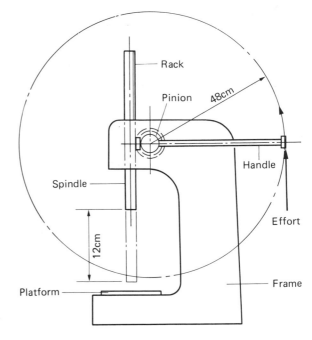

Mandrel press

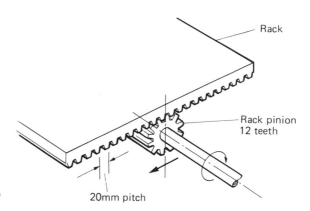

Rack and pinion mechanism

Crank and connecting rod mechanism to obtain linear movement

Automatic feed is provided to the table cross-slide of a shaping machine, since:

1 This is usually the motion required to feed the work across the greatest width of face required to be machined.

2 The physical exertion to move the mass of the table vice and work across is too great.

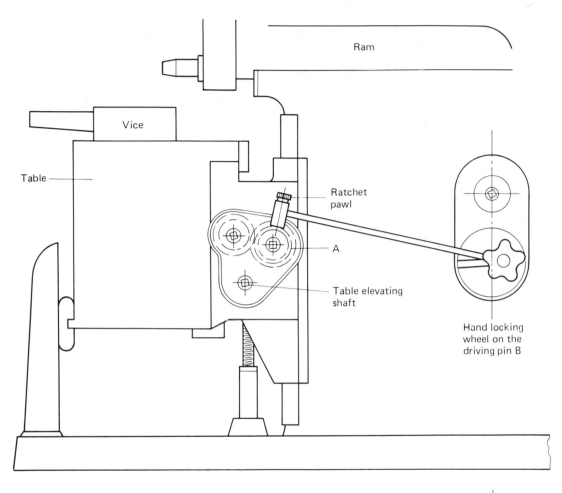

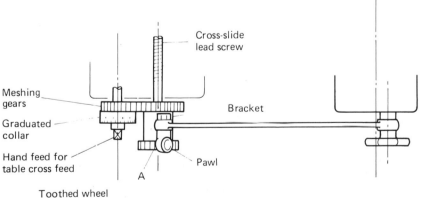

Layout of a table feed mechanism on a shaping machine

The shaper feed must be intermittent, occurring during the end of each return stroke of the tool. It is therefore necessary to turn the cross-slide lead screw a part of a turn at this instant. If we require a feed of 0.1 mm per stroke and the table cross-slide lead screw has a single start pitch of 5.0 mm, the screw must rotate $^{0.1}/_{5.0} = ^1/_{50}$ revolution per stroke.

If a toothed wheel A of 50 teeth is fitted to the end of the lead screw, a rotation of the amount of one tooth will give the required feed of 0.1 mm per stroke, rotation to the extent of two teeth will give a feed of 0.2 mm per stroke and so on.

This feed of a few teeth at a time can be arranged by mounting a *ratchet pawl* on the *toothed wheel* A in a *bracket* which rocks about the lead screw axis, the rocking motion being

provided by a *connecting link* attached to a *crankpin* B, on a *disc* which rotates at the same speed as the bull wheel.

The ratchet pawl is square on one side and bevelled on the other, so that it carries the toothed wheel as it rocks in one direction but rides over the teeth as it rocks in the other direction.

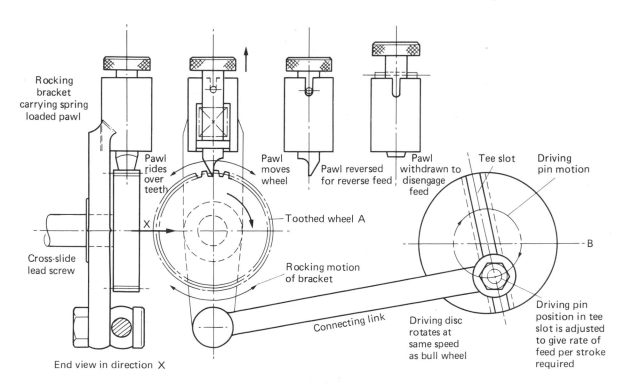

Crank and connecting rod — feed mechanism for a shaping machine

Slotted link mechanism

In a shaping machine the very strong slotted link oscillates in the vertical plane about the pivot C. The throw of the crank can be varied by a screw located in the very large bull wheel which also rotates about O. The top of the slotted link is connected to the ram.

The rotation of the crank OA causes linear movement to the ram and shaping tool. The cutting takes place while the crank rotates through the angle greater than 180° as shown, the return stroke through the angle EOA less than 180°.

Because the crank rotates at constant speed the time to rotate through the cutting angle is longer than to rotate through the smaller return angle. The return tool stroke therefore occurs more quickly than the forward cutting stroke.

Pulley and worm arrangement and table

Complete columns 1, 2, 3 and 4 in the table.

Movement ratio
Rotating the hand wheel for 1 revolution, the distance moved by the effort = the circumference of the wheel = $2 \times \pi \times R = 2\pi\,50$ mm.

Because the worm A is a single start thread, it will displace one tooth on the worm wheel B which has a total of 40 teeth.

This will cause a rotation of the worm wheel B and pulley dia. C of $\frac{1}{40}$ of a revolution. Then the load W will be raised a distance of $\frac{1}{40} \times$ circumference of 80 dia. pulley C = $\frac{1}{40} \times 2 \times \pi \times 40 = 2\pi$ mm.

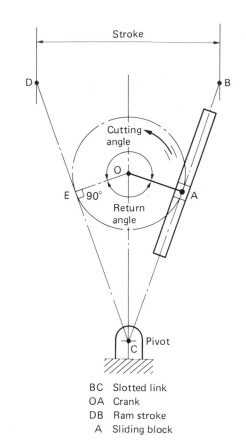

BC   Slotted link
OA   Crank
DB   Ram stroke
A   Sliding block

Principle of the quick return mechanism

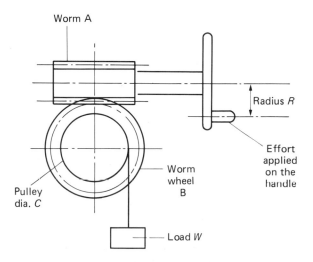

Pulley and worm arrangement

Movement ratio =

$$\frac{\text{the distance moved by the effort}}{\text{the distance moved by the load}}$$

$$= \frac{2\pi\,50}{2\pi} = 50$$

Force ratio $= \dfrac{\text{Load}}{\text{Effort}} = \dfrac{100\,\text{N}}{5\,\text{N}} = 20$

Efficiency of lifting machine (%)

$$= \frac{\text{load} \times \text{load's distance} \times 100\%}{\text{effort} \times \text{effort's distance}}$$

$$= \frac{20}{1} \times \frac{1}{50} \times 100 = 40\%$$

TABLE				
PULLEY AND WORM ARRANGEMENT	1	2	3	4
Worm A single double start	Single	Double	Single	Double
Number of teeth on wheel B	40	50		40
Diameter of pulley C (mm)	80	100	120	80
Radius R (mm)	50		70	50
Movement ratio		30	70	
Effort applied at radius R (Newtons)	5	10		10
Load W (Newtons)	100		140	
Force ratio				
Efficiency of lifting machine (%)		50	40	50

The three answers must now be entered in column 1. In a similar procedure complete the columns 2, 3 and 4.

Note:
For a double start worm A, one revolution of the hand wheel displaces 2 teeth on the worm wheel B.

Toothed gearing
A toothed wheel is made from a circular blank which then has an equally spaced whole number of teeth formed into the outside diameter.

The width of the disc is the face width of the teeth.

The majority of toothed wheels in machine tools are *spur gears*.

When two spur gears are in contact with each other the size and shape of the teeth are the same.

When centre distances between shafts are small, space is restricted and a great number of different speeds is required, then toothed gearing is used.

The slip which is possible in friction drives such as flat belt drives is completely eliminated with toothed gearing.

Simple train of gears

Only some of the teeth are shown on the gears which locate onto shafts.

W is the face width of teeth,

OD the outside diameter of gear,

RD the root diameter and

PD the pitch diameter, also called the pitch circle diameter.

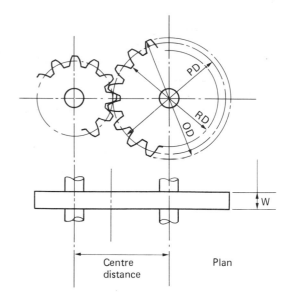

If wheel A has 55 teeth and rotates at 260 rev/min and wheel B has to rotate at 220 rev/min, find the number of teeth on wheel B. Speed of A × teeth on A = speed of B × teeth on B.

$$260 \times 55 = 220 \times \text{teeth on B}$$

$$\frac{260 \times 55}{220} = \text{teeth on B}$$

$$65 = \text{teeth on B}$$

A rotates clockwise, B anticlockwise.

When two shafts are too far apart for the available gears to engage, then a third wheel is introduced to produce the necessary transmission of power. A and B are shown far apart, no transmission being possible.

Gear C is introduced to produce transmission. Notice for clockwise rotation of A, C is anticlockwise and finally B is clockwise. C is called an *idler* wheel. It does not affect the speed of B, but only bridges the space between A and B.

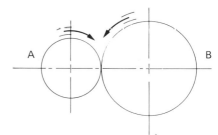

Diagram of two spur gears rotating

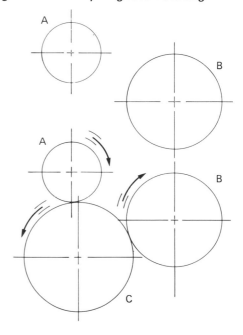

Compound train

The diagram shows a compound gear train, in which B and C move together on the same shaft. Thus a clockwise rotation at A causes B and C to rotate anticlockwise at the same rev/min. D rotates clockwise, A gears with B and C gears with D.

If A has 40T, rotates at 100 rev/min, B has 60T, C has 30T, D has 80T, find the rev/min of D.

Rev/min of A × teeth on A = rev/min of B × teeth on B

$$100 \times 40 = \text{rev/min of B} \times 60$$

$$\frac{100 \times 40}{60} = \text{rev/min of B}$$

$$\frac{200}{3} = \text{rev/min of B, also is the rev/min of C}$$

Rev/min of C × teeth on C = rev/min of D × teeth on D

$$\frac{200}{3} \times 30 = \text{rev/min of D} \times 80$$

$$\frac{200}{3} \times \frac{30}{80} = \text{rev/min of D}$$

$$25 \text{ rev/min} = \text{rev/min of D}$$

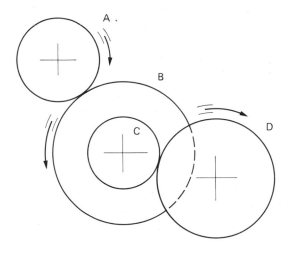

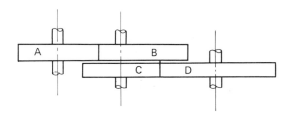

Compound train

Question

The motor shaft drives the three pulleys A, B and C, which are used to belt-drive pulleys F, E and D respectively. Thus the gear wheels G and K may be driven at three speeds.

The output shaft has on it two sliding gears H and L, H meshing with G and L with K. G has 100 teeth, H 80, K 140 and L 40.

1   Calculate all the speeds for the output shaft.
2   What is the slowest speed? State the pulleys and gears used.
3   What is the highest speed? State the pulleys and gears used.

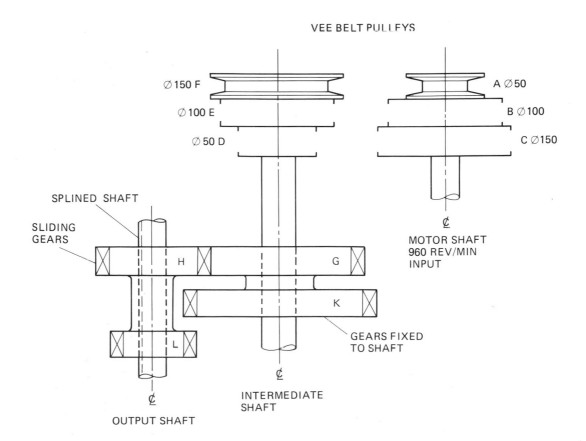

VEE BELT PULLEYS

Ø 150 F

Ø 100 E

Ø 50 D

A Ø 50

B Ø 100

C Ø 150

SPLINED SHAFT

SLIDING GEARS

H

G

K

L

MOTOR SHAFT
960 REV/MIN
INPUT

GEARS FIXED
TO SHAFT

OUTPUT SHAFT

INTERMEDIATE
SHAFT

Gearboxes

On a machine tool, to obtain a range of speeds for the workpiece on a lathe, or for a milling cutter on a milling machine, the gearbox is used. For a certain speed, generally, two levers are moved to definite location stops. Levers are only moved when the workpiece or cutter has stopped.

On a lathe the gearbox occupies part of the headstock.

Moving the levers results in different gears meshing and the drive from the input pulleys through the gear trains produce different speeds at the spindle output.

Plates secured to the machine tool state the various rev/min possible.

The Norton gearbox

A quick-change type of gearbox on a lathe, is often known as a *Norton gearbox* and it covers all the ratios likely to be wanted.

The input shaft, which is driven from the headstock, drives a long roll gear R. Through the tumbler gears T_1 and T_2, shown in the end view, gear R can be engaged with any one of the gears numbered 1 to 9 in the 'cone cluster' of gears. A sliding cluster of three gears a, b and c is engaged with gears 10, 11 and 9 respectively on the cone cluster shaft to give three alternative output ratios.

Since this three-speed output gearbox is compounded with the nine speeds from the cone cluster, the gearbox provides a total of $3 \times 9 = 27$ different gear ratios which cover a very wide range of screw pitches and satisfy most needs.

Layout of Norton-type screw cutting gearbox

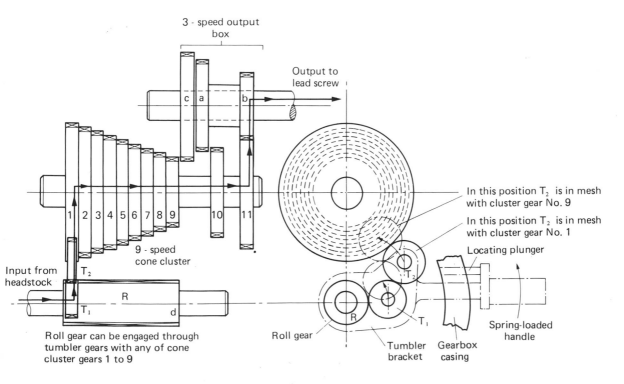

In the engagements shown the drive is from R to cluster gear number 1, and from gear number 11 to gear b and the overall ratio is:

$$\frac{\text{Roll gear R}}{\text{Gear 1}} \times \frac{\text{Gear 11}}{\text{Gear b}}$$

A lathe headstock

Find all the speeds available from the gearbox.

Note:
The drawing shows the drive from gear B, to gear E, to gear H.

Therefore, revs B × teeth B = revs E × teeth E from which revs E is found.

Then revs E × teeth E = revs H × teeth H from which revs H is found, i.e. one of the spindle speeds required.

By then moving A to mesh with D, leaving G, H and K in the position as shown, the drive is A to D and E to H. Then another spindle speed is calculated.

C meshes with F and also G with D and K with F.

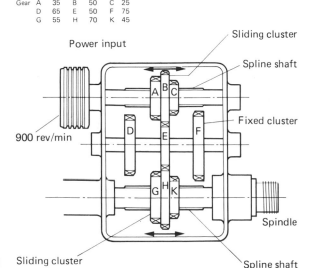

			Teeth			Teeth			Teeth
Gear	A	35		B	50		C	25	
	D	65		E	50		F	75	
	G	55		H	70		K	45	

A lathe headstock

Arithmetical progression

Speed rev/min 40 160 280 400 520 640 760 880
Speed No.　　1　2　3　4　5　6　7　8

If a machine had eight speeds as shown, plotting the graph produces a straight line.

Subtracting the speed No. 1 from speed No. 2

$$= 160 - 40 = 120$$

Subtracting the speed No. 2 from speed No. 3

$$= 280 - 160 = 120$$

and so on. The speeds are therefore in an arithmetical progression; the difference

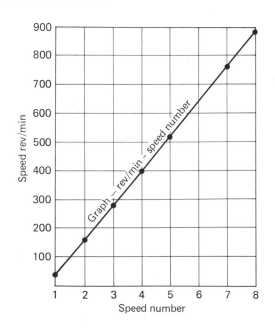

between any two adjacent speeds is always the same. The speeds increase by a constant number.

Speed	Arithmetic progression rev/min	Geometric progression rev/min
1	19	19
2	82	30
3	145	47
4		
5		
6		
7		
8	458	458

Problem
A gearbox has to be designed to have eight speeds. Calculate (a) the speeds, if arranged in an arithmetic progression, and (b) the speeds in geometric progression.

It can be shown that if the first speed is 19 rev/min and the 8th 458 rev/min then the ratio between adjacent speeds is 1.575. That is, speed 2 will be $19 \times 1.575 = 29.9$, i.e. 30 rev/min approximately, speed 3, $29.9 \times 1.575 = 47.1$, i.e. 47 rev/min etc.

Draw the graphs, 'AP rev/min — speed number' and 'GP rev/min — speed number'.

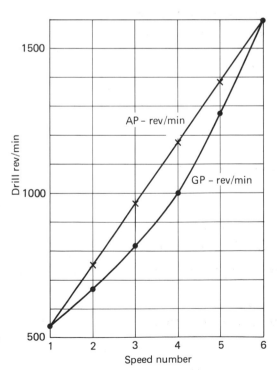

Comparison of diameters for a range of rev/min (GP) and rev/min (CAP)

Questions

1   A lathe has eight speeds arranged in geometric progression. Draw the graph. On the graph, draw the arithmetic graph, and by reading the graph state the rev/min.

Speed No.	1	2	3	4	5	6	7	8
Rev/min (GP)	14	23	38	63	103	170	280	460
Rev/min (AP)	14							460

2   Plot speed No. — rev/min (GP) and speed No. — rev/min (AP) for the eight speeds on a milling machine given in the table below.

Speed	1	2	3	4	5	6	7	8
Rev/min (GP)	28	44	70	111	176	279	442	700
Rev/min (AP)	28	124	220	316	412	508	604	700

3   A machine tool has a range of five spindle speeds from 10 to 223 revolutions per minute. The speeds are arranged in a geometrical progression. The constant multiplier is 2.173.

Calculate all the speeds and draw a graph of 'speed numbers' against the 'spindle speeds in rev/min'.

Preference of geometric progression speeds to arithmetic progression speeds

This can best be explained by considering a machine tool which has six speeds, and to draw up the speed numbers and the corresponding diameter of drills. The range of drills is to be from ϕ 4 mm to ϕ 12 mm and the cutting speed 20 m/min.

For a given cutting speed S, the number of revolutions of the drill, N, will be given by

$$\text{rev/min} = \frac{\text{cutting speed (m/min)}}{\text{drill circumference}}$$

i.e. $N = \dfrac{S}{\pi d}$

So for the 4 mm diameter drill

$N = \dfrac{20 \times 1000}{\pi \times 4} = 1591$ rev/min

For the ϕ 12 mm drill,

$N = \dfrac{1000 \times 20}{3.142 \times 12} = 530$ rpm.

All the GP and AP speeds are shown.

Conversely, given the cutting speed S and the rev/min, the appropriate drill size can be calculated, from the relation $d = S/\pi N$. For example, taking the same cutting speed of 20 m/min, and 660 rev/min,

$d = \dfrac{20}{\pi \times 660}$ mm

$= \dfrac{20 \times 1000}{\pi \times 660}$ mm $= 9.64$ mm.

Similarly, all the diameter drills can be calculated. By comparing the full range of drill diameters, it can readily be seen that, because the distribution of speeds in GP is much better than with AP, so is the distribution of drill sizes. The above method could also be carried out on a milling machine, where d = diameter of cutter, on a lathe, where d = diameter of workpiece. Again it would be shown that the preference is for a machine tool with speeds arranged in a geometrical progression. For a milling machine, a more convenient distribution of cutter diameters, and on a lathe, a more convenient distribution of diameters could be possible.

Speed No.	1	2	3	4	5	6
rev/min (GP)	530	660	823	1025	1277	1591
Drill Dia. mm	12	9.64	7.73	6.2	4.98	4
rev/min (AP)	530	742	954	1167	1379	1591
Drill Dia. mm	12	8.57	6.66	5.45	4.61	4

Hydraulic circuitry

Many industrial processes and operations entail the use of hydraulically controlled machines. Oil is normally the fluid used and can be used to very high pressure if required of 3500 KN/m². It has the advantages of being a lubricant and has rust preventive properties.

Hydraulic equipment is light, compact, versatile and trouble-free. On machine tools hydraulic control is used, because of its convenience rather than because a lot of power is wanted.

Any circuit is made up of:
1 A *motor* which can be electric, internal combustion engine or a diesel engine and this in turn rotates the *pump*.
2 A *pump* rotates and is supplied with oil from a *reservoir*. There are three common types:
(a) *Gear pump*
    Two gears meshing with each other, contained in a close fitting housing; has an oil inlet port on one side. The meshing of the gear traps the oil and forces it out, under pressure, through the outlet port into a delivery pipe in the circuit.

(b) *Vane pump*
Consists of a circular chamber in
which there is an eccentric rotor
carrying a number of blades or vanes.
As the rotor rotates oil is drawn into
the large variable spaces and compressed into the small spaces and out
into the line.

(c) *Plunger type*
A number of plungers in cylinders
either 'in-line' or 'radial' positions are
moved by an eccentric shaft so drawing in fluid and then compressing it.
The oil under pressure then operates
through pipelines, through valves and
into a cylinder to act on a piston.
Other lines exhaust oil into reservoirs.

Basic hydraulic circuitry
BS:2917 lists the symbols for hydraulic and
pneumatic systems. Arrow heads on pressure
lines in valves and in pumps indicate the
direction of the pressure flow.

In drawing hydraulic circuits the components
can be represented by drawing rectangles and
printing in their titles. This is called the *black
box treatment.*

Cylinders
Hydraulic power is most commonly applied by
a ram, cylinder or jack. Each consists of
cylinder barrel, with end fittings and a piston.
In a cylinder or jack there is a piston rod. In a
single acting cylinder the pressure is exerted on
the full piston area; in a *double acting* cylinder
the pressure, in turn, acts on the full and
annulus area of the piston, that is, the back of
the piston, to which the rod is attached.

Four-port control valves
By moving the inside parts, the pressure and
the exhaust oil can be directed in different
directions.

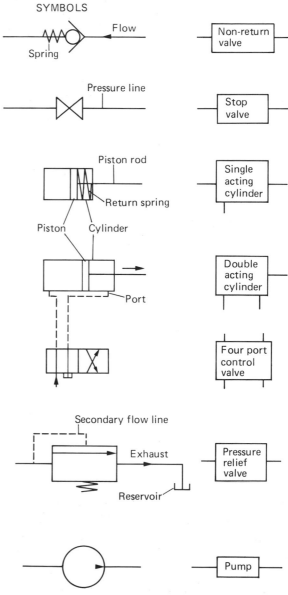

*Symbols (BS 2917) for hydraulic and
pneumatic systems*

Spool valve

This type of valve is used a great deal. Its name arises from the 'spool' part of the sliding part of the valve. Three spools are shown, fixed to the shaft. As the valve rod moves, the spools open or close the ports to which they relate. The spool can be operated mechanically, manually, electrically, hydraulically, or pneumatically. The spools are a lapped fit in the body of the valve, and therefore no sealing rings are required.

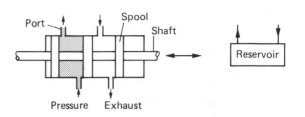

Spool valve

Clamping device with accumulator

An *accumulator* stores energy either by compressing gas (either air or nitrogen) or by raising a weight. When an operation is intermittent but must, when it does take place, be steady, an accumulator can be added to the circuit with advantage. The pump charges the accumulator during off periods and when a sudden demand for power is required it is drawn from the accumulator. It smooths out the system for power requirements.

In the circuit the pump is delivering pressure to open the *vice jaw* and when fully open it can charge the accumulator to full capacity, and then the oil pressure will operate the relief valve and exhaust to reservoir. To close the vice jaws, the four-part control valve is moved over to the right so that pressure acts on the full area of the piston.

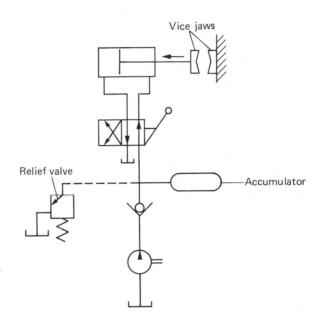

Circuit to operate a vice

Single-acting cylinder

The piston is being lowered, oil is being exhausted from the cylinder to the reservoir. At the same time the pump delivering·oil under pressure cannot pass through the lever operated valve, so will operate the relief valve to exhaust. When the lever moves the valve, oil pressure will then pass through the valve into the cylinder, so raising the piston.

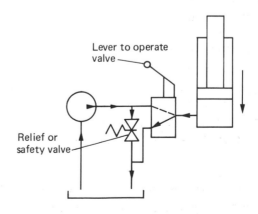

Single-acting cylinder with a three part valve

A shaft could carry gears, pulleys, cams, etc., and in order to rotate the shaft must have supports, each of which will support some of the load and permit rotation of the shaft. A simple support is the plain bearing or bush whose outside diameter is a push fit in the bore of the housing. The internal diameter of the bush is a clearance fit for the shaft. That part of the shaft resting in the bearing is the *journal*.

When the shaft rotates, sliding of shaft material on the bearing material takes place; sliding friction results. Plain bearings can be:
(a) lubricated by oil or grease, or
(b) self-lubricated e.g. nylon or sintered.

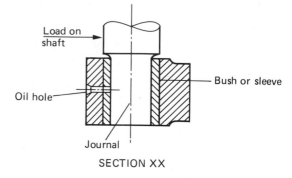

SECTION XX

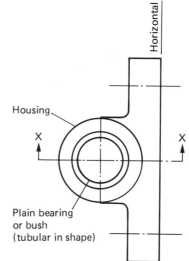

Plain bearing

Bearings

A bearing material must have
1 The ability to support the load or thrust.
2 A minimum resistance to rotation, i.e. the coefficient of friction of the shaft and bearing has to be as low as possible.
3 The ability to assume a highly polished finish under running conditions.
4 High thermal conductivity so that the heat generated by friction is readily conducted away.
5 An appreciable resistance to corrosion.
6 A long life.

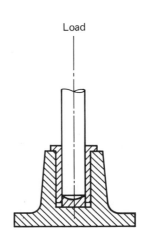

Bushed footstep

Bearing metals — white metal anti-friction alloys

Metals employed are copper, tin, lead and antimony.

The copper-tin alloys are bronzes. In making any alloy of the above, the object is the production of a soft matrix with hard particles embedded in it. The hard particles resist wear and produce a low coefficient of friction, whilst the soft matrix allows the bearing to adjust itself to the journal, thus tending to yield even distribution of the load and prevent local heating and seizing.

Tin-base alloys are called Babbit metals. The main constituents of white-metal bearing alloys are either lead or tin.

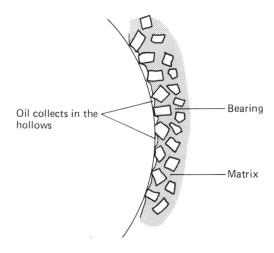

Cubes of hard antimony in the tin rich or lead rich matrix

Methods of locking plain bearings

1 The flanged bearing can be a press or slide fit in the housing and is then locked in position by tightening up the countersunk screws.
2 The plain bearing has a flat on its outside diameter. When pressed into position as shown, the end of the grub screw is then tightened onto the flat.
3 The bearing is pressed into the housing against the shoulder. The bolted plate retains the bearing against the shoulder.

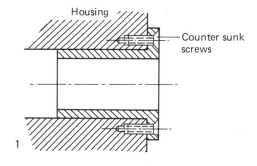

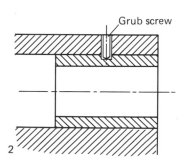

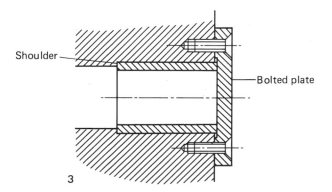

4 The bearing is pressed against the shoulder. Into the milled slot in the bearing locates the lugged end plate.
5 The bearing when pressed into the housing is then drilled. The bolt screws into the tapped hole in the housing and locates in the hole in the bearing.

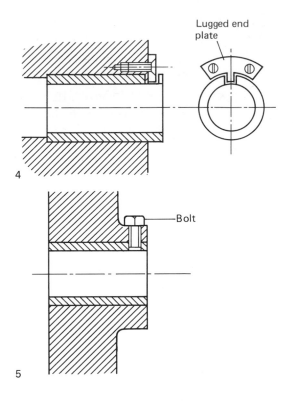

Basic principles of lubrication

When a block of mass m on a dry horizontal surface requires a force P to slide it along at a slow uniform motion then the ratio $P/mg =$ coefficient of friction μ.

Applying a lubricant
The block is at rest. When the force P is applied, the block rides over the lubricant, taking up an inclined position on a wedge of lubricant. Because of the viscosity or oiliness of the liquid there will now be a much lower value of μ.

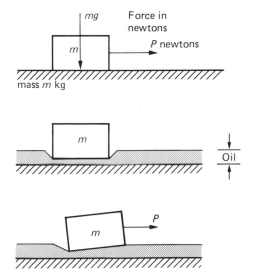

Lubrication

Efficient lubrication is essential because:

1 It prevents metal-to-metal contact.
2 It carries away local heat produced in a bearing and promotes uniform temperature throughout the bearing.
3 It protects the highly finished working surfaces from corrosion.
4 The life of the bearing is much longer than without lubrication.

Choice of lubricant

Oil is important when very high speeds or when temperatures of 100°C and above are involved. In these conditions the bearings are enclosed in casings containing other components for which oil is essential. In other cases grease is used.

Advantages of grease

1 Grease is easier to retain in a bearing housing.
2 Grease combines effective lubrication with permanent coating properties and therefore does not leave the surfaces; oil tends to drain away.
3 Grease excludes dirt and moisture.
4 It is easy to handle and extra grease, if needed, can be applied quickly.
5 Greased bearings can operate for a very long time between inspections for additional lubricant to be added.

Advantages of oil

1 Oil is easy to drain and refill, and the level of oil in a reservoir can readily be controlled.
2 The oil for a bearing might also be available for other parts of the machine.
3 Oil is very effective in carrying heat away.
4 It has a greater range of operating speeds and temperatures than grease.

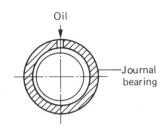

Single oil inlet hole on unpressurised area

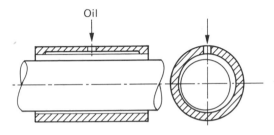

Straight axial groove feeds oil all along the shaft

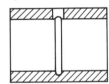

Circular oil groove

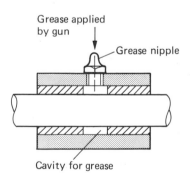

Spaced journal bearings

5 Oil readily feeds easily into any spaces and can carry away dirt and wear particles.
6 Passing through filters in a machine, the oil may then be circulated again through the machine.

Action of simple oil bearing

When rotation starts the journal tends to climb up, the bearing builds up a wedge of oil and the pressure produced causes the journal to take up the position as in A.

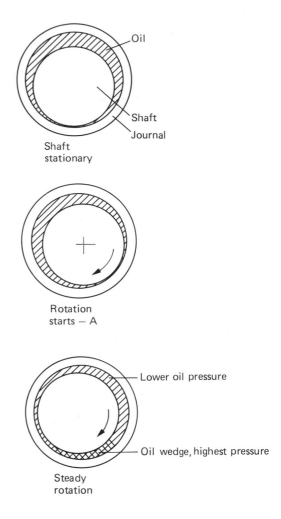

Constant centre-line or hydrodynamic bearings

These are used when a spindle is required to run at high speeds under light load and must be as free from vibration as possible.

When the spindle rotates, oil enters between the shoes and the journal, lifting each shoe and forming a wedge shaped oil film which grips the journal. This bearing is found mainly in wheel-head spindles on precision grinders and boring machines.

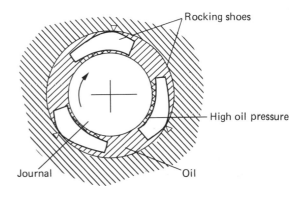

1 **The single row rigid ball-bearing**
Probably the most frequently used type of
bearing. It is designed to handle radial
loading only, or thrust (axial) loading, or a
combination of both loadings in any proportions up to the rated capacity of the
bearing.

2 **The single row rigid roller bearing**
Has approximately twice the radial load
capacity of similar size ball-bearing. The
type shown has a lipped inner ring and
plain outer ring. It is for radial loads only.
It does not handle axial loading or provide
an axial fix of the shaft.

3 **The angular contact single row ball-
bearing**

It is similar to the ball-bearing, has an
inner ring, outer ring, cage and set of balls.
It differs due to the run out shape of the
inner surface on the outer ring. This run
out feature permits the use of a one-piece
brass cage into which can be fitted the
maximum possible number of balls. This
gives the angular contact bearing a higher
load-carrying capacity than a similar size
ball-bearing.

4 **The taper roller bearing**
These are suitable for heavy combined
radial and axial loads. A taper roller
bearing locates the shaft in one direction
only; therefore, it must be paired with a
bearing which locates in the other
direction.

5 **The needle roller bearings**
These are a type of cylindrical roller
bearing with a wide sphere of use in
applications where space is limited. They
are frequently used for oscillating conditions and when fitted with a cage are also
suitable for relatively heavy loads and high
speeds.

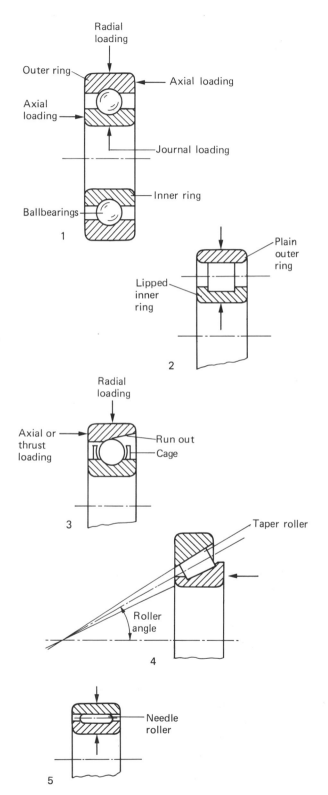

The cage

The purpose of the cage is to maintain the balls a fixed distance apart as they roll around the ring tracks. Some cages are made from steel pressings, in two halves which are finally rivetted together, and are shaped to freely locate on the balls.

Construction of a ball or roller bearing

The bearing consists of the following parts:

1 Two rings, an outer and inner ring on which the raceways are formed.
2 A set of rolling elements which run on the raceways.
3 A cage for separating the rolling elements from one another.

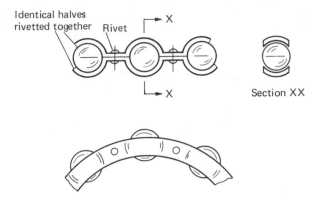

Ball-bearing cage — ball riding type

Lubrication

To renew the grease, the plug screw is withdrawn and fresh grease is forced under pressure through the nipple and into the grease spaces. Old grease leaves through the plug hole. This process is known as 'packing' the bearing.

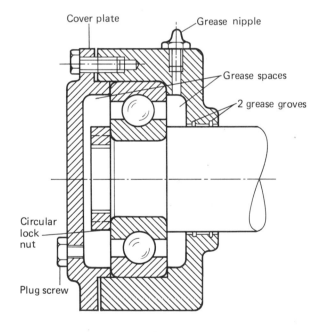

Independent housing for grease lubrication with grease sealing grooves

Questions

1 Name a list of rolling elements.
2 What materials are used in making the cage?
3 Make a sketch of a cage.
4 What metal is used for manufacture of the rolling elements and rings?
5 What is the 'metal-to-metal' contact possible in a bearing?
6 Some of the bearings in the following list are represented in the diagrams.

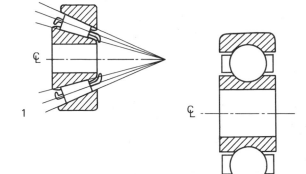

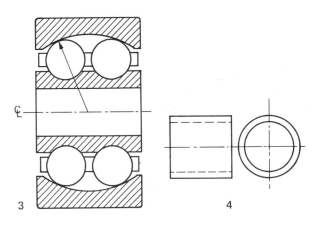

Bearing	No.
Thrust	
Radial roller	
Self-aligning	
Needle roller	
Plain	
Single row radial ball	
Taper roller	

Indicate the type of bearing by putting the appropriate number in the above column.

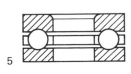

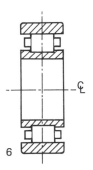

7   *Rotating centre*
  (a)   Name the three bearings at positions 1, 2 and 3.
  (b)   State the reasons for your choice.
  (c)   Sketch them on the drawing.

8   *Drilling machine spindle*
  What type of bearings are used and what are the reasons?

9   *Lathe headstock*
  What type of bearings are used and what are the reasons?

10 *Milling machine spindle*
  (a)   Name the three bearings at positions 4, 5 and 6.
  (b)   State the reasons for your choice.

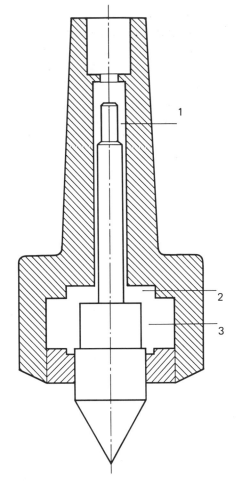

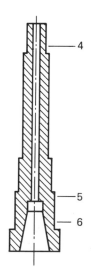

Preloaded bearing
To keep bearings firmly in place it is sometimes desirable to apply an axial thrust, independent of the normal load. This is called preloading. The two commonest preloading methods are shown.

Preloading methods
(a) The tightening of an adjustment nut on the shaft to axially displace one bearing ring. The reaction to this thrust is taken on the shaft shoulder.
(b) The use of springs to apply the necessary axial thrust. The nut secures the two inner rings and the spacer against the shaft shoulder.

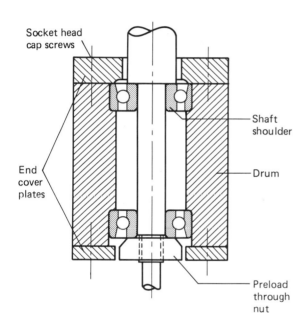

Axial adjustment nut for bearing preload

Springs displace the outer race for proper preload. The inner races are firmly fixed by a spacer

Gas bearings
Any fluid capable of forming a lubricating film between moving parts may be used in bearings. Fluids consist of both liquids and gases, but if gases are used then, to maintain a 'lubricating film', they must be under pressure. Various gases under pressure, e.g. argon, carbon dioxide, nitrogen or air are used. The advantage of gas bearings is that the load carrying capacity increases with speed, temperature and pressure. Gas bearings are almost frictionless.

Air bearings are becoming popular in machine tools. One example is an air bearing giving friction-free running to the wheelhead spindle on a grinding machine. It is found that it:

1   eliminates the warm-up period necessary with oil bearings,
2   increases the production time,
3   makes savings on oil change and topping up, and
4   produces faster metal removal by the wheel due to full power applied instantly.

The journal is rotating about its own axis in space.

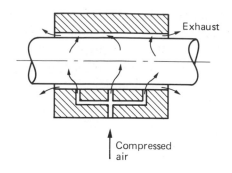

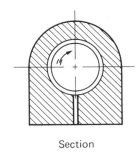

Section

Air bearing

Plastic bearings

1   The material polytetrafluoroethylene (PTFE) is commercially known as Teflon. It is commonly used in moulded bushes, with fillers such as graphite and bronze, or incorporated in porous bronze bearing liners. The PTFE gives a very low coefficient of friction, does not require lubrication and can be used up to a temperature of 320°C.
2   The material polyamide, is known as nylon.
    It can be moulded into bushes, does not require lubrication, and is used for office and food-processing machinery.

Lubrication of sliding surfaces by oil under pressure

Oil is fed under pressure to all bearing surfaces so that there is no metal-to-metal contact.

1   The slideways have a low coefficient of friction. The only friction is the internal fluid friction of the lubricant.
2   They enable the positioning of tables to be more accurately predictable.
3   They use less power for the drive and therefore savings can be made on this.

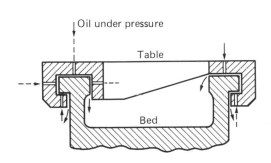

Rolling element linear motion bearings
Balls or rollers are set between slideway
surfaces, thereby achieving the low friction
and accuracy of rolling element bearing
arrangements.

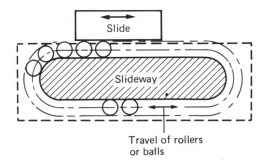

Vee and flat roller slide

Linear motion is also obtained by using
recirculating balls or rollers, which travel in a
channel guide.

Recirculating roller system

5 Materials

Objectives
A student will be able to:
(a) Compare the basic properties of the listed non-ferrous alloys and state the reasons for their use.
(b) State the basic reasons for the use of the listed alloying elements in steels.
(c) Identify the effects of primary forming processes.
(d) Identify the listed plastics forming processes.
(e) Recognise the factors which influence the choice of bearing materials.
(f) Identify listed heat treatment processes and state their purpose.
(g) Interpret load/extension graphs and simple iron/carbon diagrams.

Basic properties of materials

For a material to be suitable for the function it is called upon to perform, it must have certain properties. For example, a milling cutter must be harder than the materials to be cut; a material to be made into wire must have the property to flow into this shape without breaking or cracks appearing in the material. A steel hawser used on cranes must have great strength to carry the load. Some basic properties of materials are *ductility*, *malleability*, *elasticity*, *toughness*, *hardness* and *strength*.

Ductility
A ductile material is one which can be drawn out permanently by a tensile force. The metal from which the finest wire is producible is the most ductile. Wires are produced by dragging rods of a convenient size through holes in dies.

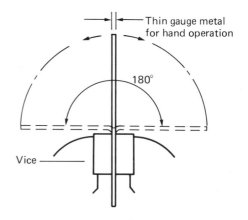

Continuous bend test (ductility)

With certain very ductile materials the *continuous bend test* is applied. A strip is alternately bent and straightened through a prescribed angle, usually 90° or 180°. The number of bends required to cause fracture is taken as a measure of ductility.

Metal	Order of ductility
Gold	Highest
Silver	
Aluminium	
Iron	
Copper	
Zinc	
Tin	
Lead	Lowest

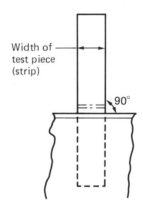

Malleability

Good malleability of a material is defined as the ability to be hammered or rolled out without cracking. Very few metals have good cold malleability, but most are malleable when heated to a suitable temperature. A *bend test* can be carried out on a bar of material. The material can be cold or hot, or in a stated treated condition. The angle to which it must be bent and the radius of bending when the angle exceeds 90° are stated. A specification might state that 'the bar is to be bent through

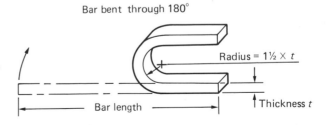

Bend test specimen (malleability)

180°, the inner radius of the bend to be one and a half times the thickness of the bar'.

Elasticity

This is the property of regaining original shape after deformation. When a material is subjected to a force, a change of shape can be detected; if the force is *tensile*, the material is elongated. The elasticity of a material is very important in structures such as in bridges and buildings, aircraft and vehicles. The loads applied are absorbed by the elasticity of the materials.

Toughness

This is the resistance to fracture which is offered by the metal when subjected to impact loads. A workshop method to test toughness is to use a bench vice, a hammer and similar size pieces of different metals. By hitting each piece in turn with a constant blow from the hammer, one is enabled to compare the toughness of the metals. Those that fracture or bend the most are the least tough. Those that bend the least are the most tough.

The *Izod impact testing machine* for testing machined specimens of metals gives the actual energy absorbed in breaking the specimen.

Hardness

It is the property of a material which allows it to resist wear and indentation. The hardness of a material is usually stated relative to the hardness of other materials. Scales of hardness usually give high numbers to hard materials and low numbers to soft materials. Hardness is decreased by heating.

Metal	Order of malleability
Gold	Highest
Silver	
Aluminium	
Copper	
Tin	
Lead	
Zinc	
Iron	Lowest

Strength

The strength of a material is its ability to withstand applied forces without failing. Depending on the way the forces acting on the material are to be applied, strength may be defined in the following ways.

1 *Tensile strength* is the maximum force per unit area the material will withstand if loaded in tension.
2 *Compressive strength* is the maximum force per unit area the material will withstand if subjected to a compressive load.
3 *Shear strength* is the maximum force per unit area the material will withstand if a shear force is applied.

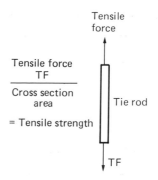

$$\frac{\text{Tensile force}}{\text{Cross section area}} = \text{Tensile strength}$$

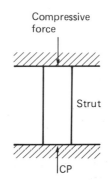

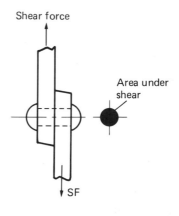

The table shows the ultimate strength of materials

Material	Approximate ultimate strength in N/mm^2		
	Tension	Compression	Shear
Cast iron	155–185	620	93
Wrought iron	360	360	280
Mild steel	435	435	340
Copper	185	185	116
Aluminium	116	116	93
Brass	185	155	125

Brittleness

This is the opposite of toughness; a brittle material breaks easily under a sharp blow, although it may resist a steady load quite well. Brittle materials are neither ductile or malleable, but they often have considerable hardness.

Machinability

This may be defined as 'that characteristic possessed by the material which permits the ready removal of the material by a cutting tool at economic speeds, producing a satisfactory finish and providing normally expected tool life'.

Examples

1 A solid bar of diameter 28 mm was subjected to a tensile force of 44 000 N. Calculate the tensile stress in the bar.

Cross-sectional area of the bar

$$= \frac{22}{7} \times \frac{d^2}{4} \text{ mm}^2$$

$$= \frac{22}{7} \times \frac{28}{4} \times 28 \text{ mm}^2$$

$$= \frac{22 \times 28 \times 28}{7 \times 4 \times 1000 \times 1000} \text{ m}^2$$

Tensile stress

$$= \frac{\text{tensile force}}{\text{cross-sectional area}}$$

$$= \frac{44000 \text{ N}}{\left(\dfrac{22 \times 28 \times 28}{7 \times 4 \times 1000 \times 1000} \text{ m}^2 \right)}$$

$$= \frac{44\ 000 \times 7 \times 4 \times 1000 \times 1000}{22 \times 28 \times 28} \text{ N/m}^2$$

$$= 71.4 \times 10^6 \text{ N/m}^2$$

2 What shear force will be required to shear off a bar 38 mm $\times$ 9 mm if the ultimate shear stress of the material is 340 N/mm^2?

The area being sheared is

$$38 \times 9 = 342 \text{ mm}^2.$$

$$\text{and stress} = \frac{\text{force}}{\text{area}}$$

$$340 \text{ N/mm}^2 = \frac{\text{shear force N}}{342 \text{ mm}^2}$$

$$\therefore \text{ Shear force} = 340 \times 342 = 116\ 280 \text{ N}$$
$$= 116.28 \text{ kN}$$

Non-destructive workshop test for twisting (lathe set-up)

Rods are used, of small equal diameters, made from mild steel, copper, aluminium and brass.

A tap wrench is fixed to the end of the rod, and the hanger and weight to the end of the wrench.

Procedure

With one rod set up as shown, release the support.
The twisting angle θ can be measured.
Repeat the test with another rod with the same length l.

Draw up a table of 'rod material' and the angle of 'twist $\theta°$'. The smallest angle gives the material that possesses the greatest shear strength.

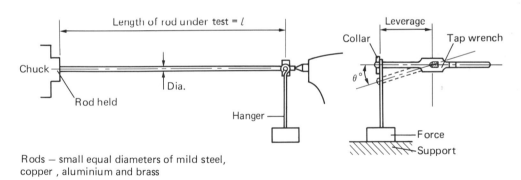

Rods — small equal diameters of mild steel, copper, aluminium and brass

Simple workshop test for twisting (lathe set-up)

Impact test

The impact test is a measure of shock-resistance or toughness of a metal.

In the *Izod machine*, a square sectioned test specimen is firmly gripped in the jaws of a vice. The small machined notch is set level with the top of the vice and facing in the direction as shown. A pendulum of known mass is locked in the initial position. The energy stored in this mass, in virtue of its height above the specimen is recorded by the pendulum's pointer on the *energy indicator scale*. On releasing the mass, it swings like a pendulum, strikes and breaks the specimen. Energy has been used up by the mass in breaking the specimen. The mass continues its swing and it reaches its final position. Under the action of the pull of gravity, the mass falls back towards the vertical centre line of the machine. It oscillates about this centre and finally comes to rest on this centre line. The *idle pointer* was moved by the pendulum and remains in the position on the scale that corresponds to the maximum swing of the pendulum after impact (final position).

The energy possessed by the pendulum in its initial position = the energy used up in breaking the specimen + the energy possessed by the pendulum in its final position. Therefore the *energy used in breaking the specimen* = the difference in the two readings on the energy indicator scale. The test procedure (for metals) is specified by BS 131: 1961 Part 1.

The result of testing a brittle metal will be that the pendulum reaches a high final position.

After breaking a tough metal, the final position of the pendulum will be at a much lower final position.

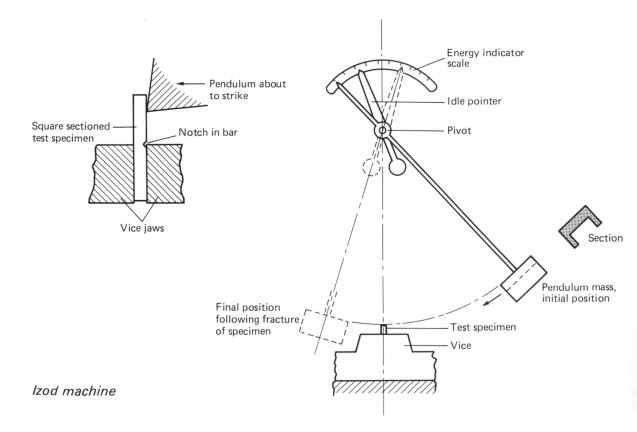

Izod machine

Cupping test

One of the most useful and widely employed tests on sheet metal is carried out on the Erichsen machine. This test produces a bulge in the strip by means of a dome-shaped die which is gradually forced onto the metal under the influence of a hand-controlled ram, until fracture occurs.

The drawing depth in millimetres is then read off on the apparatus and the values thus obtained are of great importance in determining the quality of the strip.

If the fracture runs around the dome, the metal will have a fibrous character and give a low drawing value. Such a metal is not suitable for withstanding further deformation by bending, folding, etc. A smooth dome indicates a material possessing good drawing properties, whilst a rough surface generally indicates a large coarse-grained material incapable of withstanding much more deformation.

Summarising, therefore, a good quality cold-stamping and cold-pressing sheet steel should yield a good Erichsen value, whilst the dome should be quite smooth and free from surface defects.

Rockwell hardness test

A common, simple method to obtain the comparative hardness of metals is by using the *Rockwell hardness testing machine*.

The hardness is determined by the depth of penetration of a penetrator into a specimen under certain fixed conditions of test. The penetrator may be either a steel ball or a conical diamond of 120° included angle. The hardness number is automatically indicated on the indicator dial. A high number indicates a hard material; a low number indicates a soft material.

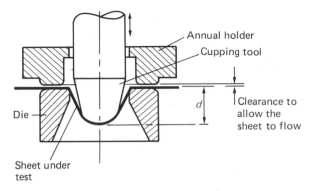

Erichsen cupping tool for testing metal sheets

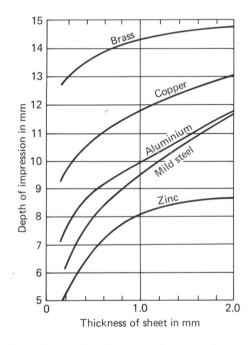

Erichsen's standard curves for metals

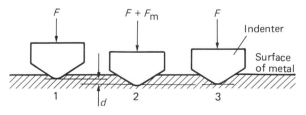

The Rockwell hardness test

From BS 891: 1962 Part 1. The procedure is as follows:

(a)   The minor load F is applied.
(b)   The major load F_M is also applied.
(c)   The F_M load is removed still leaving load F acting.

The Rockwell hardness number
$$H_R = K - 500d$$
where d = distance in mm
K = a constant, 100 when using the diamond indenter and 130 when using a steel ball.

Brinell hardness test

The Brinell test for determining the hardness of metallic materials consists in applying a known load to the smooth surface of the material to be tested, through a hardened steel ball of known diameter. A 300 kilogram mass is applied on a 10 mm diameter ball for soft metals and a 3000 kilogram mass on a 10 mm diameter ball for harder metals. The diameter of the indentation is measured by means of a micrometer microscope and is used as a basis for calculating comparative figures — hardness numbers.

The Brinell hardness number
$$= \frac{\text{force applied } F}{\text{curved area of the indentation A}}$$
where $A = \frac{1}{2}\pi D[D - \sqrt{(D^2 - d^2)}]$
the test procedure is specified in BS 240: 1962 Part 1.

Hardness comparison table

Brinell dia. of impression	Brinell 10 mm ball 3000 kg load	B scale Rockwell 1.587 mm ball 100 kg load
2.8	477	118
3.1	389	114
3.5	301	107
3.6	286	105
3.7	269	104
3.8	255	102
4.1	217	96
4.4	187	91
4.6	170	87
4.8	156	83
5.0	143	79
5.2	130	72

Tested metals and range of Brinell hardness numbers obtainable

Tested metals	Brinell hardness	Penetrator
Hardened steels, alloy steels, stellites and carbides	over 400	Diamond with 120° cone
Alloy steels, carbon steels, cast irons	from 400 to 230	Diamond with 120° cone
All mild steel and medium carbon steels, soft CI copper-aluminium alloys	from 240 to 100	Steel ball ∅ 1.587 mm
Copper alloys	below 125	,,
Magnesium alloys	50 to 30	,,
Steels, cast irons and other alloys	from 400 to 140	steel ball ∅ 2 mm

The recommended *test load* must be applied in each case. This is obtained from the manufacturer's handbook.

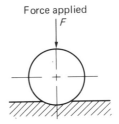

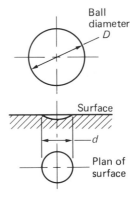

The Brinell hardness test

Non-ferrous alloys

Aluminium alloy

Wrought — non heat treatable
One type of alloy contains about 1.25 per cent *manganese* as a means of improving the resistance to corrosion and making the alloy easier to weld. This is obtainable in the form of strip, sheet etc. Various degrees of hardness or temper can be obtained, but the alloys are not subjected to heat treatment. They are given mechanical properties of the order 92 to 200 MN/m^2 according to the temper supplied. The hardness values vary between Brinell hardness number 27 and 54. The alloy is used for roofing sheets and the like as well as canning of fruit and vegetables.

Other types of wrought alloy contain about 5 per cent magnesium which are widely used on account of their combination of high strength and corrosion resistance. These aluminium-magnesium alloys, which develop further strength as a result of cold-working, as distinct from heat-treatment, are used in the construction of all types of sea-going vessels.

Heat treatable wrought duralumin 4 per cent copper
Duralumin is an alloy composed of copper 4 per cent, 0.4 to 0.7 per cent manganese, 0.4 to 0.7 per cent magnesium, the remainder being aluminium. It is widely used in the wrought condition for forgings, stampings, bars, sheets, tubes and rivets in the aeronautical, automobile, shipbuilding and civil construction industries. The alloy is readily hot-worked by heating to a temperature of about 500°C.

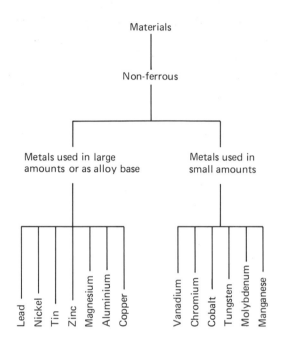

After forging or annealing, duralumin may be cold-worked to quite an appreciable degree, and a combination of both hot and cold-working is indeed generally employed for the production of sheets. The alloy is obtained in the fully softened state by annealing at about 400°C.

Duralumin exhibits the phenomenon of *age-hardening* to a very pronounced degree. If the alloy is heated to about 480°C and quenched in water, its hardness increases rapidly for the first day and then slowly up to a maximum value after 4 or 5 days. When it has *aged* it is too hard for work to be done on it, and must be annealed.

When in the heat treated and aged condition duralumin has a tensile strength of about 310 MN/m².

The alloy has good machining properties. In its annealed condition the Brinell hardness number is about 64; in the aged condition it is about 98. Its density is little more than that of pure aluminium.

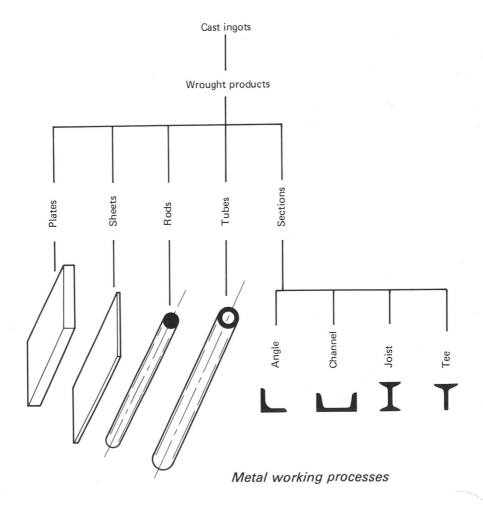

Metal working processes

Cast — non heat treatable alpax
Alpax is an alloy of about 10 to 13 per cent
silicon, the remainder being aluminium.
These alloys have a close-grained structure, are
ductile, can be mechanically worked and have
a silvery white tint. Alpax is used sand-cast
and also die-cast, being ductile and of medium
strength with excellent corrosion resistance. It
is extremely castable and will produce thin
cross-sections of complicated form. The castings are dense, non-porous and will withstand
fluid pressure without leakage. Since silicon is
lighter than aluminium, alloys of the two are
lighter than most other aluminium alloys and
it is this property which has made its greatest
appeal in those instances in which lightness is
of primary importance. For this reason,
together with its excellent corrosion
properties, this alloy finds considerable
applications for marine purposes. The alloys
retain their strengths very well at moderately
high temperatures, a property which renders
them suitable for moving parts of internal
combustion engines.

Cast heat-treatable 'Y' alloy
This alloy is used for aircraft castings and the
pistons of diesel engines and sometimes for
other types of pistons. The composition is
typically 2.5 to 4.5 per cent copper, 1.8 to 2.3
per cent nickel and 1.2 to 1.7 per cent
magnesium, with a little iron and silicon as
impurities, the balance aluminium. A small
titanium content is sometimes introduced.

A great improvement in the strength of castings is observed if the alloys are cast in cast
iron moulds, rather than sand, by the gravity
diecasting process. The alloy can be forged.

The strength of this alloy can be increased 50
per cent by age-hardening and it can be heat-
treated either in the cast or wrought conditions. 'Y'-alloy subsequently provided the

Metal	Melting temperature °C
Tin	232
Lead	327
Zinc	419
Aluminium	657
Magnesium	651
Silver	955
Copper	1062
Gold	1064
Cast iron	1200–1350
Nickel	1452
Iron	1503
Tungsten	3267

basis of a number of special aluminium alloys developed by Rolls-Royce Ltd.

The tensile strength of the alloy is about 340 MN/m^2.

Solution heat-treatment and *ageing* are required for the best properties. The hardness given by ageing may be accompanied by lower ductility.

Solution heat-treatment
The first step consists of heating the alloy to some temperature below the melting temperature, usually in the range 510° to 520°C for aluminium alloys, to put as much as possible of the alloying constituent into solid solution. The temperature is maintained for about 20 minutes to 60 minutes, according to the thickness of the piece. This permits the entire piece to reach a uniform temperature and the dissolving of the alloying elements in the solid solution to take place throughout. In effect the alloying constituent has been dissolved in the aluminium and dispersed as completely as when sugar is dissolved in water. The alloy is quenched and in contrast to steel after quenching, is in a relatively soft condition.

Ageing
Following the solution heat-treatment the hardness of the alloy increases, rapidly at first, and then more slowly, up to a maximum value after a period of about four to five days. This phenomenon is called *ageing*. The *age-hardening* process may be considerably accelerated and completed in a few hours by reheating the quenched alloy in boiling water, or some other medium, so long as the temperature does not exceed 150°C.

Brass
The term 'brasses' is usually understood to apply only to alloys of copper in which zinc is the main alloying element. A brass made of

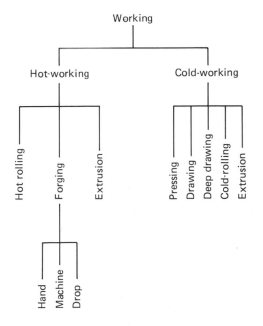

Manipulation of metals

70% copper and 30% zinc is referred to as *cartridge* brass. This alloy can be cold-rolled into sheets, drawn into wire, formed into tubes, pressed and otherwise cold-worked.

To manufacture a cartridge case, a calculated size of a circular blank of a certain thickness is used. The blank is pressed into the shape of a shallow cup. By a series of further pressing operations the cup is pushed and squeezed through successively smaller and smaller holes in a steel die, resulting in the walls of the cup being elongated until eventually a tube with a relatively thick base and thin walls is obtained. Further operations are carried out to the base to form the recess for the detonating cap and ensure that the cartridge fits only one type of breech. The rim of the cartridge is also softened by annealing so that it may be bent in to clip the bullet.

Machining of 70/30 brass
It is an unpleasant material to machine, as the swarf comes away in long ribbons at a fast rate. It has sharp, jagged edges and the machined surface is usually torn and rough.

Season cracking
When 70/30 brass has been severely cold-worked, season cracking may occur. This happens when the article is brought into contact with mild corrosives, such as slightly salty water or air containing traces of acid. Cracks suddenly appear, sometimes after years of service. They are caused by internal stresses. The remedy is to anneal at 280°C after cold-working; this treatment relieves internal stresses, but has little effect on the hardness.

Another important brass in engineering is *Muntz metal* or *red brass* of composition 60% copper and 40% zinc. This alloy can be particularly adaptable to casting and hot working by rolling, extrusion and hot stamping.

Muntz metal machines readily. Castings are very suitable for pump parts. Machined components manufactured are bolts, pins, spindles etc.

Bronze

Tin bronze
An alloy of copper and 15 per cent tin produces a castable tin bronze. It is used for the manufacture of heavily loaded bearings, pumps, gears, nuts etc., demanding reasonable mechanical strength. It also resists acid corrosion very well.

Phosphor bronze
This alloy is composed of 5 per cent tin, about 0.1 per cent phosphorus, the remainder being copper; it has a close-grained microstructure. Phosphor bronze can be mechanically worked without difficulty, but is liable to become brittle if heated to too high a temperature. It has considerable toughness, high tensile strength and in colour it has a yellowish tint. The alloy's tensile strength ranges from 340 MN/m^2 to 741 MN/m^2 and the Rockwell hardness B numbers between 33 and 99.

It is readily cold-worked into rods, wires and sheets. Typical applications include bellows, Bourdon tubes, clutch discs, diaphragms, fuse springs, switch parts, perforated sheet, chemical equipment and welding rods. In wire form it should withstand being bent cold through an angle of 120° without fracture.

Specific gravity, or comparative density, is the weight of the metal compared to water. Water = 1.

Metal	Specific gravity
Magnesium	1.74
Aluminium	2.56
Zinc	7.1
Tin	7.2
Iron	7.8
Copper	8.6
Nickel	8.8
Silver	10.5
Lead	11.36
Mercury	13.6
Gold	19.3

Aluminium bronze
Two copper-base alloys containing aluminium are important.

One is a copper-base alloy containing *5 to 7 per cent aluminium* which has a fine golden colour. It is highly ductile and may be cold-worked into tubing, sheets, strip and wire. It is made into parts that require strength at elevated temperatures, a low coefficient of friction against steel, or where a combination of strength and corrosion resistance is required. Aluminium bronze is used for bushings, gears, valve parts, bearings, sleeves, screws, pins and fabricated sections.

The second is a copper-base alloy containing *10 per cent aluminium* and a castable alloy. It cannot be cold-worked to the same extent as the previous aluminium bronze, but can be readily mechanically worked in the hot state. This aluminium bronze or aluminium copper alloy is the most widely used in engineering for diecast parts. The castings produced possess high yield strength and good ductility, combining their hardness and wear-resistance properties, making them useful for pump castings, rods and shafts, valve fittings, nuts and bolts, propellers for small vessels, electrical work and heavy duty bearings.

This alloy can be heat treated in a manner rather similar to a medium-carbon steel.

Magnesium alloys
When alloyed with aluminium, manganese and zinc, the magnesium alloy acquires sufficient mechanical strength and corrosion-resistance to produce useful constructional alloys. Magnesium alloys can be subjected to all the usual metallurgical treatments, including casting, diecasting, rolling, forging, extruding and pressing. By far the greater number of magnesium alloys are used as castings, but some alloys are available in wrought form. Certain precautions have to be taken when magnesium alloys are machined owing to the possibility of frictional heat at the tool nose generating sufficient heat to ignite the chips or powder produced. Tools are

therefore kept as sharp as possible and turnings etc. are not to be stored where exposed to air, but in a container with a lid.

Wrought magnesium alloys
These contain about 1.5% manganese and are called *manganese-aluminium* alloys. The manganese improves the corrosion resistance properties and gives greater welding facility. Usually the alloys are manufactured in five different tempers, ranging from soft to hard. The tensile strengths vary from 92.67 MN/m^2 to 200.77 MN/m^2. The Brinell hardness number varies from 27 to 54.

The magnesium alloys have a specific gravity about two-thirds of that of an aluminium alloy. Due to its lightness, the alloy is used a great deal in the construction of aircraft, space vehicles and automobiles.

Forms of supply are sheets, extruded rods, angles, sections and tubes.

Cast magnesium alloy
The cast 'electron' alloy, from the company called the Magnesium Elektron Ltd has a composition of 9.5 per cent aluminium, 1.5 per cent zinc and 1.0 per cent manganese and the remainder magnesium.

The aluminium and zinc act as hardeners to raise the mechanical property of the alloy. Permanent-mould and diecasting produce large complicated thin-walled cast parts used in aircraft and space vehicles. Other castings are made for hand trucks, power drill parts, chain saw parts, textile and printing machinery parts, crank cases and gearboxes for vehicles, cameras etc.

The lightness and the relatively high mechanical strength of the alloy make it an ideal alloy for the stated uses. Its minimum tensile strength varies from 138 MN/m^2 to 220 MN/m^2.

Alloying elements in steels

Carbon steel is an alloy of carbon and iron. The presence of carbon, usually in excess of 0.60 per cent is essential for assuring the *hardenability* of steels to the levels needed for tools. Raising the carbon content by different amounts up to a maximum of 1.3 per cent increases the hardness slightly and the *wear resistance* considerably.

Hardenability is the depth to which steel can be hardened to martensite under stated conditions of cooling.

During the present century, *alloy steels* have developed to a great extent and may be regarded as steels which contain specific added

amounts of other elements in addition to iron and carbon. The carbon is necessary for hardening and tempering; the alloying elements *modify* the effect of the treatment.

Alloying elements in steels are nickel, chromium, vanadium, molybdenum, tungsten, manganese and silicon.

Examples of the use of alloy steels are to be found in components for vehicle engines, modern heavy guns, tanks, cutting tools, crushing machinery, dredger parts, oil drilling equipment, railway crossings, dies, 'tin' helmets, turbines, gear wheels, jet engines, chemical vessels etc.

Alloy steels are used for the following reasons:

1 To enable the effect of heat treatment to appear uniformly in large masses of steel without the outer skin behaving differently from the inside, as would be the case if bulky sections of 'straight' carbon steel were treated.
2 To obtain a combination of mechanical properties by less drastic heat treatment than would be necessary in a plain carbon steel.
3 To enable special qualities to be imparted to the metal, such as great strength, hardness, resistance to wear, springiness, or resistance to corrosion.

Nickel (Ni)

A *nickel steel* usually contains from 3.0 to 3.5 per cent nickel and from 0.2 to 0.4 per cent carbon. It possesses toughness and good wear-resistance properties. It is used in the manufacture of armour plate, gun manufacture, bridge construction, in railway lines and in the automobile and aircraft industries. One of the properties required for armour plate is that it will not crack when perforated by a projectile.

A steel containing 36 per cent nickel and 0.2 per cent carbon is called *invar*. It is non-magnetic and stainless and has a low coefficient of thermal expansion. It is used in clocks and measuring instruments.

A 'case-hardening nickel steel' contains 3 per cent nickel and 0.15 per cent carbon.

Chromium (Cr)

High alloy tool steel

This element is added in amounts up to 12 per cent for tool steels. It improves hardenability and, together with high carbon, provides both wear resistance and toughness , a combination valuable in certain tool applications. However, high chromium raises the hardening temperature of the tool steel and thus can cause proneness to hardening deformations. A high percentage of chromium also affects the grindability of the tool steel. The chromium reduces the grain size.

Stainless steel

If not less than 13 per cent chromium is added to steel, the corrosion resistance is greatly increased. A steel with 13 per cent chromium and less than 0.1 per cent carbon is used for stainless steel turbine blades. The effect of carbon in raising the hardness is very rapid. Consequently, the stainless cutlery steel contain 13 per cent chromium and only 0.3 per cent carbon and can be hardened and then ground to a good cutting edge.

Chromium carbon steels

Carbon steels containing chromium characterised by their great hardness, mostly contain 0.5 to 2.25 per cent chromium and 0.8 to 1.2 per cent carbon. They also have the properties of toughness and stiffness. Typical applications of this steel are in the manufacture of files, saws, ball-bearings, safes, armour piercing projectiles, crushing and grinding machinery parts and permanent magnets for which purposes they are used in their hardened condition.

Chrome and nickel steels

Termed 18/8 steel, this very important stainless steel contains 18 per cent chrome and 8 per cent nickel. If heated and quenched it is quite soft and is very suitable for cold-working of all descriptions. The cold-working leads to considerable work hardening, but annealing can be repeated by heating and quenching. Many vessels and tools for chemical plants are worked up cold to shape in 18/8 steel.

Vanadium

This element contributes to the refinement of the carbide structure and thus improves the forgeability of alloy tool steels. Vanadium has a very strong tendency to form a hard carbide which improves both the hardness and the wear properties of tool steels; however, a large amount of vanadium carbide makes the grinding of the tool very difficult. Vanadium increases the temperature at which the *grains* begin to enlarge. Other effects are a greater retention of hardness in the tempered steel, a secondary hardness shown by the high speed and some other steels and a superior and finer microstructure. Vanadium steels are used for high speed tool steels, spring steels, heat-resistant and nitriding steels etc.

Molybdenum (Mo)

Molybdenum apparently has a similar effect to that of tungsten on steel, but in a more marked degree, 1 per cent of the element being as effective as about 2.5 per cent tungsten. The steels containing nickel and chromium some-times suffer from *temper-brittleness*. This is a defect which arises if the steel is held at a temperature between 250° and 500°C. The tensile strength remains high, but the shock resistance becomes dangerously low. This temperature range is often found in steam plant. This trouble can be overcome by the introduction of 0.5 per cent molybdenum. A typical alloy contains 3.0 per cent nickel, 0.8 per cent chromium, 0.5 per cent molybdenum and 0.25 per cent carbon.

Small quantities of molybdenum yield a finer 'grain' and improve the properties of many of the heat-resistant alloys. Nickel-chrome steels containing small amounts of molybdenum, used for such purposes as dies in drop-forging, do not scale so readily and have a longer life than those free of molybdenum. This element is also a constitutent of some of the 'super high speed' steels of composition of about 0.9 per cent carbon, 3.0 to 3.75 per cent chromium and 3.0 to 3.75 per cent molybdenum.

Tungsten (W)

This is one of the important alloying elements of tool steels, particularly because of two valuable properties: it improves '*hot-hardness*', that is the resistance of the steel to the softening effect of elevated temperatures and it also forms hard, abrasion-resistant carbides, thus improving the wear properties of tool steels.

The property that tungsten imparts to steel is that of *hardening in the air*, after heating to the required temperature. These alloys are termed *self-hardening* steels. The composition of tungsten steels is usually 5.0 to 15.0 per cent tungsten and from 0.4 to 2.0 per cent carbon.

Air hardening steels
These are steels adequate in carbon content, completely hardened by cooling in air or a suitable gas when at a temperature above the critical or transformation point at which the pearlitic or austenitic microstructure changes to martensitic form, i.e. the steel is above its transformation temperature range before cooling.

Classification of tungsten steels are as follows:

Chisel and punch steels for cold work
These are medium deep-hardening, harden in oil and have reasonable resistance to wear, together with good strength of resistance and impact. They are used for shear blades and can be used for dies.

Tungsten die steels for hot work
These have a fine grain microstructure but are liable to crack if hardened in water, so they are better hardened in air or oil. They have a

reasonable wear resistance, low distortion and high red-hardness. They readily carburise and are extensively used for hot-shaping of metals, dies for forging brass and punches and shears for hot work. They can also be used for diecasting aluminium and permanent moulds for brass and bronze.

Tungsten chromium die steels for hot work
They harden well in either air or oil, have reasonable resistance to wear and fairly high strength together with red-hardness. They have greater strength than the tungsten die steels and are much more resistant to impact, but readily carburise. They are mostly applied to dies for diecasting aluminium and aluminium alloys where impact is severe on occasions.

Manganese (Mn)
Manganese carbon steel can be classified into three common compositions.
1   Up to 1.5 per cent manganese but not exceeding 2.5 per cent, which has higher forging properties than ordinary carbon steel.
2   Up to 1.5 per cent manganese with not more than 0.4 per cent molybdenum for automobile crankshafts, medium tensile bolts, shafts and spindles in machinery.
3   11 to 14 per cent manganese and from 0.8 to 1.25 per cent carbon known as *Hadfield manganese steel*. With the high manganese content the steel becomes ductile and very hard. The ductility of the steel is brought out by sudden cooling, the process being opposite to that employed for carbon steel. This alloy has very pronounced work-hardening properties. It can be hot forged, but is very difficult to machine as cutting quickly leads to a hardened surface. It is machined with high cobalt, high-speed steel tools. The steel is *wear-resistant* to a

high degree, particularly when under severe pressure and abrasion. With the work-hardening surface, still retaining the toughness and ductility of the core, this steel is applied extensively to such duties as railway switches and crossings, dredger parts, such as pins, links, bucket lips and bushes, steam shovel parts, parts of crushing and grinding machines, pulverisers and conveying plant.

The steel can be cast, rolled into bars and rails or forged. Its strength in the rolled condition can vary between 896 MN/m^2 and 1081 MN/m^2.

Silicon
The element silicon is a *non-metal* and occurs widely in combination with other elements in sands, clays and other minerals. For most engineering purposes, the silicon should be kept below 0.5 per cent, since, although higher proportions cause slightly better resistance to corrosion, particularly as regards attack by dilute sulphuric acid, they result in drastic lowering of the tensile strength, ductility and resistance to shock. Silicon steels for corrosion resistance are made up with up to 15 per cent silicon. They have reasonable strength but cannot resist severe shock, nor corrosion by acids. With up to 4 per cent of silicon, the hot-forming properties of the steel is improved. In combination with other certain alloying elements the silicon content is sometimes raised to 2 per cent for increasing the strength and toughness of steels used for tools which have to sustain shock loads.

Primary forming processes

Sand casting

There are several ways of producing a casting
from molten metal and, of these, castings from
sand moulds are perhaps the best known.

The method used is that a cavity or mould is
made, approximately of the size and shape of
the required part, and is filled with molten
metal which is then allowed to solidify. The
mould is opened and the casting removed.

Let us assume that a casting is to be made
shaped like a letter T. The equipment
required will be a pair of metal or wooden
moulding boxes, flat wooden boards,
moulding sand, a pattern, molten metal and a
ladle.

Pattern making

The process of making a copy of the metal
casting in wood is called *pattern·making*. The
pattern is made of soft wood, usually yellow
pine. It can be easily worked and takes varnish
readily in order to make it more durable.

The moulding of the sand is done in a pair of
metal or wooden moulding boxes which
contain the sand and help it to hold together.

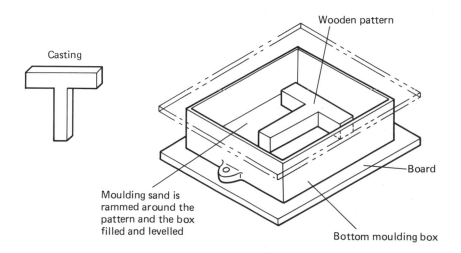

Casting

Wooden pattern

Moulding sand is
rammed around the
pattern and the box
filled and levelled

Board

Bottom moulding box

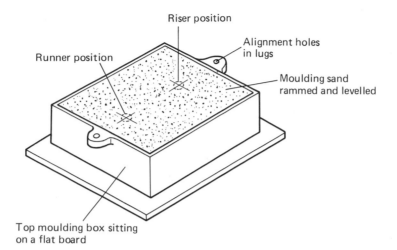

Riser position

Runner position

Alignment holes
in lugs

Moulding sand
rammed and levelled

Top moulding box sitting
on a flat board

The boxes are open at the top and bottom. One box is laid on a board and the wooden pattern is put face downwards on the board in a central position.

The box is filled with sand which is rammed firmly round the pattern, and another wooden board is placed on top of the moulding box, which is then turned over so that the pattern is uppermost.

The pattern is now carefully extracted from the sand leaving a T-shaped cavity. The top box, containing sand with a carefully smoothed surface is placed on top of the first moulding box containing the cavity, so that the cavity is now completely enclosed in sand. A channel or 'runner' must be cut through the sand in the moulding sand so that liquid metal can be poured down this runner and flow into the cavity at its lowest level.

One channel, called a 'riser' must also be made, so that the cast metal fills the cavity and rises up the riser; the provision of a riser assisting the complete filling of the mould, helping to ensure soundness in the casting, and providing an outlet for the air in the mould.

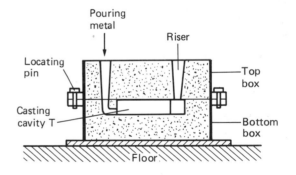

Pouring
metal

Riser

Locating
pin

Top
box

Casting
cavity T

Bottom
box

Floor

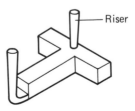

Riser

Solidified casting removed
from the mould

When the metal has solidified and the two halves of the mould separated, the casting remains attached to two columns of metal, representing the runner and riser. The surface texture on the casting is improved by *blast cleaning* in order to remove adhering sand. The methods employed include blasting with sand, metal shot, or grit, carried by a stream of compressed air or water.

The columns of metal can be removed by a hammer, sawing, shearing or burning off. Portable abrasive wheel tools can also improve the surface texture. Finally, painting of all areas, other than machined areas greatly improves the finish on sand castings.

Diecasting

Diecasting is a method of producing finished castings by forcing molten metal into a suitable die, which is arranged to open after the metal has solidified so that the casting can be removed. The diecasting process makes it possible to secure accuracy and uniformity in castings, excellent surface texture and machining costs are either eliminated altogether or greatly reduced. The dies are generally made of steel, although cast iron and non-metallic materials of a refractory nature have been used. Their design must permit the molten metal to rapidly flow to all parts of the impression and at the same time allow the air to escape.

The alloys used in modern diecasting practice may be divided into six main classifications as follows:
1 zinc-base alloys,
2 tin-base alloys,
3 lead-base alloys,
4 aluminium-base alloys,
5 copper-base or brass and bronze alloys,
6 magnesium-base alloys.

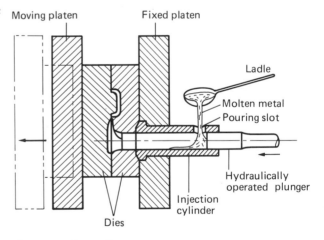

Sequence of operations
1 A molten shot is poured into the cylinder.

2 The plunger moves the molten metal into the die. Pressures up to 68 MN/m^2 may be used.

3 The moving platen and its attached die moves to the left and the cast component is removed.

Cold chamber die casting system

Parts produced are used in cash registers, meters, small housings, washing machines, gear wheels, automotive bearings, vacuum cleaners, camera parts etc. The strength of the castings relative to their weights is high for magnesium-base alloys and aluminium-base alloys. The tensile strength of copper-base alloys is also very high.

Due to the contraction of castings in cooling the size of patterns must be carefully calculated, allowance being made for the type of casting metal, the size and shape of the casting and the resistance of the mould to the normal contraction of the casting during cooling.

The amount added to a pattern to allow for machining the casting varies widely. On small castings to be finished by milling about 4 mm is usually allowed. On large castings allowances of 18 mm to 25 mm will be necessary.

Cast iron castings have very high compressive strengths.

Alloy cast iron castings have high tensile strengths of about 480 MN/m^2.

Extruded section for wrist watch cases

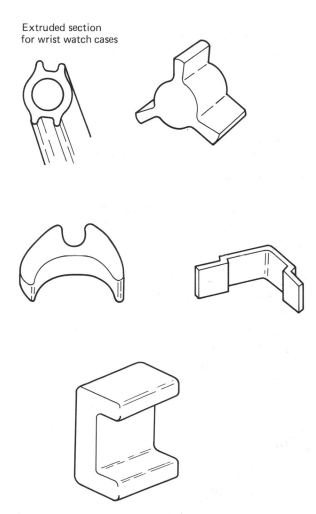

The extrusion process

By means of the extrusion process, certain fairly plastic metals are formed into various shapes by forcing the metal, which is usually heated, under high pressure through an aperture of the shape to be produced. In this manner, a continuous bar section or pipe of the cross-section of the aperture or die is produced.

The heated temperature for copper and brass is between 700° and 800°C and for aluminium alloys between 400° and 500°C.

Typical extruded steel sections

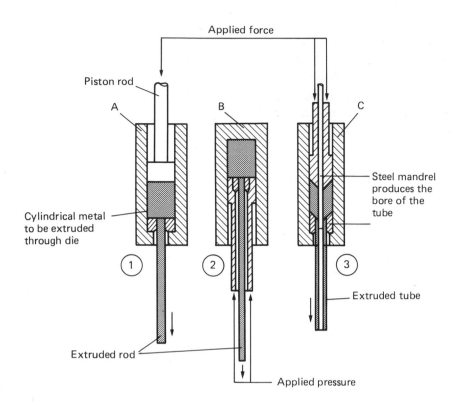

Applied force

Piston rod

A

B

C

Cylindrical metal
to be extruded
through die

Steel mandrel
produces the
bore of the
tube

① ② ③

Extruded tube

Extruded rod

Applied pressure

A, B and C fixed containers

① Direct extrusion process

② Indirect extrusion process
An average size press details.
Heated size of metal: $\varnothing$ 130 mm
$\times$ 600 mm long pressure applied
450 MN/m².
A rod $\varnothing$ 31 mm $\times$ 9m long is
extruded in 15 seconds.

③ Extrusion of lead pipe for plumbing.
The pipe can also be extruded and
shrunk on to finished cotton
covered insulation wire.

Die orifices are made in a variety of different shapes so as to produce different sections, such as curtain rails, windscreen and window sections for automobiles, glazing bars and window sections for double glazing, gear wheels, ratchet wheels, etc. The process is so economical that for copper, aluminium, magnesium and lead alloys, extrusion is a normal production procedure for such products as rods, bars, tubes and strips. The extruded rod or section is sometimes finally drawn through another die in the cold state. This is in order to improve the finished dimensional accuracy and surface texture and the work hardening effect increases the strength of the material.

Forging

Forging is the process whereby a piece of metal heated to a high temperature is subjected to hammering, pressing or bending into shape. Village blacksmiths forge metal pieces that they can handle, using a hammer, an anvil and a variety of tools.

Machine forging

For larger pieces of metals, power operated hammers are used, driven by water power, compressed air, steam or friction. In most of these machines the hammer becomes an upper anvil called a *tup* which is controlled to lift up, and falls, or is driven down, onto the lower anvil which is built into the base. The forging supported by chains from overhead cranes can be moved horizontally and rotate about its axis. This enables, for example, a billet to be forged to a circular cross-section. The surface texture and the accuracy of size depends on the skill of the operator.

Drop forging

This is a machine-forging process used to produce large numbers of similar parts. A pair of dies with appropriate cavities, one fitted to the tup and one to the floor anvil, are aligned when they come together. The heated blank is usually preformed to a suitable size and shape before it is placed in the bottom die. The top die at a predetermined height is released and the energy of its fall squeezes the metal into the two halves of the die. Any excess metal squeezes out and forms a fin or flash between the faces of the dies.

Removing the flash by mechanical methods does leave a tell-tale mark on the forging. As in sand casting, allowance has to be made by the dies for contraction of the forging. Nevertheless, a more or less finished shape with a very

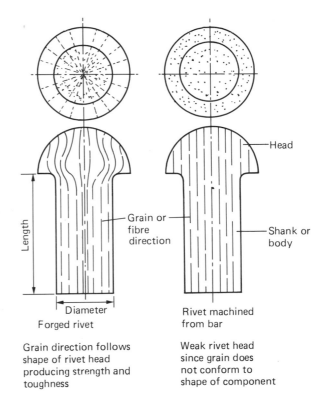

Length

Diameter

Forged rivet

Grain or fibre direction

Head

Shank or body

Rivet machined from bar

Grain direction follows shape of rivet head producing strength and toughness

Weak rivet head since grain does not conform to shape of component

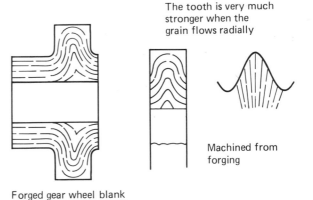

Forged gear wheel blank

The tooth is very much stronger when the grain flows radially

Machined from forging

Grain flow

good surface texture is obtained. Drop forging
reduces machining costs and also gives a better
flow of the grain in the finished articles, so
giving a greater tensile strength to withstand
applied loads.

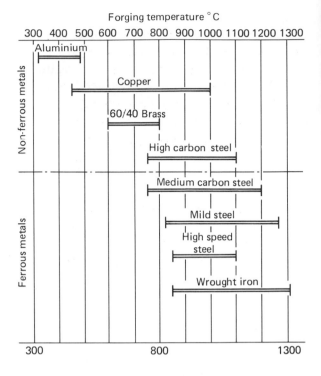

Typical forging temperature for metals

Drawing

Drawing is a process of producing wire or
bright bars. The raw material for making wire
is hot-rolled bar about 6 mm diameter. After
annealing, cooling and removal of scale, the
steel bar is pointed at one end and then
inserted through a hole in the die slightly
smaller than the size of the rod. The pointed
end is gripped from the other side and the bar
pulled through, thus reducing its diameter. In
modern continuous methods, particularly
applied to copper, the wire is drawn through a
first die, turned round a roller, then passed
through a second die, and the same procedure
is repeated eight or nine times, using
successively smaller holes and rollers of
increasing peripheral speed.

By drawing black mild steel bars through dies,
bright-drawn mild steel bars or rods are
produced. The drawing process causes the
grains to be elongated in the direction of
drawing and tends to increase the tensile
strength of the metal. The surface is also work-
hardened by the action of the die on the metal.
A very smooth surface texture is obtained but
if any 'built-up' edge is formed on the hole in
the die, then horizontal lines will be formed on
the surface.

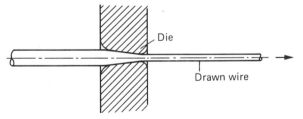

Die material can be hardened
alloy steel, sintered carbide or
diamond

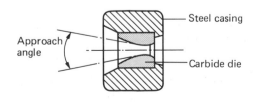

Wire drawing

Rolling

This is a process of reducing ingots of metal into finished sections such as rectangular, round, joists, railway lines, square, etc. The metal is squeezed between pairs of rolls, their contours depending on the shape of rolled section required. Metals may be rolled either hot or cold. The advantage of working the metal hot is that it may be reduced in thickness more easily, on the other hand, the surface condition and accuracy are not so good as those obtained by cold-rolling. The most general use of hot-rolling, therefore, is for breaking down large ingots; cold-rolling may then be used to complete the shaping very accurately. In practice, a number of pairs of rolls set in mill-housings are used so that each in turn reduces the metal by rolling.

For cold-rolling, the material supplied is initially hot-rolled near to size and has been pickled in acid to remove the scale. To produce sheet steel for the car industry, the metal is rolled between rolls that have been ground accurately to a smooth finish. The sheet is passed through a number of rolls in housings in order to obtain the required width and thickness. The surface texture of the sheet is the same as the finishing rolls. The sheet's thickness across the width is very accurate; the grains have been elongated due to rolling and its tensile strength has increased. Work-hardening of the surface has also taken place.

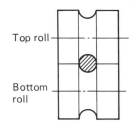
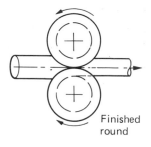

Finished round

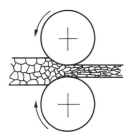
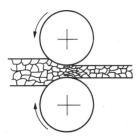

Cold rolling
Elongated distorted grain structure: hard, internally stressed structure

Hot rolling
Reformed grain structure: hardening and internal stresses alleviated

Rolling

Pressing

Pressing is the operation of forcing blanks of sheet metal into dies. The sheet metal then bears an exact reproduction of the die. Buttons and similar articles are stamped from sheet metal, using dies which bear an exact reproduction of the design to be embossed. Circular blanks of annealed brass or nickel silver are punched from a strip and each blank is placed in turn on the anvil of a stamping machine. One half of the die is mounted on a heavy steel block which is raised to a given height and dropped on the metal blanks, thus stamping the pattern on the front of the button.

Making a cartridge case by pressing is described in the section on 70/30 brass.

Motor car bodies are made from a number of parts each shaped by pressing in great hydraulic presses and finally welded together. The material used is annealed bright mild steel sheet.

The articles produced are accurate in size and detail, do not require machining and have very good surface texture. Due to the flow of the sheet metal work-hardening takes place. Work-hardening is an advantage for its use in buttons. In the pressing of a cartridge annealing is necessary.

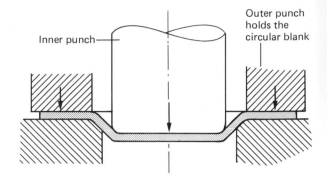

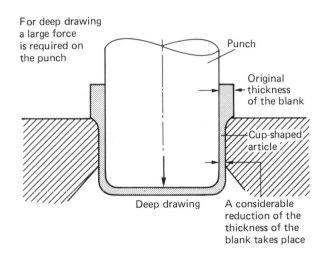

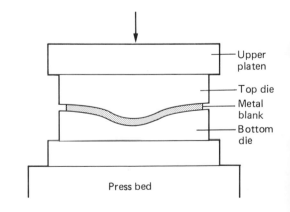

Pressing

Metals under the microscope

The microscope is the most useful scientific instrument assisting the metallurgist in every-day work; with its aid, a skilled observer can learn a great deal about the structure, the manufacturing history, the effect of heat-treatment and the causes of breakage of any given piece of metal or alloy. Usually a camera is also provided so that the structure can be photographed.

The preparation of a metal specimen entails the following:

1 A piece of metal approximately 12 mm × 12 mm × 12 mm is cut off.
2 One face is then filed flat, ground with successive finer grades of emery paper and finally polished with a polishing powder. The metal possesses a flat, mirror-like surface. At this stage the specimen is examined under the microscope by means of reflected light to see if there are any cracks, inclusions or holes.
3 The polished surface is now 'etched'. This etching is carried out by immersing the metal in a chemical solution until the polished surface appears slightly dulled. Replacing the specimen under the microscope, the etched surface of a polished metal reveals that metals (and alloys) are built up of innumerable small *grains* or *crystals*. The grain boundaries have been more readily attacked by the solution than the interior of the grains or crystals.

If the crystals or grains are small, the metal is usually strong, hard and tough: if the grains are large the metal is weak and ductile.

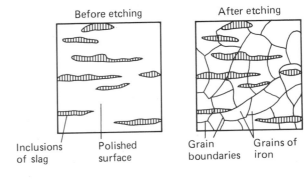

Wrought iron
Viewed under the microscope

Before etching   After etching

Inclusions of slag   Polished surface   Grain boundaries   Grains of iron

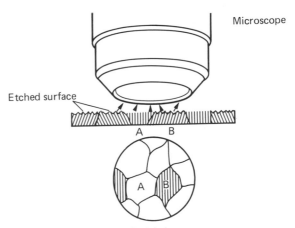

Microscope

Etched surface

When light falls on the grain A it is reflected back and this grain appears light.

For grain B the light is reflected sideways and appears dark.

Microstructure

Tensile testing

The tensile strength and the ductility of a material are determined by performing a tensile test. The tensile testing machine grips each end of the prepared specimen.

Increments of load are then applied to stretch the specimen and in each case the load applied and the specimen's extension are recorded. In the case of a Hounsfield testing machine, a complete graph of load against extension up to the point of destruction is produced for the specimen under test.

Important points on the graph for a mild steel specimen are:

A The *limit of proportionality*; up to this point, Hooke's law applies — 'that the extension is directly proportional to the load applied'.

B The *elastic limit*: beyond this point the specimen has 'permanent set' and will not return to its original length if unloaded.

C The *yield point*: a sudden extension occurs without any increase in load.

D The *ultimate load*: corresponding to the ultimate tensile stress (alternatively called the *tensile strength*) and hence the maximum nominal stress, recorded during the test.

E The *breaking load*: corresponding to the *nominal stress at break*: this is less than that at D because of localised narrowing or 'necking' of the specimen.

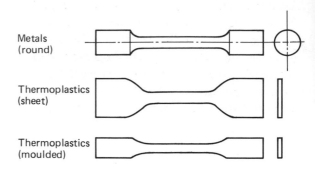

Metals (round)

Thermoplastics (sheet)

Thermoplastics (moulded)

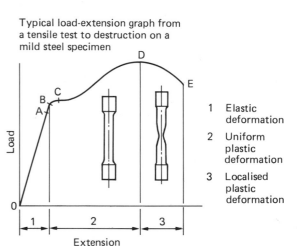

Typical load-extension graph from a tensile test to destruction on a mild steel specimen

1 Elastic deformation

2 Uniform plastic deformation

3 Localised plastic deformation

Forms of tensile specimen

Tensile testing using a Hounsfield tensometer

Constructional details

When the *handle* is rotated it operates a *worm and wheel mechanism* which rotates the *screw*. The screw moves the *movable crosshead* along its *guide rods*.

Attached to the crosshead is the *collet chuck* A. When a load is applied to collet chuck B, it is transmitted through the *tension head* to the *spring beam*, the defection of which is proportional to the load, and this deflection is measured by the movement of the mercury in the *glass tube*. The *cursor* slides along the *load graduated scale* and the *pricker*, also set in the cursor, makes a small hole in the *graph paper*. When the square thread screw rotates, its wheel meshes with a gear keyed to a shaft, which passes through the centre of the top guide rod on the diagram. This rotation is magnified by the *drive to drum* mechanism.

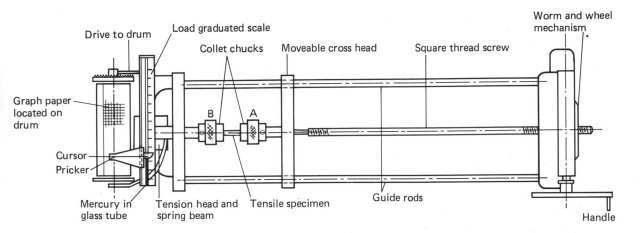

Hounsfield tensometer

Procedure to carry out a tensile test
1 A prepared specimen is gripped in collets A and B.
2 The handle is rotated to 'bed in' the specimen and the cursor lined up with the top of the mercury.
3 The graph is pricked.
4 A further load is applied by rotating the handle. Again the cursor is moved to line up with the mercury reading and the paper is pricked.
5 This procedure is repeated until the specimen breaks.
6 By removing the graph paper from the drum, the load extension graph is visible by the series of holes produced by the pricks. Joining the holes with a pencil or pen then completes the graph.

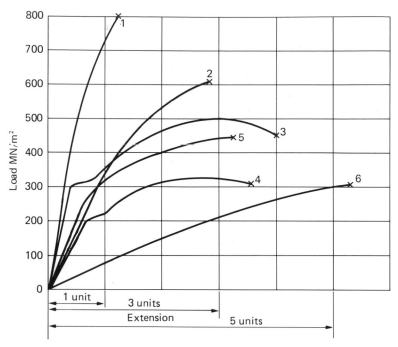

Load extension diagrams for different materials, the results being obtained from test pieces of identical dimensions

Tensile tests

Tensile tests for different materials

Curve 1 is for heat-treated *alloy steel*. The alloy steel has no clearly defined yield point and is not particularly ductile. Its tensile strength is about twice that of mild steel.

Curve 2 represents a fully heat-treated (solution heat-treatment and aged) wrought aluminium alloy.

Curve 3 is that for *mild steel*, of the form already shown.

Curve 4 is the same alloy in the annealed, or softest possible, condition. The tensile strength of the heat-treated aluminium alloy is about twice that of the annealed aluminium alloy.

Curve 5 is for a 70/30 brass.

Curve 6 is for an annealed, virtually pure copper, and showing high ductility.

The extension of the mild steel is about three and one third times that of the alloy steel. The extension of the copper is about four and a half times that of the alloy steel.

Types of fracture

It will be seen that cast steel, cast iron and heat-treated alloy steel, being brittle materials, break with little extension, while the rest, being ductile, such as mild steel, aluminium and copper, show considerable extension during the plastic stages.

The extent of the ductility of a material is shown in the form of the actual fracture. Brittle materials give a clean fracture with practically no decrease in diameter, while ductile materials undergo considerable necking, or reduction in area, and always give a crater-like fracture due to the part sliding, part tearing action at the moment of final breakdown.

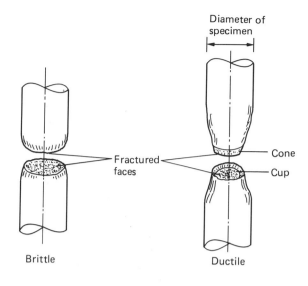

Examples of how materials appear after tensile fracture

Compression testing

Machines used for tensile testing can also be used for compression testing. The specimen may be in the form of a cylinder (for metals, and certain plastics) or a cube (for building materials such as concrete and stone).

For a ductile material, such as mild steel, the load-compression graph will be as shown. As in a tensile test, there is an elastic range followed by a yield point Y. After the yield point the diagram has an increasing upward slope; this is due chiefly to the increase in the cross-sectional area of the specimen as its

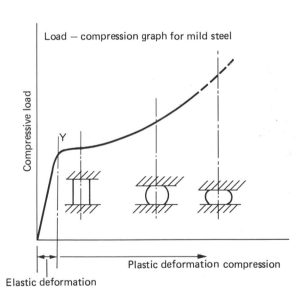

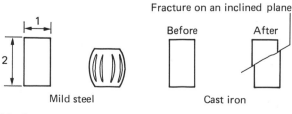

Various materials before and after compression loading

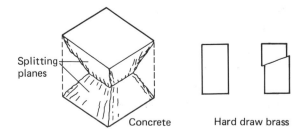

length is reduced. Eventually, surface cracks may develop, but no 'maximum load' can be identified as in a tensile test.

In the case of metals, the turned specimens are used with a ratio of height to diameter of 2:1.

Metals of a plastic character show no breakdown point. The tests can be made comparative by stating the force required to reduce the length by a definite proportion — usually 50 per cent. Brittle metals in compression behave elastically up to a certain load, then fail suddenly by splitting or cracking on an inclined plane.

For such materials the ultimate compressive

$$stress = \frac{maximum\ compressive\ load}{original\ cross\text{-}section\ area}$$

For concrete and stone, 100 mm cubes are compressed to destruction. Again the brittle material fails on inclined planes of 45°.

Basic plastic-forming processes

Injection moulding
This process, which grew out of the diecasting of metals was developed and first used for making articles of cellulose acetate by Eichengrun in 1921 and is now one of the most important methods of plastic manipulation, both in terms of the variety of products made and the amount of material handled;

The injection moulding process

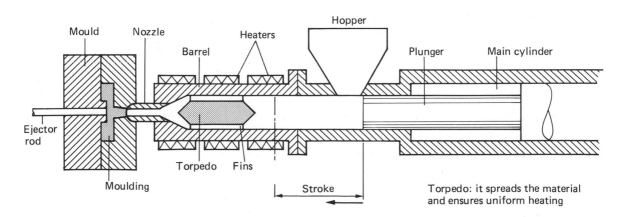

Torpedo: it spreads the material and ensures uniform heating

practically every known plastic material (including rubber) can be processed in suitable injection machines, to make items from about 50 g up to 16 kg at one 'shot', using a single-cavity mould for large articles or a multi-cavity mould for small ones. The process differs from compression moulding in that the plastic material is rendered fluid in a separate chamber outside the mould, and is transferred by pressure from this into the cooled mould. The mould is split, the two halves being locked together by pressure, opening automatically when the cavity in the mould has been filled by a 'shot' of the liquefied plastic, the opening of the two halves giving access for the removal of the moulded article.

The moulds which are usually made of special steels, involve complicated design considerations and are very expensive, making long 'runs' essential to offset their capital cost.

Different plastics have differing moulding temperatures and pressures. Low density polythene is an ideal injection material, whereas polypropylene requires moulding pressure fifteen times as great as that required by polythene.

Blow moulding

A particularly important development of tube-extrusion is the process of blow moulding, by which enormous numbers of plastic bottles are manufactured. Polythene, rigid PVC and many other plastics are operated on based on glass-bottle technique. An intermediate form is produced by extruding a molten tube length into a split mould which is closed, nipping the tube at the lower end, and then introducing air to blow it to fill the inside face of the mould.

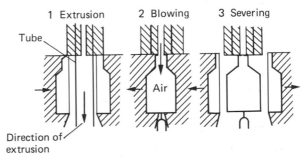

Blow moulding

Compression moulding

This form of moulding is used in the production of articles from thermosetting materials. For the production of a simple cup-like unit, split-steel moulds would be used. The process operated in compression mould-ing is a relatively simple one. The moulds are pre-heated by electricity to a temperature of 95°C to 200°C. The necessary quantity of powder or tablets is then introduced into the mould. The mould is then closed under high pressure for a certain calculated time and the temperature required is maintained. During this period the powder is first liquefied and caused to flow throughout the mould. Being of the thermo-hardening type, however, it is then converted into the infusible state at the temperature of the mould. When the mould is re-opened by retracting the plunger of the press, the solid moulded unit can be ejected. The moulding pressure required varies from 15 to 46 MN/m².

The *cure* time is the time the mould is under pressure and temperature, which varies from a half to two minutes.

Vacuum forming

All permanently thermoplastic sheets can be shaped by a process known as *vacuum forming*, which is an important method of fabrication. The basic feature is that the sheet of plastic to be formed is heated by a heater plate above it and subjected to light pressures of 170 to 250 KN/m². In simple vacuum-forming the plastic sheet is clamped over an air-tight box, to which vacuum is applied rapidly, drawing the heated plastic down onto a 'former' within the box where it sets to the required shape; this can only be shallow if thinning and rupture are to be avoided.

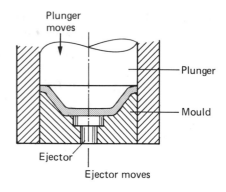

Compression moulding

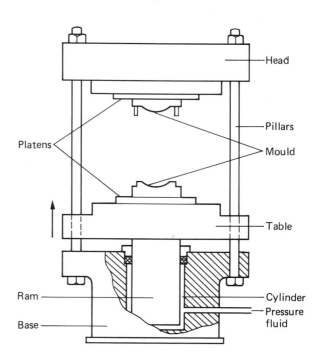

Simple upstroking compression — moulding press

Bearing materials
Factors which influence the choice of bearing materials, when considering plain bearings and machine tool slideways, where the moving parts slide over each other are as follows:

1 *Coefficient of friction* (μ)
   This should be as low as possible to avoid wasting energy. Friction causes heat which heats the bearing up. Excessive heat could result in the bearing seizing up, the shaft becoming welded to the bearing.
2 *Wear resistance*
   The bearing material must resist wear due to the rubbing action taking place. If wear does take place it is better that the bearing material wears out rather than the journal. It is less costly and easier to replace the bearing than the journal.
3 *Strength*
   The material must have sufficient compression strength to carry the load when the journal is at rest and also when it is rotating.
4 *Plasticity*
   A bearing material should be capable of slightly distorting in order to allow the journal to 'bed-in' to ensure alignment.
5 *Surface texture*
   The ideal material should consist of facets of hard anti-friction material dispersed through a soft matrix. The hard particles stand out in slight relief, the softer matrix wearing to yield a series of microscopic channels which form an effective irrigation system for the lubricant. Antimony is an example of hard anti-friction material.

6 *Corrosion resistance*
   The bearing material should resist corrosion by:
   (a) impurities in the lubricant,
   (b) impurities that may form in service, and
   (c) attack of any additives in the lubricant intended to give it greater lubricity.
7 *Thermal conductivity*
   Since some friction is always present in a bearing, the heat resulting can only be dissipated through the lubricant or the conduction through the bearing walls. The bearing material must have a good thermal conductivity value.

The tables show bearing materials, their properties and applications.

Category	Composition (%)					Properties and applications
	Tin	Antimony	Copper	Lead	Phosphorus	
White metal	93.0	3.5	3.5	—	—	Combines maximum toughness with strength. Uses for big-end bearings for light and medium duty high-speed internal combustion engines. High cost bearings.
	86.0	10.5	3.5	—	—	Harder than the above but still tough. Used for main bearings for the same type of engines as above.
	80.0	11.0	3.0	6.0	—	Very useful for heavy loads and high speeds: diesel engines, turbines, rolling mills, locomotives. Lead improves plasticity where alignment is a problem.
	60.0	10.0	1.5	28.5	—	Heavy duty marine reciprocating engines, dynamos and other electrical machines.
	40.0	10.0	1.5	48.5	—	Generally useful for heavy pressure and medium speed or medium pressure and high speed. Low cost bearings. Used in automobile and railway engines.
Bronze	10.5	—	89.0	—	0.5	This alloy has a low coefficient of friction, great hardness and very pronounced resistance to wear. Suitable for heavy load bearings.
	10.0	—	79.9	10.0	0.1	Phosphorus has a deoxidising influence on the alloy and causes a sounder cast bearing. Alloy called phosphor-bronze. Lead reduces rigidity but helps alignment. Good anti-friction bearing.
	5.0	—	65.0	30.0	—	So-called plastic bronzes. Due to the high lead content it has excellent self-alignment properties. Used for railway axle and other bearings where no considerable pressure is involved.

Category	Composition (%)						Properties and applications
	Iron	Carbon	Silicon	Manganese	Sulphur	Phosphorus	
Cast iron	94.4	3.0	1.3	0.7	0.1	0.5	The flakes of graphite (carbon) in grey cast iron gives it self-lubricating properties. Used for heavy duty, low speed applications such as machine tool slideways. Cast iron is the only material that can be used for a journal and its bearing.
Plastic	Polytetrafluoroethylene						*Teflon*: Can withstand much higher temperatures than most plastics. Very expensive anti-friction coating. It has a very low coefficient of friction. Does not require lubrication.
	Polyamide						*Nylon*: Does not require lubrication. Can be moulded, machined and extruded. Used in office, food-processing, kitchen equipment, etc.
	High density polyethylene						Low cost bearings. Does not require lubrication. Cannot support such high loads as nylon or Teflon.

Heat treatment

Metals are heat-treated for many reasons, the more common of which are:

1   To improve mechanical properties.
2   To relieve internal stresses.
3   To impart hardness and wear resistance.
4   To soften for further working operations.

The process of heat-treatment involves heating the metal to a certain temperature, holding for a period of time and controlling the rate of cooling.

Structure of fully annealed carbon steel

In carbon steel that has been fully annealed there are normally present two constituents: the element iron in the form metallurgically known as *ferrite* and the chemical compound iron carbide in the form metallurgically known as *cementite*. This latter constituent consists of 6.67 per cent carbon and 93.33 per cent iron. A certain proportion of these two constituents will be present as a mechanical mixture. This mechanical mixture, the amount of which depends upon the carbon content of the steel, consists of alternate bands or layers of ferrite and cementite. Under the microscope it frequently has the appearance of mother-of-pearl and hence has been named *pearlite*. Pearlite contains about 0.85 per cent carbon and 99.15 per cent iron. A fully annealed steel containing 0.8 per cent carbon would consist entirely of pearlite. Such a steel is known as *eutectoid* steel and has a laminated structure characteristic of an entectic alloy.

Steel which has less than 0.85 per cent carbon (*hypo-eutectoid* steel) has an excess of ferrite above that required to mix with the cementite present to form pearlite; hence both ferrite and pearlite are present in the fully annealed state.

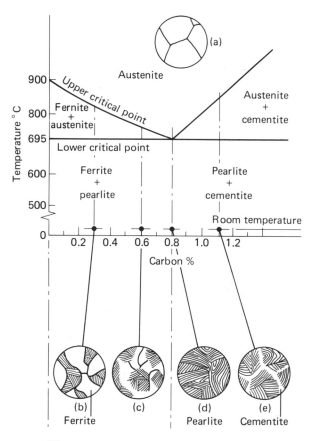

Microstructures

(a) Austenite

(b) About two thirds ferrite, remainder pearlite

(c) About two thirds pearlite, remainder ferrite

(d) Completely pearlitic

(e) Pearlite plus free cementite

The iron/iron carbide equilibrium diagram

Steel having a carbon content greater than 0.85 per cent (*hyper-eutectoid* steel) has an excess of cementite over that required to mix with the ferrite to form pearlite; hence both cementite and pearlite are present in the fully annealed state. The structural constitution of carbon steel in terms of ferrite, cementite, pearlite and austenite for different carbon contents and at different temperatures is shown in the iron/iron-carbide equilibrium diagram.

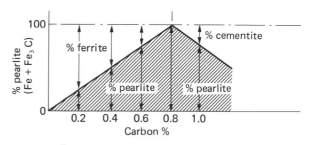

Graph of pearlite content against carbon

Hardening

Effect of rapid cooling or quenching carbon steel
Observations have shown that as the rate at which carbon steel is cooled from an austenitic state is increased, the temperature at which the austenite begins to change into pearlite drops more and more below the slow cooling transformation temperature of about 700°C. (For example, a 0.8 per cent carbon steel that is cooled at such a rate that the temperature drops 260° in one second will show transformation of austenite beginning at 500°C.) As the rate of cooling is still further increased, this transformation temperature suddenly drops down to around 260°C or lower, depending on the carbon content of the steel. The cooling rate at which this sudden drop in transformation temperature takes place is called the *critical cooling rate*.

When a piece of carbon steel is quenched at this rate or faster, a new structure is formed. The austenite is transformed into *martensite* which is characterised by an angular needle-like structure and a very high hardness. It is, however, very brittle and has practically no ductility. Such a steel would have a Brinell hardness of at least 700 as against about 200 in the annealed (pearlitic) state. The *hardening* of steel is entirely dependent on the formation of martensite, since austenite is comparatively soft and ductile.

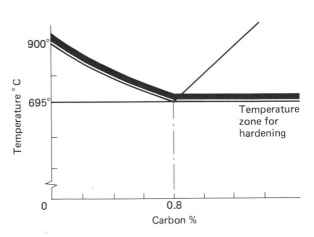

Iron/iron carbide diagram showing hardening temperatures for plain carbon steels

Annealing

The purpose of annealing may be:

1   To remove stresses that have occurred during casting or as a result of cold-working on steel.
2   To soften steel for greater ease of machining, cutting, stamping, drawing etc.
3   To alter ductility, toughness, electrical or magnetic characteristics or other physical properties.
4   To refine the grain structure and make the steel homogeneous.
5   To produce a desired microstructure.
Annealing is applied also to other materials as well as steel.

The *full annealing* of carbon steel consists in heating it slightly above the *upper* critical point for hypo-entectoid steels and slightly above the *lower* critical point for hyper-entectoid steels, holding it at this temperature until it is uniformly heated and then slowly cooling it to 540°C or below. This is performed by switching off the heat to a furnace and leaving the steel to cool down with the furnace or burying the steel in warm sand. The resulting structure is layer-like or lamellar due to the pearlite which is formed during the slow cooling.

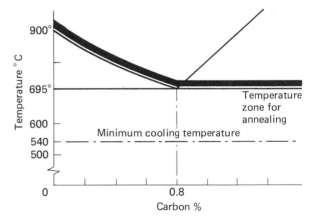

Iron/iron carbide diagram showing annealing temperatures for plain carbon steels

Normalising

The *normalising* of steel consists in heating it to some temperature above that used for annealing, usually about 50°C above the *upper* critical range and then cooling it in still air at room temperature. Normalising is intended to put the steel into a uniform unstressed condition of proper grain size and refinement so that it will properly respond to further heat-treatments. It is particularly important in the case of forgings which are later to be heat-treated. Normalising is also carried out as an intermediate treatment on steels requiring further machining and although normalised

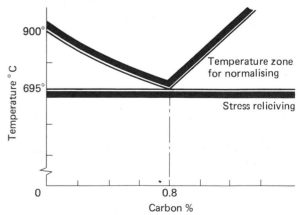

Iron/iron carbide diagram showing normalising and stress relieving temperatures for plain carbon steels

steels are somewhat stronger and harder than annealed steels due to their finer grain size, give a better machined finish. It is also used as a finishing treatment for steels of less than 0.35 per cent carbon content giving the best combination of mechanical properties.

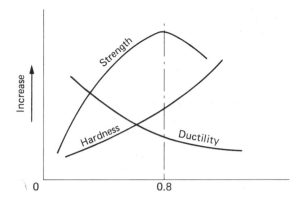

Effect of carbon content on normalised plain carbon steel

Tempering

The object of *tempering* or *drawing* is to reduce brittleness in hardened steel and to remove internal strains caused by sudden cooling. The tempering process consists in reheating the steel to a certain temperature and then cooling. It causes the hard martensite to break down and the steel loses some of its hardness and gains in toughness.

Tempering temperatures

If steel is heated in an oxidising atmosphere a film of oxide forms on the surface which changes colour as the temperature increases. These oxide colours can be used, as a workshop method, as a means of gauging the approximate amount of temper given to a hardened steel.

The availability of reliable pyrometers (high temperature measuring instruments) in combination with tempering baths of oil, salt or lead make it possible to heat the work uniformly and to a given temperature within close limits.

Temperature °C	Tool	Colour
200	Scribers, gauges	Faint straw
230	Lathe tools	Pale straw
240	Drills	Dark straw
250	Taps	Brown
260	Centre punches	Brown/purple
270	Press punches	Purple
280	Cold chisels	Dark purple
300	Springs	Blue

Tempering temperatures and oxide colours

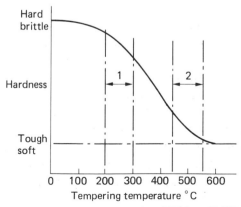

1 Low-temperature tempering, 200°C to 300°C.
2 High-temperature tempering, 450°C to 550°C, to obtain a hardened plain carbon steel in its toughest state

Effect of tempering temperature on hardness

Stress relief

This is a thermal treatment in which the locked-up stresses in a metal caused by cold-working, machining and other fabrication processes, are removed by heating the material close to but below the lower limit of the critical temperature range, or to approximately 40°C below the tempering temperature. Stresses incurred during fabrication may become unbalanced and because of this could result in distortion and warping. In severe cases, cracking may result. Another result of internal stress is stress corrosion, for example around spot welding areas on cars.

Pack carburising

Carburising is the oldest method of *case-hardening*, a process which consists of treating the surface of a piece of low carbon steel in such a way that it absorbs additional carbon and so forms a *case* or *outer skin* of high carbon steel.

Case-hardened Steels

These are steels low in carbon content hardened in such a manner that the external surface or 'case' has a much higher hardness than the central mass or 'core'. The case-hardening effect can be produced by various processes such as carburising with a carbonaceous substance, but also by cyaniding, nitriding, carbon-nitriding, induction-hardening and flame-hardening. The steels suitable for the carburising process include carbon steels and alloy steels such as nickel steel, nickel-chromium steels, molybdenum steels, etc.

Pack carburising is a method of carburising in which the articles to be carburised are cleaned and packed loosely in a metal box with carbonaceous material or with a commercial carburising compound. Carbonaceous materials that have been used include coal,

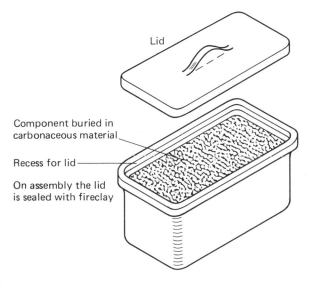

Lid

Component buried in carbonaceous material

Recess for lid

On assembly the lid is sealed with fireclay

Carburising box (heat-resistant cast alloy)

charcoal, charred bone, wood and hide scraps. Commercial compounds usually are hard-wood, charcoal or bone charcoal and include carbonates of barium, calcium and sodium. Plain carbon steels with carbon content between 0.12 and 0.18 per cent, and steels which contain amounts of nickel or nickel and chromium, are suitable.

In general, the higher the carburising temperature and the longer the process time, the greater is the carbon content of the case and the greater is its depth. During the prolonged carburising process, the outer skin could be 1.1 per cent carbon content and the core could be say 0.3 per cent carbon from an initial say 0.15 per cent carbon composition. It will be in an annealed state.

Heat-treatment is now necessary to produce a hard skin or case and a tough core. From the iron/iron carbide diagram, the temperatures are obtained. Thus the temperatures and quenches used in the process are:

1 Carburising 930°C.
2 Core refining 870°C with an oil quench.
3 Case hardening, 750°C with a water quench.

Finally, a low temperature tempering at 200°C may be used with prolonged heating and slow cooling for the purpose of stress relieving.

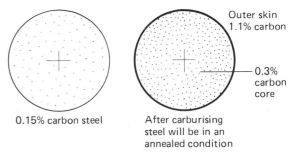
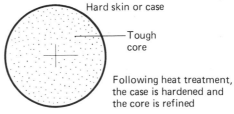

Circular cross-section component

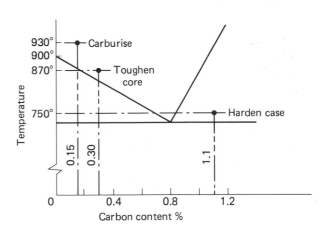

Application of iron/iron carbide diagram to case hardening

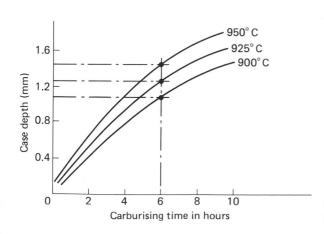

Effects of carburising time and temperature on depth of case produced

Flame-hardening

This is a *surface*-hardening process in which a highly concentrated oxy-acetylene flame is passed rapidly over the portions of the pieces of work which are to be hardened. The flame is followed immediately by a jet of water or an air blast to quench the heated surface layer.

The process is used to harden cams, gears, shafts, lathe beds and similar articles which might crack and warp if hardened by conventional furnace heating and subsequent quenching. Carbon steels of 0.4 to 0.6 per cent carbon are used and the depth of case obtainable by the flame-hardening process is up to 5 mm.

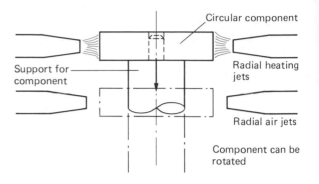

Flame hardening

Induction hardening

This is a surface-hardening process based upon the heating effect produced in a piece of carbon steel by placing it in a high-frequency electric field generated in a suitably shaped water-cooled coil of copper wire or tubing. One of the major disadvantages of the flame-hardening process is the risk of overheating and burning; induction heating overcomes this problem. The heating effects due to the induced current are confined mainly to the surface regions. The depth of 'case' heated can be controlled with great accuracy. The component can then be quenched in water or oil.

The induction-hardening process may be operated on an automatic cycle when once set up and, because of the accuracy of timing, the product has a high degree of uniformity. Because the heating of the surface is extremely rapid, little heat is conducted to the core and the core retains its original structure with consequent minimum internal stresses.

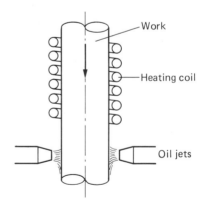

Induction hardening

Heat-treatment furnaces

Safety precautions

There are two main dangers when heat-treating metals:

1 Burns that can be both serious and painful.
2 Fire.

In heat-treatment shops the operators must be provided with adequate protective clothing, including goggles or, better still, a transparent face visor, leather apron and leather gloves.

1 Always wear the clothing provided.
2 Assume everything is hot until you have proved it cold.
3 Oil-quenching baths should have an air-tight lid. If the oil catches fire, closing the lid stops the air from feeding the flames and puts the fire out. Leave the lid on until the oil cools down.
4 Oil-quenching baths should be provided with a circulating and cooling system to keep the temperature below the flash point of the oil, especially when ·production-quenching large quantities of work. Lubricating oil must *never* be used for quenching, only the special oils developed for quenching are safe and give the desired results.
5 Never light up a furnace until you have been properly instructed and have been given permission.
6 Never use a salt-bath furnace without first drying and pre-heating everything that is put into the salts.
7 Never tamper with temperature-recording and controlling devices.
8 Learn where the fire extinguishers are kept and learn how to use them.
9 Learn what to do if your workmate's clothes catch fire.
10 Learn how to give the alarm if a fire breaks out.

Types of heat-treatment furnaces

Various types of furnaces heated by gas, oil or electricity are used for the heat treatment of steel. These include the muffle and radiant furnaces and the salt bath.

Muffle furnace

The work is charged into a chamber of muffle constructed of refractory materials and is then sealed with a door. The outside of the muffle is heated and radiating heat from the walls falls onto the work contained inside. Initial heating up of the furnace is slow but has the advantage that the products of combustion are unlikely to cause contamination of work. In other muffle-type furnaces, heat resistant alloy steel muffles are used which can be placed over the work and a seal made between the muffle and the furnace base. A 'furnace' bell is then lowered over the whole and heating takes place. An advantage of this process is that once the heating cycle has been completed the bell can be removed allowing the work to cool down in the muffle without contamination.

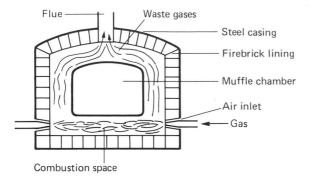

Natural-draught gas-fired muffle furnace

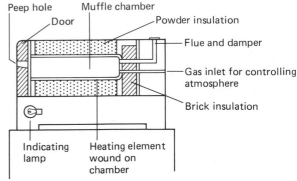

Electric muffle furnace

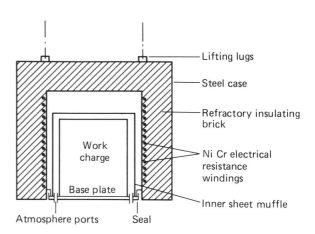

A lifting bell type muffle furnace

Radiant furnaces

Tunnel furnaces utilise radiant tube heating. Radiant tubes are made of ceramics, alloy cast iron, or alloy steel in which the fuel burns. Gas and oil burn in the radiant tubes but they can also be heated using internal electric elements. Tubes heat up rapidly and radiate energy onto the work charge. Controlled atmospheres can readily be used in radiant tube furnaces. The furnace can cater for large quantities of charges and of varying sizes from small to large.

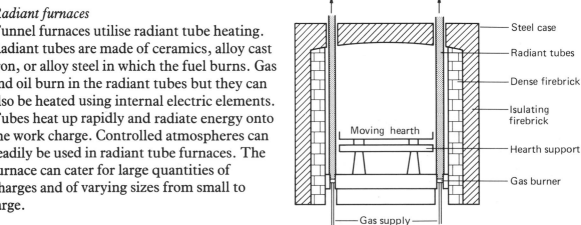

Section through a radiant tube furnace (gas fired)

Salt bath furnaces

Salt baths have a number of advantages over gas atmosphere furnaces for heat-treatment, such as:

1   Low installation and capital costs.
2   Temperature uniform due to convection currents within the liquid.
3   The work is heated much more rapidly in a molten bath.
4   Buoyancy effect of the liquid limits distortion.
5   Salts can provide neutral, oxidising, carburising, nitriding and carbon-nitriding atmospheres.

Liquid salts can be used between 150°C and 1350°C depending upon the salt chosen and the atmosphere required.

The salt is held in a small cylindrical pot made of pressed or forged mild steel which is aluminised (surface treated with aluminium and alumina) on its outer surface. A longer pot life is obtained, at more expense, with cast nickel-chromium alloy.

Nitrate-based salts are used for low-temperature applications such as tempering ferrous alloys and the solution treatment of light alloys.

Chloride-based salts are used for quench-hardening temperatures of about 800°C and above.

Cyanide salts are used for case-hardening low carbon steel components. Since these salts are exceptionally and fatally poisonous, extreme care must be exercised in their use and disposal. Special sections of the Factory Acts govern their use.

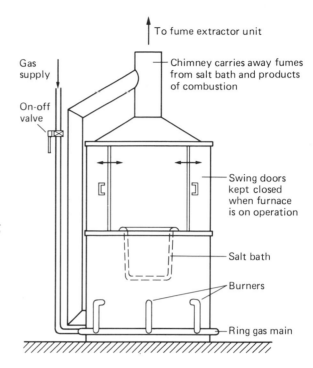

Natural-draught salt bath furnace

Seger cones

These are conical in shape, about 75 mm high and composed of metallic and mineral substances which fuse at certain known temperatures. A range of mixtures can be obtained giving about 900° to 1700° melting temperature, in steps of 20°C. To obtain a certain temperature in a furnace 3 cones can be used. The middle cone will be the required temperature and on either side will be a temperature below and above. The furnace will be at the correct temperature when the lower temperature cone melts, the middle one is just beginning to melt at the tip, and the third cone is still at its original shape.

Pyrometers

These are used for measuring high temperatures and can be divided into the following classes.

Thermo-electric pyrometer

This is the most commonly used pyrometer. It makes use of the property that when temperature variations occur on the junction of two dissimilar wires, welded together as a part of a circuit, an electric current is generated. The thermal e.m.f. generated varies with temperature so that a meter in the circuit can be calibrated directly in degrees. The magnitude of the current will depend upon the *difference in temperature* between the hot and cold junctions.

If the temperature of the cold junction varies, the reading correspondingly varies. The measuring instrument is normally placed some distance away from the furnace. This enables a simple means of cold-junction correction to be used, by making the leads from the thermo-couple to the instrument also of dissimilar metals so that they form, in effect, a second

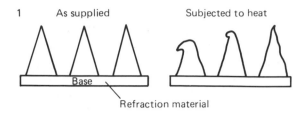

Seger cones

BASE METAL COUPLES	Up to Max. temp.
Copper — constantan	500° C
Iron — constantan	900° C
Chromel — alumel	1200° C
RARE METAL COUPLES	
Platinum — platinum + 10% rhodium	1600° C

Constantan or 'eureka':
an alloy of 60% copper, 40% nickel

Chromel: 80% nickel, 20% chromium

Alumel: 94% nickel, 2% aluminium

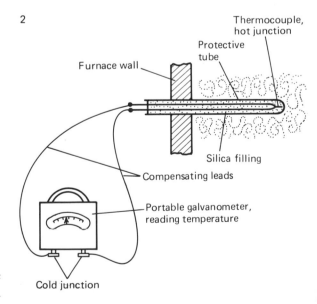

Thermo-electric pyrometer

thermocouple to compensate for changes in temperature at the cold junction. These leads are called *compensating leads*.

The wires of the thermocouple must be insulated from each other by small ceramic insulators, and in the furnace the thermocouple is protected from damage by a silica sheath.

Radiation pyrometer

Radiation pyrometers measure radiated heat and are adopted for high temperatures. The Foster radiation pyrometer is a reflecting telescope having a concave mirror which focuses the radiant heat of the object upon the 'hot' junction of a small thermocouple. It can be held in the hand or on a tripod and pointed towards a heat source, which could be an aperture in a furnace wall. Temperatures of up to 2000°C can be recorded.

Foster fixed focus pyrometer

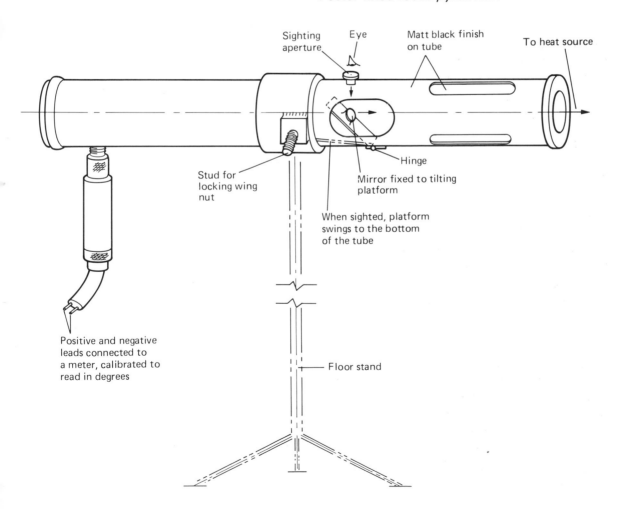

Sighting aperture

Eye

Matt black finish on tube

To heat source

Stud for locking wing nut

Hinge

Mirror fixed to tilting platform

When sighted, platform swings to the bottom of the tube

Positive and negative leads connected to a meter, calibrated to read in degrees

Floor stand

Optical pyrometer

In the disappearing-filament pyrometer light from the hot body is compared with the light emitted by the filament of a lamp. The operator, when viewing say a furnace, can alter the current flowing through the lamp. When the filament has the same brightness as the furnace, the temperature is read off. The instrument is accurate, simple to operate and portable. It is suitable for temperatures between 800° and 3000°C.

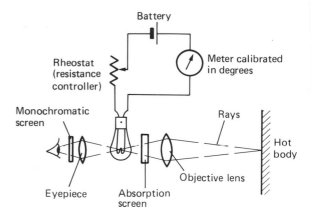

Appearance of filament image

Low reading

Correct

High reading

Disappearing-filament pyrometer

Questions

1 Define the following basic properties of materials: ductility, malleability, elasticity, toughness, hardness, strength and brittleness.

2 Give two examples of materials which possess:
   (a) ductility,
   (b) hardness,
   (c) toughness,
   (d) malleability.

3 A rod has a cross-sectional area of 100 mm^2. If it is subjected to a tensile force of 150 kN, what is its tensile strength?

4 A rivet 10 mm diameter is subjected to a shear force of 120 kN. What is its shear strength?

5 What is the Brinell hardness test and how is it conducted? Metal A has a hardness number of 420 whilst the hardness number of metal B is 230. Which is the harder?

6 What are 'wrought' products?

7 For the following alloys, state compositions, forms of supply and properties:
   (a) alpax,
   (b) duralumin,
   (c) Y

8 Define *solution heat-treatment* and *ageing*.

9 Explain what is meant by *season cracking* and describe a treatment for preventing its occurrence.

10 Distinguish between 70/30 brass and 60/40 brass and state the main physical properties of each. Which is the more suitable for cold-working?

11 For the following alloys, state compositions, forms of supply and properties:
   (a) tin bronze,
   (b) phosphor bronze,
   (c) aluminium bronze.

12 What danger is there, when machining magnesium alloys? What are the differences between manganese-aluminium alloys and 'electron' alloys?

13 What advantages do alloy steels possess when compared with straight carbon steels? Give five examples of parts and equipment that are made of alloy steels.

14 What is 'invar'?

15 (a) What mechanical properties does chromium impart when combined with carbon steel to produce a high alloy tool steel?
   (b) What is stainless steel?

16 What are the properties of an 18/8 steel?

17 How does vanadium affect the properties of alloy tool steels?

18 What are the mechanical properties of alloy steels when molybdenum is part of the composition?

19 What are:
   (a) 'hot-hardness', and
   (b) 'self-hardening' steels?

20 What are the two valuable properties that tungsten imparts to alloy steels?

21 What is the composition of 'Hadfield' manganese steel? State its properties, forms of supply and uses.

22 Compare sand casting and diecasting. What is the difference between the two?

23 Describe the difference between pressure and gravity diecasting. Which alloys make the best diecastings?

24 What are the advantages of the extrusion process? What is the main limitation of this process?

25 (a) Briefly describe machine forging and drop forging processes.
   (b) What is a flash and why does it occur?

26   What is 'grain flow'? With which processes is it likely to occur? What important properties does it give to the metal?

27   What is 'rolling'? Describe the following processes:
     (a)   hot-rolling, and
     (b)   cold-rolling.

28   Describe briefly the following basic plastic moulding processes:
     (a)   injection moulding,
     (b)   blow moulding, and
     (c)   compression moulding.

29   Why are metals subjected to heat-treatment?

30   State the purpose of annealing a steel.

31   Why is it necessary to temper a hardened steel?

32   What is 'carburising' and 'pack carburising'?

33   Describe the heat-treatment process that takes place, following a component that has been pack carburised.

34   What are the advantages of induction-hardening as compared with flame-hardening?

35   What are muffle furnaces, radiant furnaces and soft bath furnaces?

6 Material removal

Objectives

(a) The student should be able to select the correct cutting tool material for a particular operation on a workpiece.

(b) The student should be able to select the correct tool holder to give maximum rigidity and safety at minimum cost.

(c) The student should be able to machine a workpiece:
  (i)   at the correct cutting conditions,
  (ii) at the most economical material removal rate,
  (iii) to obtain the required surface finish.

(d) The student should be able to:
  (i) identify grinding wheels, and
  (ii) select the correct wheel for a particular grinding operation on a workpiece.

Cutting tool materials

Before a metal cutting job is undertaken an important decision which has to be taken is the choice of material for the cutting tool tip. High carbon steel (0.83% carbon) is suitable for low speeds only, and special tips have been developed for higher speed work. There are five common tip materials, namely, high-speed steel, stellite, cemented carbide, ceramics (cemented oxides) and diamond. Their main properties are listed below and the diagrams show (a) how hardness varies with temperature (b) how toughness compares, and (c) how cutting speeds compare.

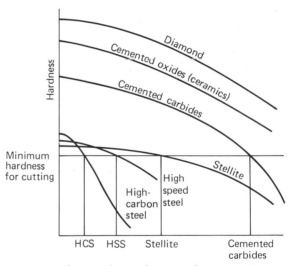

Comparative maximum cutting temperatures

Comparative values of maximum cutting temperatures for various tool materials

High-speed steel

Since its introduction in 1898, this has been and still is widely used for single-point turning tools, milling cutters, taps, reamers, etc. Its advantages are:

1 It has a good combination of hardness with toughness.
2 It is cheaper than either carbide or ceramics.
3 In its softened state it can be shaped.
4 It obtains its final hardness as a result of heat treatment.

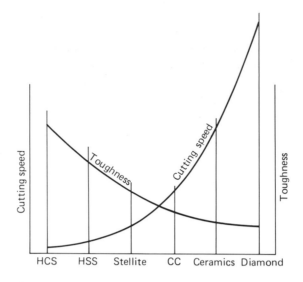

Comparison graphs

Stellite

1   This is a cast non-ferrous alloy. Cutting tips are cast in chilled moulds.
2   The tips are brazed into position.
3   Its cutting speed is higher than HSS.
4   The tips must be well supported by the use of small clearance angles.

Cemented carbide

1   This has very great hardness even at high temperature and therefore operates at high cutting speeds. It resists abrasion.
2   It is expensive.
3   Very brittle, so shocks are to be avoided and machine to be in a good rigid condition.
4   Easily brazed to a medium carbon shank or clamped indexable insert on a shank.
5   Used on a wide field of metal-cutting operations.

Ceramics

1   Ceramics are suitable for clamped tip applications only.
2   Because of its very high hardness at elevated temperatures, it is used at high cutting speeds.
3   It has a low or medium toughness; therefore, it is sensitive to shock.
4   Ceramics, because they are brittle, are prone to tool fracture. Because of this fact, when machining satisfy the following:
   (a)   stable machine and workpiece,
   (b)   minimum of vibrations,
   (c)   minimum overhang of cutting tool,
   (d)   approach angle desirable in order to reduce chip thickness,
   (e)   largest possible nose radius.
5   Frequently used on finish machining brake drums, brake discs etc.

Diamond

1 It is the hardest known natural substance.
2 Limited application as a cutting tool, due to the small size of the stones, brittleness and high cost.
3 As a cutting tool, two types of cutting edge are produced. A radiused cutting edge and a faceted cutting edge. As one facet or section of a radius becomes dull, the tool can be moved to provide a new keen cutting edge.
4 Speeds of around 400 m/min are used.
5 Used for finish turning of soft materials (low feeds), e.g. aluminium alloys (pistons) non-ferrous metals, plastics, carbon etc.
6 Vibration from the machine to be a minimum, hence the use of endless belts.

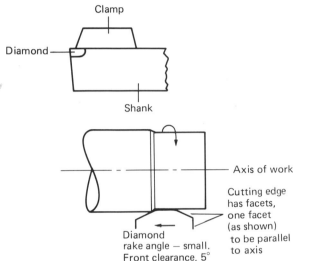

Diamond cutting tool

High	Toughness	Cold Hardness	Hot Hardness	High
↑	HSS	Diamond	Diamond	↑
	Stellite	Ceramic	Ceramic	
	Carbide	Carbide	Carbide	
	Ceramic	HSS	Stellite	
↓	Diamond	Stellite	HSS	↓
Low				Low

Property comparison of cutting tool materials

Cutting tools

The first set of diagrams show 1 the tool profile for a square tool bit, and the bit located in a straight tool holder; and 2 a sloping tool bit, with its cam-operated locked holder.

The three views of a *solid single butt-welded tool*, shows all the recommended ground, angles for the tool to undertake general machining.

Three different methods (a), (b) and (c) are shown for clamping of *indexable inserts*.

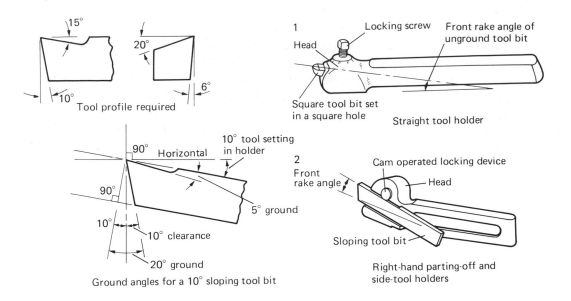

15°
20°
10°
6°
Tool profile required

1   Locking screw   Front rake angle of
unground tool bit
Head
Square tool bit set
in a square hole
Straight tool holder

90°   Horizontal   10° tool setting
in holder
90°
10°   5° ground
10° clearance
20° ground
Ground angles for a 10° sloping tool bit

2
Front
rake angle   Cam operated locking device
Head
Sloping tool bit
Right-hand parting-off and
side-tool holders

Tool holder bit

In (a) each of the two inserts has its own
clamp. By screwing the socket head cap screw
into the body, it acts on the clamp to hold the
insert in place.

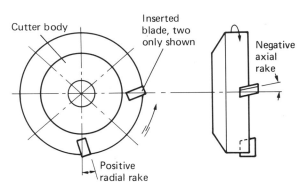

Cutter body   Inserted
blade, two
only shown   Negative
axial
rake
Positive
radial rake
Inserted blade negative-rake milling cutter

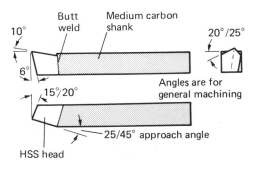

Butt
weld   Medium carbon
shank
10°   20°/25°
6°   Angles are for
general machining
15°/20°
25/45° approach angle
HSS head

A solid single butt welded tool

Indexable insert

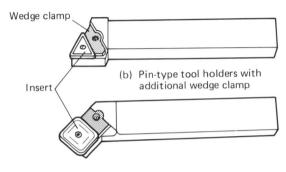

Mill body

Insert 'nestling' in a recess

Clamp

Socket head cap screw

(a) An insert-type end mill

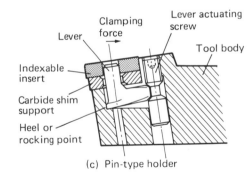

Wedge clamp

Insert

(b) Pin-type tool holders with additional wedge clamp

Lever actuating screw

Clamping force

Lever

Tool body

Indexable insert

Carbide shim support

Heel or rocking point

(c) Pin-type holder

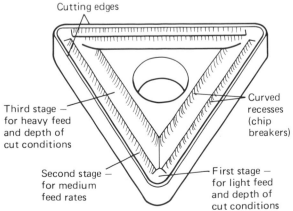

Cutting edges

Third stage — for heavy feed and depth of cut conditions

Curved recesses (chip breakers)

Second stage — for medium feed rates

First stage — for light feed and depth of cut conditions

Triple chip-breaker insert

Tool holder bit

1 Great skill is required when producing the correct cutting tool shape, due to the inclination of the square hole location.
2 It can also be further complicated if the holder is right-hand or left-hand.
3 Calculations for rake and clearance are necessary before attempting to sharpen the tool in its holder.
4 A new tool already ground can be easily and quickly set up (cross-section must always be the same).
5 Due to the overhang of the head, the tool point is well away from the tool box support. Rigidity is not as good as with other tool set-ups.

Solid single point butt-welded

1 The butt-welding of an HSS cutting head to the medium carbon shank produces a rigid tool for cutting.
2 The cost is much less than a complete HSS tool.
3 It can be easily reground.
4 A range of different tools offers differing rakes and angles to machine various metals.

Indexable insert (carbide or ceramic)

1 As the words suggest, a new cutting edge can be offered by turning the insert.
2 Its shape, e.g. triangular or square, and the rake, determine the number of cutting edges on an insert.
3 When all edges are used up it is then thrown away.
4 Replacing, or indexing, is carried out quickly and simply.
5 Rake and clearance angles are automatic due to the seating, for the insert, on the tool.

Inserted milling cutter

1 The body of a cutter is very robust.
2 The carbide inserted tooth bits sink deep into slots in the body with the minimum of the inserts showing. Locked by screws, tapered wedges or serrated edges, the inserts are rigidly fixed.
3 The rake and clearance angles are automatic.
4 When cutting edges become blunt they are removed and thrown away.
5 New cutting edges are supplied by the new replaced inserts.

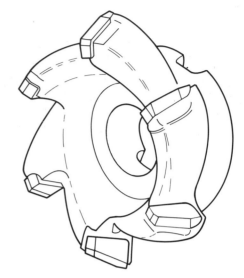

A brazed carbide milling cutter

Tipped single tool

1 A carbide or stellite tool bit is brazed to a carbon steel shank.
2 Different shaped carbide or stellite bits are supplied for different machining operations.
3 The tool bit can be ground by a silicon carbide (green) wheel.
4 A diamond lap for burnishing gives the final finish to the cutting edge.
5 For stellite the best cutting properties are found at the outside chilled surfaces. The cutting edge should be kept as close as possible to these chilled faces.

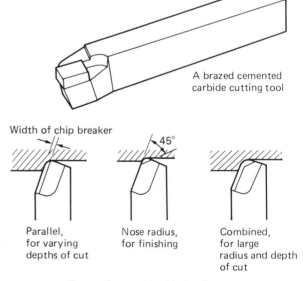

A brazed cemented carbide cutting tool

Width of chip breaker

45°

Parallel, for varying depths of cut

Nose radius, for finishing

Combined, for large radius and depth of cut

Types of ground-in chip breakers

Tipped single tool

Deposit-tipped single point

1 Stellite, a non-ferrous alloy, is deposited by welding onto a steel shank.
2 It can be applied to lathe tools, drills and milling cutters.
3 The cutting edges can be ground with the normal aluminium oxide grinding wheels.
4 A well supported cutting edge is necessary, so the clearance angles must be small.
5 A better finish and tool life will be obtained by a final operation of machine or hand lapping or honing.

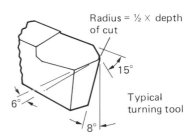

Radius = ½ × depth of cut

15°

6°

8°

Typical turning tool

Side and front clearance face angles 8°

Regrind *only* on these angles

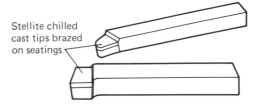

Stellite chilled cast tips brazed on seatings

Tipped stellite tools

Metal cutting

If a piece of hardened tool steel is ground so that its end is square, with all corners and edges sharp, and it is pressed into a piece of soft steel, and if a force F is then applied parallel to the surface as in diagram 1, the tool will not cut. The heel of the tool will foul the work and prevent the leading edge from entering it.

The situation can be greatly improved by clearing the heel away, by grinding a *clearance angle*, as in diagram 2. By applying the force P and F the tool can now cut the work and metal is removed in the form of *chips*.

Clearance

The clearance angle may be defined as the angle between the flank face of the tool and a tangent to the work surface originating at the cutting edge.

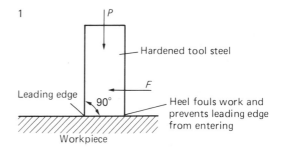

1

P

Hardened tool steel

Leading edge

90°

F

Heel fouls work and prevents leading edge from entering

Workpiece

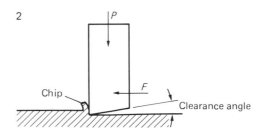

2

P

F

Chip

Clearance angle

Clearance necessary to allow cutting to take place

The clearance angle is generally fixed, depending upon the geometry of the surface being cut, at the following values:

2   flat surfaces 6° to 8°

3   external cylinder surface 5° to 7°
4   internal cylindrical surface 8° to 10° plus secondary (heel) clearance.

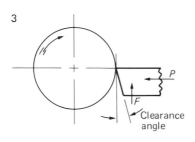

External cylinder

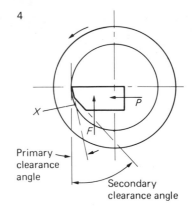

Internal cylinder

Shear plane

The chip parts from the parent metal along a path called the *shear plane* AB. The length of the shear plane multiplied by the width of the cut gives the area in shear for the metal being cut. For any given material, the smaller this area can be made, the lower will be the cutting efficiency.

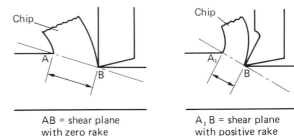

Comparison of length of shear plane

It has been shown by experimentation that if the *rake face* of the tool is inclined away from the perpendicular, the shear plane:

1   Tends to become normal to the rake face.
2   Decreases in length AB.

Also an inclined rake face enables the chip to peel away from the parent metal without having to turn through such an acute angle. Thus, a high rake angle reduces the cutting force by reducing the shear area, and it also reduces the pressure of the chip on the rake face of the tool. Both these factors lead to increased cutting efficiency.

Too much rake angle would tend to weaken the tool, so a suitable rake angle becomes a compromise between adequate strength of tool and good cutting action.

For a *tool considered as a wedge* it can be seen that three angles are involved:
1 Clearance angle.
2 Rake angle.
3 Wedge angle.
The wedge is forced into the work by the resultant R of forces P and F.

The table gives values of typical rake angles for high speed tools cutting with positive rake. The values given are for roughing cuts and can be slightly increased, with advantage, for finishing cuts.

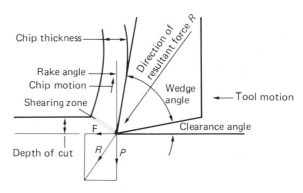

Positive rake — tool considered as a wedge forced into work by a resultant force R

Material being cut	Typical rake angles for HSS tools
Cast iron	0°
Free-cutting bras	0°
Ductile brass	14°
Tin bronze	8°
Aluminium alloy	30°
Mild steel	25°
Medium carbon steel	20°
High carbon steel	12°
'Tufnol' plastic	0°

The simple wedge tool
For the simplest type of cutting operation, the cutting edge is straight, parallel to the original plane surface of the work, and perpendicular to the direction of cutting, and the length of the cutting edge is greater than the width of chip removed. Such an operation is called *orthogonal cutting*.

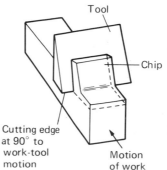

Orthogonal cutting

A second cutting operation is when the cutting edge is again straight and parallel with the original plane surface of the work but is *inclined* to the cutting direction. This is called *oblique cutting*. The wedge forms the basic element of all cutting tools.

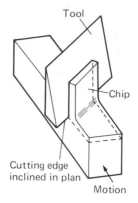

Oblique cutting

Single-point tool geometry

For both the orthogonal and oblique cutting lathe tools the depth of cut d and the feed is the same. It can be seen that the length of the cutting edge d_1 for the oblique cutting tool is longer than d, the actual depth of cut. Therefore, the oblique cutting tool will provide a greater area of cut than the orthogonal cutting tool, to the force F. This results in less cutting power being required. Thus, an oblique tool has a higher cutting efficiency than an orthogonal tool. This results in a longer tool life and less wear and tear on the machine tool being used.

It is advisable to have the *plan approach angle* as large as possible without causing chatter. The *plan relief* or *trail angle* is ground to give clearance and prevent rubbing, and is usually at 90° to the approach angle. A small nose radius on the tool improves the cutting, reduces tool wear and produces a good surface finish to the work.

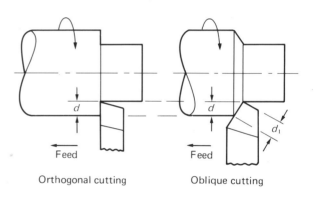

Turning

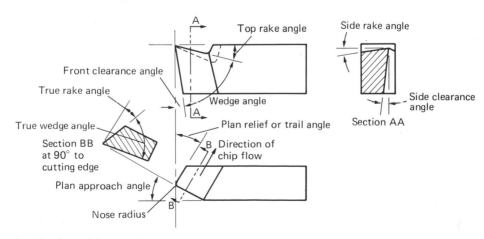

Features of a single point positive rake cutting tool

Because the tool shown is ground with top rake and side rake, the actual or true rake is a combination of the two. The true rake may be defined as the rake angle measured in the direction of chip flow at the cutting edge, and will normally be measured at 90° to the cutting edge.

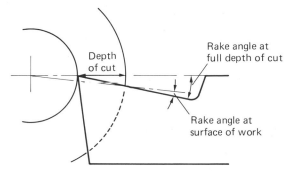

1 Difference in rake angle at nose and back of tool, due to top rake

The straight-edged cutting tool
In diagram 1 the tool shown has top rake and it can be seen that the rake angle at the back of the cutting edge is less than at the front. If the idea of top rake with side rake is abandoned, and the true rake is ground with the cutting edge horizontal, this error is avoided, as shown in diagram 2.

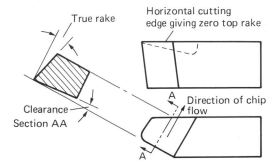

2 Tool given zero top rake by grinding the rake angle in a direction at right angles to the cutting edge

The straight edged cutting tool

Various effects of incorrect tool settings
Diagrams (a), (b), (c) and (d) indicate the effects on the rake angle and the clearance on tools due to incorrect tool settings.

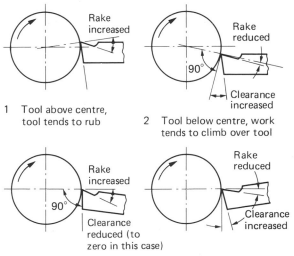

1 Tool above centre, tool tends to rub

2 Tool below centre, work tends to climb over tool

3 Tool on centre but inclined upward at front, tool rubs

4 Tool on centre but inclined downward at front, work tends to drag tool in

Various effects of incorrect tool settings

Forces on a lathe tool

Orthogonal cutting is a particular case where only *two* forces are acting and the cutting edge is at right angles to the direction of feed.

When machining the end of a tube the forces are:

1 *Tangential force*, which acts tangentially to the work surface. In association with the cutting speed this is the main power-consuming force.

2 *Axial force*, parallel to the work axis and resisting the feed motion. In association with the slow feed motion this also consumes power, but its amount is small.

Forces on a lathe tool

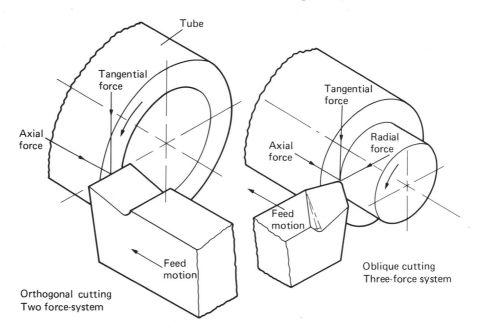

Orthogonal cutting
Two force-system

Oblique cutting
Three-force system

Oblique cutting is a case where *three* forces are acting. Because the cutting edge is not at right angles to the direction of feed a third force acts, called a *radial force*, which tries to force the tool out of the work and is resisted by the screws in the tool post. As no motion is associated with the radial force it does not consume power but influences the axial force.

Positive- and negative-rake cutting

For positive-rake cutting the chip force normal to the rake face acts towards the unsupported part of the tool and tends to break off the tip.

The more brittle cutting-tool materials such as metallic carbides and metallic oxides (ceramics) have very low transverse strengths and are normally used to cut high-strength materials. In order to provide adequate support for the cutting-tool material a different tool geometry is used. By employing a *negative* rake angle, the chip force is resisted by the full cross-section of the tool shank. Due to the increased cutting speeds possible with carbide and ceramic-tipped tools, coupled with the negative rake geometry, it has the effect of transferring the greater part of the work done to the chip. The chips may become red hot. The advantages of using negative-rake cutting tools are as follows:

1 Reduced chip force on the rake face of the tool.
2 Reduced abrasive wear of the tool.
3 Less tendency for the chip to weld to the tool.
4 The tool tends to remain cool.
5 A very high rate of removal of metal.

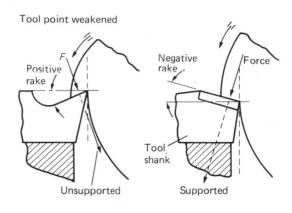

Positive and negative rake cutting (turning)

Positive- and negative-rake milling

The cutting action, in milling as for turning, consists of:

1 the formation of a crack in the metal which runs ahead of the cutting tool.
2 the subsequent passage of the chip across the face or breast of the tool.
3 the cutting edge producing the finish on the metal.

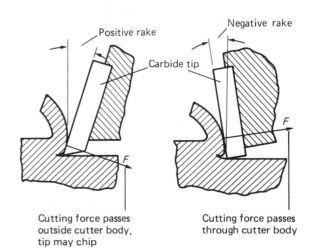

Positive and negative rake milling

Surface texture

When work is rough-machined the surface consists of hills and valleys. When work is ground the surface consists of much smaller hills and valleys as compared with the previous case. This quality of the surface finish on a work-piece may be compared to *surface texture comparison blocks*. A series of blocks with different known finishes (CLA values) set in a holder, can be scratched by an operator's nail and visually inspected. Then by scratching and visually inspecting the work surface the nearest standard block finish is noted.

A more accurate method is by using special instruments which have a very sensitive stylus and moves across the hills and valleys on the work. The movement of the stylus is magnified and a graph is drawn.

The unit of measurement for surface finish is the *micrometre* (one-millionth of a metre) called μ (Greek letter mu). A finish of 5 micrometres is 5 μm.

Centre-line average (CLA) method

With the graph produced a *mean line* is drawn so that the total of the areas above equals the total of the areas below.
Then $A_1 + A_3 + A_5 = A_2 + A_4 + A_6$
The CLA number
$$= \frac{\text{the total of the areas above and below the mean line}}{\text{the length of the mean line}}$$
$$= \frac{A_1 + A_3 + A_5 + A_2 + A_4 + A_6}{L}$$

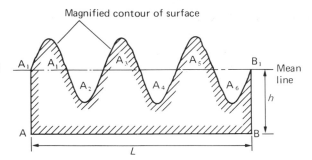

Magnified contour of surface

The position of the mean line is obtained as follows:

1   Draw AB parallel to the general line of the trace

2   AA_1 and BB_1 perpendicular to AB

3   With a planimeter (or calculations) find the enclosed area

Then $h = \dfrac{\text{Total area}}{L}$

Process	CLA Values Surface finish produced μm
Rough turning	6
Shaping	1.6
Milling	0.8
Grinding	0.05 – 3.0
Honing	0.05 – 1.0
Lapping	0.025 – 0.1

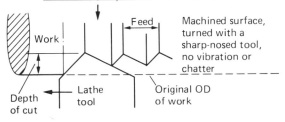

Machined surface, turned with a sharp-nosed tool, no vibration or chatter

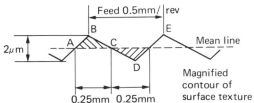

Magnified contour of surface texture

Given that the peak to valley height is 2 μm.
Calculate the CLA value for surface.

A₁ = area of triangle

A_1 = area of triangle
    = ½ × 0.25 × 1.0

ABC = ½ × base × height
    = 0.125 units².

A_2 = area of triangle
    = ½ × 0.25 × 1

CDE =
    = 0.125 units²

$$\text{CLA value} = \frac{A_1 + A_2}{L}$$

$$= \frac{0.125 + 0.125}{0.5} = 0.5 \ \mu m$$

Machining symbol (BS 308: Part 2: 1972)
Where it is necessary to indicate that a surface
is to be machined, without defining either the
surface texture grade or the process to be used,
a symbol of the form shown should be used.

Indication of surface texture
Where it is necessary to indicate a particular
quality of surface texture and the surface is to
be machined, a machining symbol with the
maximum permissible roughness in
micrometres (μm) is used.

Production processes
Where it is a design requirement that a surface
be produced by a particular process, such as
grinding, lapping, honing etc., the appropriate
process should be specified by the symbol
shown.

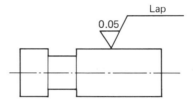

Surface texture value applied

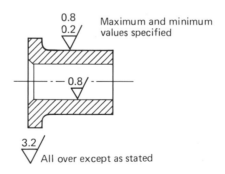

Indication of finishing process

Form of symbol

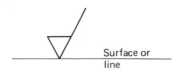

Application of symbol

Heat transfer

James Prescott Joule was an English physicist who lived in the nineteenth century, and he established the relationship between *mechanical energy* and *heat energy*. His name is honoured by the use of the *joule* as the unit of energy. When a piece of metal or a quantity of water is heated up, then the quantity of heat used in joules is:

mass (kg) × Specific heat × Temperature
of the mass in rise in °C
joules/kg °C

Substance	Specific heat J/kg °C
Water	4187
Aluminium	921
Steel	480
Cast iron	544
Copper	400

Heat exchanges

When a piece of carbon steel is heated to a bright red and quenched in water the steel is hardened. The temperature of the water rises as a result of heated steel giving up its quantity of heat. This is a system of heat exchange:

Heat lost by = Heat gained by
the hot body the cold body

$$\begin{aligned}&\text{Mass of} \times \text{Specific heat} \times \text{Temperature}\\&\text{steel} \qquad \text{of steel} \qquad \text{fall}\end{aligned}$$

$$= \begin{aligned}&\text{Mass of} \times \text{Specific heat} \times \text{Temperature}\\&\text{water} \qquad \text{of water} \qquad \text{rise}\end{aligned}$$

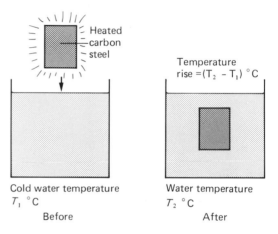

Heated carbon steel

Temperature rise = $(T_2 - T_1)$ °C

Cold water temperature T_1 °C

Before

Water temperature T_2 °C

After

Another example of heat exchange is when the heat from a cutting tool, when removing metal, is cooled by a quantity of cutting fluid passing over the cutting operation. The work and tool lose heat to the cutting fluid, the temperature of the fluid rises. If we assume that all the heat energy generated at the tool cutting edge is carried away by the cutting fluid, then:

Heat generated by = Heat carried away by
the tool per the cutting fluid per
second second

Heat carried away by the cutting fluid per second, J/s

$$= \begin{aligned}&\text{Mass of} \times \text{Specific} \times \text{Temperature rise}\\&\text{fluid kg/s} \quad \text{heat of} \qquad (T_2 - T_1)\text{°C}\\&\qquad\qquad \text{fluid}\end{aligned}$$

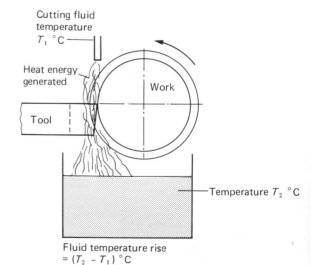

Cutting fluid temperature T_1 °C

Heat energy generated

Work

Tool

Temperature T_2 °C

Fluid temperature rise = $(T_2 - T_1)$ °C

Heat transfer examples

1   A piece of steel having a mass of 12 kg is
    heated from 15°C to 240°C. How much
    heat is used?
    Specific heat of steel $= 460 \text{ J/kg°C}$
    Temperature rise
    $$= 240°C - 15°C = 225°C$$
    Quantity of heat used
    $$= \text{Mass} \times \frac{\text{Specific}}{\text{heat}} \times \frac{\text{Temperature}}{\text{rise}}$$
    $$= 12 \times 460 \times 225$$
    $$= 1242\,000\text{J} \quad \text{or} \quad 1242 \text{ kJ}$$

2   A piece of steel at 900°C is taken out of a
    furnace and allowed to cool to a room
    temperature of 20°C. The steel has a mass
    of 10 kg. How much heat does the steel
    lose?
    Temperature drop
    $$= 900°C - 20°C = 880°C$$
    Quantity of heat lost
    $$= \text{Mass} \times \frac{\text{Specific}}{\text{heat}} \times \frac{\text{Temperature}}{\text{drop}}$$
    $$= 10 \times 460 \times 880$$
    $$= 4048\,000 \text{ J} \quad \text{or} \quad 4048 \text{ kJ}$$

3   A mass of steel 2 kg is removed from a
    furnace at a temperature of 800°C and
    plunged into cold water at a temperature
    15°C. The mass of cold water is 120 kg.
    Find the final temperature of the steel and
    water. Let t = the final temperature.

    Heat lost by the steel = heat gained by the
    water
    $$\frac{\text{Steel}}{\text{mass}} \times \frac{\text{Specific}}{\text{heat}} \times \frac{\text{Temp.}}{\text{fall}}$$
    $$= \frac{\text{Water}}{\text{mass}} \times \frac{\text{Specific}}{\text{heat}} \times \frac{\text{Temp.}}{\text{rise}}$$
    $2 \times 460 \times (800 - t)$
    $$= 120 \times 4187 \times (t - 15)$$
    $920\,(800 - t) \quad = 502\,440\,(t - 15)$
    $736\,000 - 920\,t = 502\,440\,t - 7536\,600$
    $736\,000$
    $\quad + 7536\,600 \quad = 502\,440\,t + 920\,t$
    $8272\,600 \quad\quad = 503\,360\,t$
    $$\frac{8272\,600}{503\,360} = t \quad t = 16.44°C$$

Heat exchange examples

1   A cutting fluid flowing over a cutting tool
    at the rate of flow of 4 kg/s has its
    temperature raised by 2°C. If the specific
    heat of the fluid is 4000 J/kg°C, calculate
    the power absorbed by the fluid.
    Heat carried away by the fluid
    $$= \text{Mass/s} \times \frac{\text{Specific}}{\text{heat}} \times \frac{\text{Temperature}}{\text{rise}}$$
    $$= 4 \times 4000 \times 2$$
    $$= 32\,000 \text{ J/s}$$
    But 1 Watt = 1 joule/s
    .. Power absorbed by the fluid = 32 000
    W = 32 kW

2   In a boring operation 340 Nm/s of
    mechanical energy is produced. The tool is
    cooled by a coolant flowing at 1½ kg/min.
    Find the temperature rise of the coolant.
    Take the specific heat of the coolant as
    3500 J/kg°C.
    Heat energy at the cutting tool = 340Nm/s
    = 340 J/s = 340 W
    Power absorbed by the coolant
    $$= \frac{\text{Flow}}{\text{rate}} \times \frac{\text{Specific}}{\text{heat}} \times \frac{\text{Temp.}}{\text{rise}}$$
    $$= \frac{1½}{60} \times 3500 \times \text{Temp. rise}$$

    But power absorbed by the coolant = Heat
    energy at the cutting tool
    $$87.5 \times \frac{\text{Temp.}}{\text{rise}} = 340 \text{ W}$$

    $$\text{Temperature rise} = \frac{340}{87.5} = 3.89°C$$

Questions

1 An aluminium component and a steel component are heated to a temperature of 900°C in a furnace. Both are then removed and dropped into a water tank. What is the final steady temperature of the water, given the following: mass of the aluminium component = 3 kg; mass of the steel component = 4 kg; mass of the water = 100 kg; initial temperature of the water = 15°C; allow 10% loss of heat to the atmosphere?

2 When drilling a component the power absorbed by a cutting fluid is 4 kW. If the specific heat of the fluid is 3900 and its temperature rise is 3°C, calculate the rate of flow of the fluid in kg/min.

3 During a milling operation the power used in cutting is 5 kW. 80% of this power is converted into heat energy which is removed by the coolant of specific heat 3200. If the temperature rise is 2°C, what is the rate of flow?

Tool posts

The English tool post
The tool is clamped by tightening the heel pin with a spanner. The end of the heel pin is forced onto the face A. This causes the right-hand end of the clamp to rise and the top face of the clamp to pivot uinder the nut located on the stud. The left-hand end of the clamp moves downwards so clamping the tool. The tool post is simple and rigid. To adjust the height of tool packing must be used.

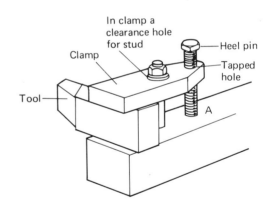

English tool post

The American tool post
This is used on light lathes. The tool can easily be adjusted for height and position. The disadvantages are that excessive overhang of the tool can occur and the method of adjustment alters the effective cutting angles.

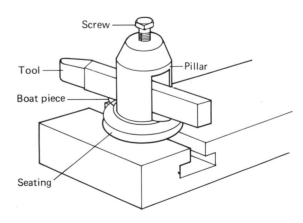

American tool post

The quick-change tool post

This type of cam lock tool post can be preferable to the turret tool post. The tools are mounted in interchangeable holders which are preadjusted for centre height. There is no limit to the number of tools that can be used.

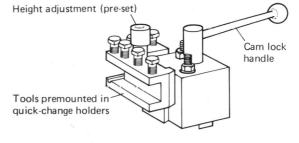

Quick-change tool post

The four-way tool post

The main advantage is that four tools can be clamped.

To index the turret, the turret lock handle is slackened off and the turret rotated. When the required tool is in position the handle is locked. The tool post is very rigid and the minimum of tool overhang is obtained.

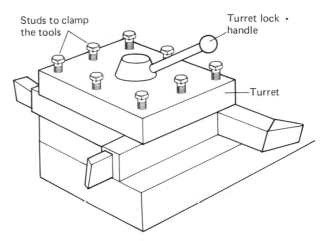

Four-way tool post

Questions

1 *Cuttting tool profiles*
   Draw and calculate the angles to grind,
front clearance and top rake for:
   (a)   tool holder bit set at 10°,
   (b)   tool holder bit set at 15°.
2 *Tool on centre, correct setting*
   With the cutting point above and below
   centre calculate the top rake and front
   clearance for each case.
3 *Lathe boring tool set below centre*
   (a)   From the diagram, place the correct
         letters in the table below.

Angle	Letter
Tool rake	
Primary clearance	
Secondary clearance	
Working rake	
Working primary clearance	

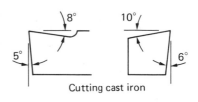

Cutting cast iron

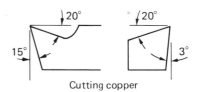

Cutting copper

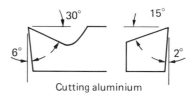

Cutting aluminium

Cutting tool profiles

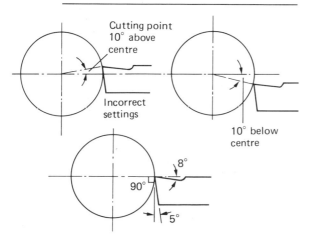

Tool on centre, correct setting

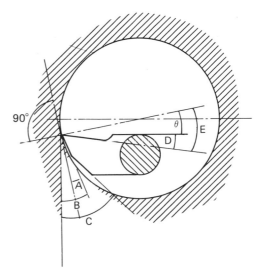

Lathe boring tool set below centre

(b)

Angle B	Tool rake angle	Primary clearance	Working rake	Working primary clearance
10°	12°	14°		
5°	10°	6°		

Complete the table.

Forces on a lathe tool

V is the vertical downward force of the work on the tool when cutting. L is the force acting on the tool, opposing the movement of the tool. R is the radial force of the work on the tool.

When $V = 1000$ N force and $L = 400$ N force, the two sides at 90° are drawn and the parallelogram completed. The diagonal is 1074 N, the *resultant force*, that force that produces the same effect as the two forces V and L acting together. Similarly, V and R produce a force diagram, their resultant force being 1170 N.

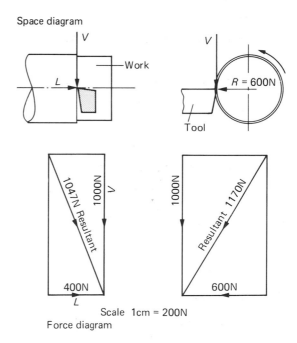

Forces on a lathe tool

Steel bar in a vee block

L is the force of the left-hand side on the bar and R is the force on the right-hand side. The pull or force of gravity on the bar is:

mass of bar (kg) $\times$ 9.81 m/s^2 = 1000 N

The lines of action of the three forces intersect at the centre of the bar.

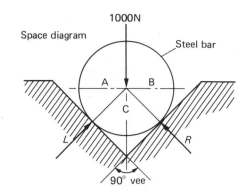

To construct the force diagram

that is, triangle of forces

1   Place capital letters in the spaces between the force lines on the space diagram.
2   Draw a line to scale and parallel to AB. This force is ab. The arrow head on the middle of the line also points the same way as on the space diagram.
3   Through b draw a line parallel to BC.
4   Through a draw a line parallel to AC.
5   Intersection for the triangle gives point C.
6   Arrow heads on bc and ca to be the same as on the space diagram.

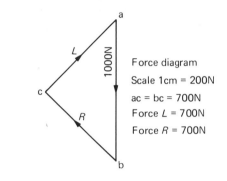

Micrometer boring head

This accessory can be used on various machine tools, such as in jig boring, universal milling, horizontal boring and drilling.

Practical application of a boring head

1   Enlargement of drilled or cored holes.
2   When a drilled hole has run out from its centre, the boring tool can bring the hole back to centre by enlarging the hole.
3   By taking cuts in a used cylinder bore of an engine, the cylinder bore is again made circular.
4   To produce drill templates, dies for press tools etc. requiring very high precision distance between hole centres.
5   On special machines, a four-cylinder engine block can be bored using four boring heads working at the same time.

Once the spindle has been located over an existing hole, the bottom slide is moved perpendicular to the spindle centre line by means of an allen key inserted into the centre of the graduated dial. The movement of the bottom slide is by means of a screw and nut mechanism.

If the screw has a lead of 1 mm and the dial has 20 divisions, then each division moved produces a tool movement of $\frac{1}{20} \times$ thread lead $= \frac{1}{20} \times 1$ mm $= 0.05$ mm. This will be the increase in the radius of the tool, then the bore when machined will increase by $2 \times 0.05 = 0.1$ mm.

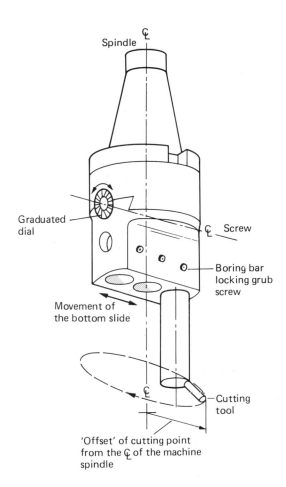

Spindle ₵

Graduated dial

₵ Screw

Boring bar locking grub screw

Movement of the bottom slide

₵

Cutting tool

'Offset' of cutting point from the ₵ of the machine spindle

Milling

A left-hand spiral side and face milling cutter, when cutting, causes a deflection force acting towards the arbor retaining nut.

A *right-hand spiral side and face* milling cutter causes a deflection force acting towards the machine housing.

In the *staggered tooth* milling cutter the deflection forces oppose each other and cancel each other out.

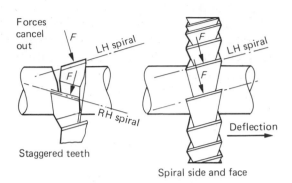

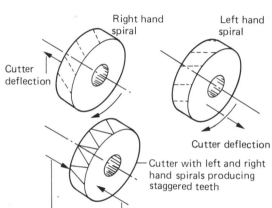

Principle and advantages of the staggered-tooth side and face cutter

Down cut milling

As a result of the downward cutting action there is a tendency to grab the workpiece and pull it under the cutter. Special machines eliminate the lead screw backlash. In conventional milling machines lead screw backlash would help the cutter to pull the work under. In 'down cut' milling the cutting edge has a clean bite at the work at the thick end of the chip. The shock load is very great on the cutting edge at the start. The advantages are that greater metal removal rates are possible, the force of the cutter acts downwards on the table, and higher speeds, higher feed rates and longer tool life between regrinds, when compared with 'up cut' milling are possible.

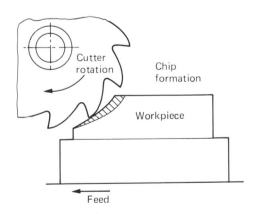

Down cut milling

Straddle milling

This operation enables parallel vertical faces to be milled at the same time. The side force into the casting by one of the cutters is cancelled by the side force from the other cutter. The width of the casting is produced accurately due to the spacing collars being equal to this width.

Up cut milling

This is the conventional method of milling. When cutting, the force of the teeth tends to lift the workpiece. The chip increases in thickness as the tooth cuts into the workpiece, and the load on the tooth increases.

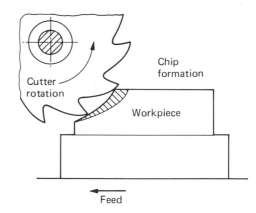

Up cut milling

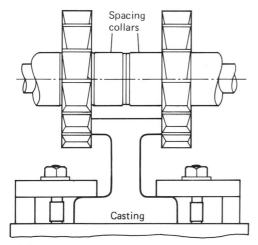

Straddle milling

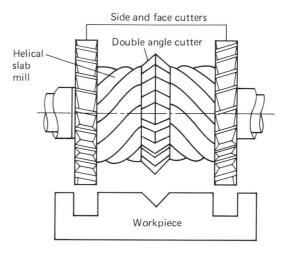

Gang milling

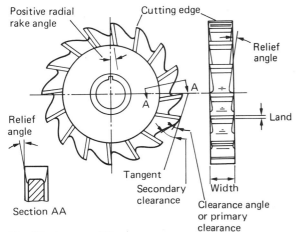

Profile type milling cutter

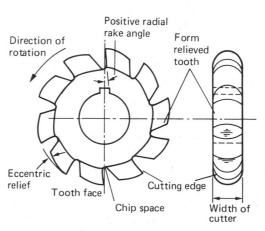

Form relieved type milling cutter

Forming and generating

If components to be produced have an unusual profile, then the machining operation can be performed by either *forming* or *generating*.

Forming
In this case a special form tool is required which bears the required profile upon its cutting edge. The shape produced on the workpiece will be the reverse image of the tool shape.

Important factors when forming:
1   When turning, the tool must be set on centre to obtain the correct profile. If the tool was set below or above centre, then an incorrect profile would be formed.
2   The accuracy of the work profile depends entirely on the form tool profile.
3   Form tools, because of the long cutting edge can cause chattering and poor finish. Cuts must be light. Form milling cutters tend to chatter, because of the inadequate clearance behind the cutting edge, leading to rubbing between the cutter and work.
4   Complex form tools and cutters are difficult to produce and are expensive.

Generating
In this case the tool shape has no effect upon the finished workpiece. The form of the profile is produced by the cutting edge of the tool being constrained to move through the required path, the required profile therefore being generated upon the work.

Important factors when generating are:
1   The work profile is independent of the tool shapes and the tool cutting angles.
2   The tool must be set on centre.
3   Much longer profiles can be generated than can be formed.

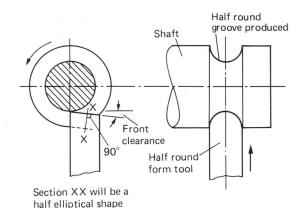

Section XX will be a half elliptical shape

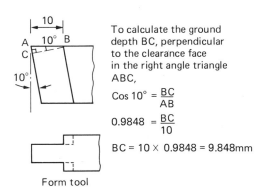

To calculate the ground depth BC, perpendicular to the clearance face in the right angle triangle ABC,

$$\cos 10° = \frac{BC}{AB}$$

$$0.9848 = \frac{BC}{10}$$

$$BC = 10 \times 0.9848 = 9.848 \text{mm}$$

Forming

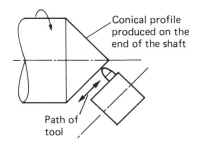

Generating

When cutting a screw thread with a single-point tool on a lathe, it has the thread shape or profile formed and the helix of the screw generated. Another example is the cutting of a helical flute on a bar, on the universal milling machine.

Generating surfaces

1 *The workpiece is required to have a flat horizontal surface* AB. The shaper tool moves forward on a cutting stroke, the workpiece being stationary. Then on the return stroke (not cutting), the workpiece moves a short distance sideways and a further cutting stroke takes place. Following complete movement of the tool over AB to further cut the surface the tool would be moved downwards before starting once more at A.

The line diagram 4, drawn isometrically, represents the relative movements of workpiece and tool, necessary to generate the flat surface AB.

2 To generate a *vertical flat surface* CD on a shaper, the feed, vertically downwards, is applied by the handle on the tool box, when the tool is at the end of the return stroke.

3 To generate a *45° flat* EF as shown in diagram 3, the tool box must be set over, away from the operator, at 45° to the vertical. The tool feed is applied by the handle on the tool box, when the tool is at the end of the return stroke.

Their *relative movement diagrams* are 5 and 6.

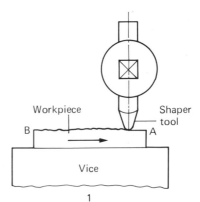

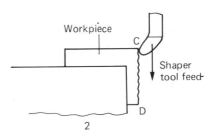

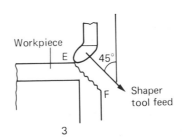

Workpiece and tool set-ups

Drilling
The rotation of a drill, combining with its axial feed, generates a *cylinder*, which is the shape of the hole in the workpiece.

Horizontal milling
The rotation of the cutter and the horizontal feed of the workpiece into the cutter, generates a *flat surface*.

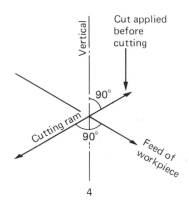

Surface grinding
The rotation of the grinding wheel and the horizontal feed of the workpiece into the wheel, generates a *flat surface*. When the wheel has traversed from A to B and returned to A, the workpiece then moves a distance about one-third of the width of the wheel, and traversing of the workpiece is repeated. This procedure continues until the width of the workpiece has been completed.

End milling
The rotation of the end mill and the feed of the workpiece as shown, generates *two flat surfaces* at right angles to each other.

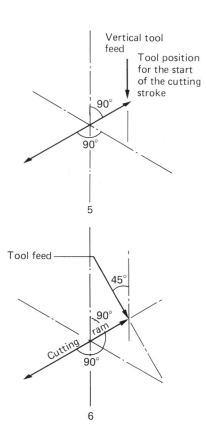

Relative movement diagrams

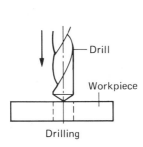

Drilling

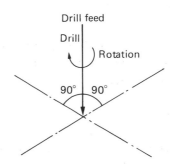

Drill feed

Drill

Rotation

90°   90°

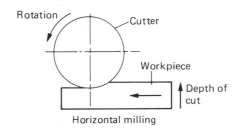

Horizontal milling

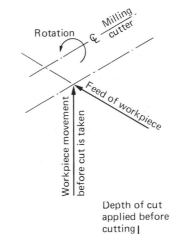

Rotation

Milling cutter

Feed of workpiece

Workpiece movement before cut is taken

Depth of cut applied before cutting

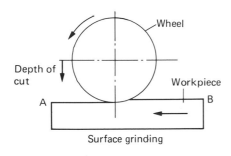

Surface grinding

Rotation

Grinding wheel

Feed of workpiece

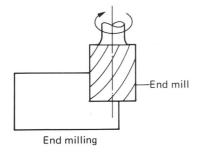

End milling

Workpiece and tool set-ups

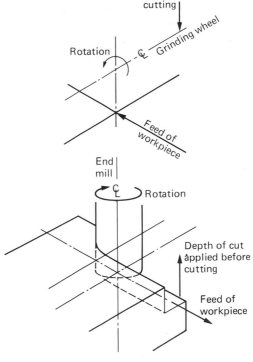

End mill

Rotation

Depth of cut applied before cutting

Feed of workpiece

Relative movement diagrams

Turning

The rotation of the workpiece about the lathe centre line, and the tool feed parallel to this centre line, results in a *cylinder* being generated.

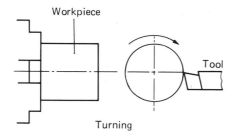

Turning

External taper turning

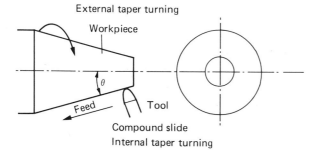

Internal taper turning

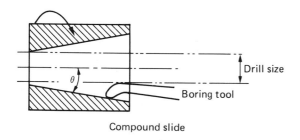

Compound slide

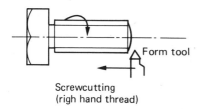

Screwcutting
(righ hand thread)

Workpiece and tool set-ups

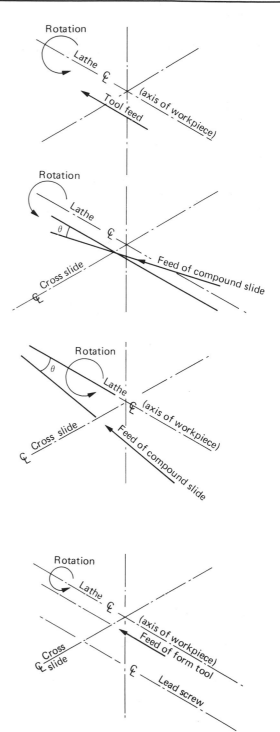

Relative movement diagrams

External taper turning

The rotation of the workpiece about the lathe centre line, and the tool feed moving at an angle B to this centre line, generates a *conical surface*.

Internal taper turning

The largest drill size, nearest to the finished small diameter of the taper, is first of all fed through the workpiece.

With the saddle locked to the bed, and the boring tool fed at an angle B using the compound slide, an *internal conical surface is* generated.

Screwcutting

The screwcutting tool, which is a form tool, moves parallel to the lathe centre line, and its feed is equal to the pitch of cut on the cylinder. The surface generated in the cylinder is a *vee-shaped helical groove*.

Cutting speeds

The distance covered by a cutting edge of a tool in *metres* in a *time* of one minute is called S, the *cutting speed* in m/min.

When drilling, turning, milling and grinding the diameter of the cutting tool or work is d mm and the rotation is N rev /min.

The cutting speed
$$S = \text{circumference mm} \times N \text{ rev/min}$$
$$= \frac{22}{7} \times d \times N \text{ mm/min}$$
$$S = \frac{22}{7} \times \frac{d \times N}{1000}$$

The $N = \frac{S \times 7}{d \times 22} \times 1000 \text{ rev/min}$ and

$$d = \frac{S \times 7 \times 1000}{N \times 22} \text{ mm}$$

Drilling

To drill through a thickness t mm, the number of revolutions of the drill required
$$= \frac{t \text{ mm}}{\text{feed mm/rev}} = \frac{t}{f} \text{ revs}$$
(ignoring the length of the drill point).
The *time* taken for this operation, by proportion N revolutions in 60 seconds:

then 1 revolution in $\frac{60}{N}$ s

$$\therefore \frac{t}{f} \text{ revolution in } \left(\frac{60}{N} \times \frac{t}{f} \right) \text{ s.}$$

Volume of metal removed = cross-sectional area × length
$$= \frac{22}{7} \times \frac{d^2}{4} \text{ mm}^2 \times t \text{ mm}$$
$$= \frac{22}{7} \times \frac{d^2}{4} \times t \text{ mm}^3$$

Metal removal rate
$$= \frac{\text{volume of metal removed}}{\text{time taken}}$$
$$= \frac{\dfrac{22}{7} \times \dfrac{d^2}{4} \times t \text{ mm}^3}{\dfrac{60}{N} \times \dfrac{t}{f} \text{ s}}$$
$$= \frac{22}{7} \times \frac{d^2}{4} \times t \times \frac{N}{60} \times \frac{f}{t}$$
$$= \frac{22}{7} \times \frac{d^2}{4} \times \frac{N}{60} \times f \text{ mm}^3\text{/s}$$
$$= \text{Area} \times \text{rev/s} \times \text{feed mm}^3\text{/s}$$

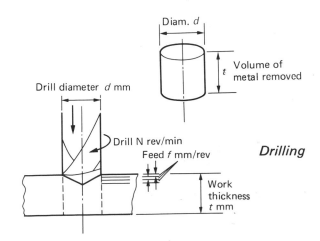

Diam. d

Volume of metal removed

Drill diameter d mm

Drill N rev/min
Feed f mm/rev

Work thickness t mm

Drilling

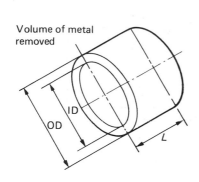

Volume of metal removed

OD
ID
L

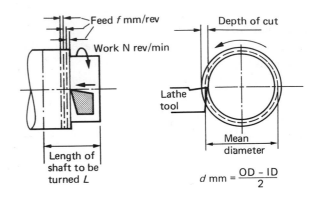

Feed f mm/rev

Work N rev/min

Depth of cut

Lathe tool

Length of shaft to be turned L

Mean diameter

d mm $= \dfrac{OD - ID}{2}$

Turning

Turning

The number of revolutions for the work to turn for the length of

$$L \text{ mm} = \frac{L \text{ mm}}{\text{feed } f \text{ mm/rev.}} = \frac{L}{f} \text{ revolutions}$$

The time taken for this operation (as for

drilling) $= \dfrac{60}{N} \times \dfrac{L}{f}$ s

Volume of metal removed = 'tube' volume
= cross-sectional area × length

$$= \left(\frac{22}{7} \times \frac{OD^2}{4} \right)$$

$$- \left(\frac{22}{7} \times \frac{ID^2}{4} \right) \text{mm}^2 \times L \text{ mm}$$

$$= \frac{22}{7} \times \frac{1}{4} (OD^2 - ID^2) \times L \text{ mm}^3$$

Metal removal rate

$$= \frac{\text{volume of metal removed}}{\text{time taken}}$$

$$= \frac{\dfrac{22}{7} \times \dfrac{1}{4} (OD^2 - ID^2) \times L \text{ mm}^3}{\dfrac{60}{N} \times \dfrac{L}{f}} \text{ s}$$

$$= \frac{22}{7} \times \frac{1}{4} (OD^2 - ID^2)$$

$$\times L \times \frac{N}{60} \times \frac{f}{L} \text{ mm}^3/\text{s}$$

$$= \frac{22}{7} \times \frac{1}{4} (OD^2 - ID^2) \times \frac{N}{60} \times f \text{ mm}^3/\text{s}$$

= area × rev/s × feed

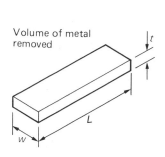

Volume of metal removed

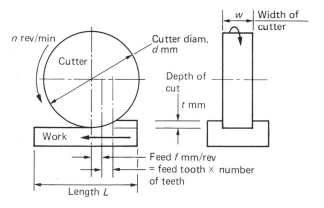

Milling

Milling

The number of revolutions of the cutter to machine a work length of

$$L \text{ mm} = \frac{L \text{ mm}}{\text{Table feed of mm/rev}} = \frac{L}{f}$$

revolutions.

The time taken for this operation, ignoring the approach length $= \dfrac{60}{N} \times \dfrac{L}{f}$ s

Volume of metal removed
$$= \text{width} \times \text{depth} \times \text{length}$$
$$= w \times t \times L \text{ mm}^3.$$

Metal removal rate
$$= \frac{\text{volume of metal removed}}{\text{time taken}}$$
$$= \frac{w \times t \times L \text{ mm}^3}{\dfrac{60}{N} \times \dfrac{L}{f} \text{ s}}$$
$$= w \times t \times L \times \frac{N}{60} \times \frac{f}{L}$$
$$= (w \times t) \times \frac{N}{60} \times f$$
$$= \text{cut area} \times \text{rev/s} \times \text{feed mm}^3/\text{s}$$

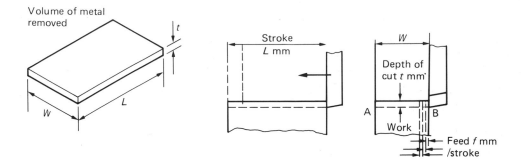

Shaping

Shaping

When cutting on a shaper the speed of the tool is maximum at the mid stroke and zero at the start and the end of the stroke. In calculations the *average cutting speed* is used.

The average cutting speed

$$= \frac{\text{the length of the cutting stroke}}{\text{the time taken}}$$

The number of cutting strokes required

$$= \frac{\text{work width} \quad W \text{ mm}}{\text{feed} \qquad f \text{ mm/stroke}}$$

$$= \frac{W}{f} \text{ strokes}$$

Volume of metal removed

= width mm × depth mm × length mm

$= w \times t \times L \text{ mm}^3.$

Metal removed rate

$$= \frac{\text{volume of metal removed}}{\text{time taken}}$$

$$= \frac{w \times t \times L \text{ mm}^3}{\frac{w}{f} \text{strokes} \times \text{time taken for 1 cycle in seconds.}}$$

$$= \frac{w \times t \times L}{\text{time for 1 cycle (s)}} \times \frac{f}{w}$$

$$= \frac{t \times L \times f}{\text{time for 1 cycle (s)}} \text{ mm}^3/\text{s}.$$

Questions

1 Production Data

The chart gives the relationship between rev/min and diameter in mm for cutting speeds in metres/min.

Component No. 1.

Cutting speed 20 m/min. Dia. 30 mm. Depth of cut 1.0 mm. Chip area 1.5 mm². Length of cut 80.0 mm.

$$\text{Feed/rev} = \frac{\text{chip area}}{\text{depth of cut}}$$
$$= \frac{1.5 \text{ mm}^2}{1.0 \text{ mm}} = 1.5 \text{ mm}.$$

$$\text{Revs required for length of work} = \frac{\text{Length}}{\text{feed/rev}}$$
$$= \frac{80 \text{ mm}}{1.5 \text{ mm}}$$
$$= 53.33 \text{ revs}$$

Time taken

210 revs in 60 s

$$1 \text{ rev } \text{in} \frac{60}{210}$$

$$53.33 \text{ revs in} \frac{60}{210} \times 53.33 = 15.23 \text{ s}$$

Column 1 can now be filled in with the values found. In a similar manner complete the remaining component numbers 2, 3, and 4.

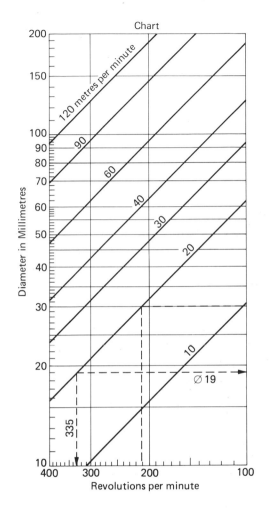

	Component number			
Production data	1	2	3	4
Cutting speed, m/min	20	40	60	90
Dia. of work, mm	30		80	
Rev/min		210		300
Cut or chip area, mm^2	1.5		5.0	7.5
Depth of cut, mm	1.0	4.0		5.0
Feed/rev, mm		0.3	1.0	
Length of cut, mm	80	100	200	180
Time taken, mm				

2 Find the lathe spindle speeds for turning:
  (a) 30 mm diameter brass, using a cutting speed of 50 m/min,
  (b) 42 mm diameter mild steel, using a cutting speed of 22 m/min,
  (c) 250 mm diameter cast iron, using a cutting speed of 20 m/min.
3 If a drilling machine is to operate with a range of drills from 22 mm to 8 mm at a cutting speed of 16 m/min, what are the highest and lowest speeds?
4 When turning a bar 250 mm long a spindle speed of 300 rev/min is used. If the feed of the tool is 1.25 mm/rev, find the time taken to make one cut.
5 Calculate the time to drill a hole 18 mm diameter and 90 mm deep, in mild steel.

Take a cutting speed of 16 m/min and a feed of 0.25 mm/rev.
6 A 60 mm diameter bar is being turned at 30 m/min. Its length is 600 mm and the feed of the tool is 1 mm/rev. Find the time taken to make one cut.
7 A milling cutter has 25 teeth and a feed of 0.2 mm per tooth. What is the feed when rotating at 100 rev/min:
  (a) in mm per revolution,
  (b) in mm per minute?
8 A drill of 22 mm has a cutting speed of 20 m/min. and a feed of 0.1 mm/rev. Find:
  (a) the rev/min of the drill,
  (b) the feed in mm/min,
  (c) the time taken to drill a hole 40 mm deep.
  (d) the volume of metal removed per minute.
9 A milling cutter 110 mm diameter × 60 mm wide has a cutting speed of 30 m/min. The cutter has 20 teeth and the feed per tooth is 0.15 mm. If it takes a 4 mm cut for the full cutter width, what is the volume of metal removed per minute?
10 When turning, a cutting speed of 28 m/min with a feed of 1.5 mm/rev is used on a ⌀ 40 bar. If the depth of cut is 4 mm find the volume of metal removed per minute.
11 A 60 mm diameter bar is being turned in a lathe at a speed of 300 rev/min. The feed is 0.75 mm/rev and the depth of the cut is 3 mm. Calculate the volume of metal removed per minute.
12 A 150 mm diameter side and face milling cutter has to cut a channel 5 mm deep in a workpiece. Calculate the minimum approach distance needed.
13 A shaping machine operates at 10 cycles/min. The forward stroke, i.e. the cutting stroke, takes ⅔ of the total time and the length of travel is 250 mm. Calculate the average cutting speed.

Cutting fluids

Their purposes
1 To cool the tool and workpiece.
2 To lubricate the chip/tool interface and reduce wear due to friction.
3 To improve surface finish of workpiece.
4 To flush away swarf.
5 To prevent corrosion.

Cutting fluids are designed to fulfil one or more of the above functions and can be broadly classified into the following groups.
(a) soluble oils,
(b) synthetic oils,
(c) chemical solutions,
(d) straight cutting oils.

Tool material	Coolants used
1 Carbon steel and medium alloy steels.	Watermix fluids
2 High-speed steel	Watermix fluids or neat oils
3 Cast alloy steels	Neat oils
4 Carbide	Watermix
5 Ceramic	Watermix

Cutting fluids in action
To get the best results, attention must be given to the correct preparation, application and control of cutting fluids.
(a) The systems must be kept clean and the solutions fresh and efficiently filtered.
(b) For maximum cooling and lubrication, the cutting fluid should flow copiously over the working area — at low pressure to avoid splashing.
(c) Where access of the fluid is restricted, high pressure jets may be applied up the rake and clearance faces of the tool.
(d) Regular checks on the 'strength' of the coolant.

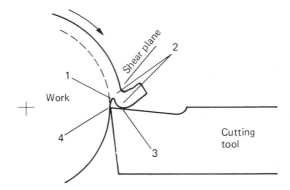

1 Internal friction due to the chip shearing from the work
2 Internal friction due to deformation of the chip
3 External friction between tool face and the chip
4 External friction between cutting edge and the work

Areas of heat generation

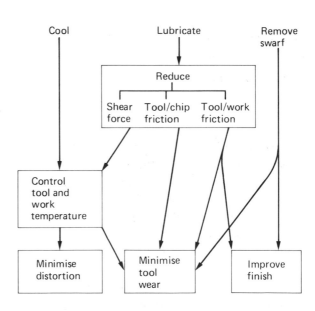

Actions performed by cutting fluids

(e) Bacteria infection of watermix fluids (infection is rare in neat oils because bacteria need water to live) leads to obnoxious smells, instability, rusting and staining of machine parts. Most watermix fluids contain bactericides which offer some protection.

(f) To further protect operators, they should wear protective clothing, keep splash guards in position and they should frequently wash and apply barrier creams.

Soluble oils
When oil and water are added together they refuse to mix, but if an emulsifier in the form of a detergent is added, the oil will break up into droplets and spread through the water. This is what happens when soluble oils are added to water. As a result of the dilution with the water, the lubricating properties of this type of fluid are much reduced, and are therefore not suitable for the very severe conditions found on many automatic machines but they are ideally suited for manually operated machines, where the operator would be affected by the fumes given off by straight oils.

A soluble oil is the 'maid-of-all-work' in metal cutting. It is adaptable, low in cost and effective. It has good cooling properties. General purpose soluble oils are used in a ratio of 1 in 20 to 1 in 50 for general machining and are milky in appearance.

Synthetic fluids
In this group of cutting fluids the mineral base of conventional cutting oils are replaced by aqueous solutions of inorganic chemicals, together with corrosion inhibitors and extreme pressure lubricating additives.

These solutions are tansparent, but colouring agents are added to differentiate them from water and soda solutions. In general, the range of materials on which the fluid may be used is wider than the cheaper soluble oils. Emulsification is easier, yielding a more stable emulsion.

Chemical solutions
These are carefully chosen chemicals in solution, which when further reduced with water possess a good flushing action and are non-clogging and non-corrosive. They are widely used for grinding. Mixtures of 1 to 100 are often employed and are transparent and more expensive than soluble oils and synthetic fluid. One of the earliest chemical solutions used was sodium carbonate (soda ash) in water.

Straight cutting oils

Straight mineral oils
Used for non-exacting work because lubricating film is unable to withstand considerable tool loading. These are suitable for light repetition work where free machining brass and steels are the main materials.

Mineral and fatty oil mixtures
These are more versatile than straight mineral oils since they possess better film properties. This is improved by the addition of fatty oils, such as rape oil and lard oil, these fatty oil blends being the most common of the straight cutting oils.

Fatty oils are rarely used alone as they tend to decompose and form sludge, but they blend well with mineral oils which inhibit the decomposition. Suitable for turning, milling, die-head screwing and general purpose duties on medium capacity bar automatics.

Sulphurised oils

These are probably the most useful of the straight cutting oils as their sulphur content can be varied to suit the work in hand. With conventional forms of sulphurised oil the sulphur present tends to stain the majority of non-ferrous alloys containing copper. These are used mainly for the lubrication factor in heavy turning, gear-cutting, thread grinding and many automatic lathes.

Method of mixing soluble oils

1   Select mixing ratio.
2   Measure off the required volume of water into a *clean* tank or drum. If water is hard, then soften before preparing emulsion.
3   Calculate the volume of soluble oil required.
4   Pour soluble oil gradually into the full volume of water and, at the same time, keep the water turning over — from top to bottom as distinct from a rotary movement. Continue the operation until the oil has been added.
5   Always add soluble oil to water and not vice-versa.

Frothing

This can arise with either soluble or straight fluids. Excessive turbulence by too powerful a pump may be the cause or the feed nozzle may be so restricted that a jet emerges instead of a low pressure gush. Further possible causes are as follows:

1   Use of too highly concentrated mixtures of soluble oil.
2   Mixing of incompatible oils.
3   Insufficient volume of coolant in the sump of the machine.

Separation (soluble oils)

This is where the emulsion is unstable and has partially separated; i.e. it has been made with excessively hard water; not mixed properly; the water has too high a proportion of dissolved acids; wrong amount of water has been used, making the emulsion weaker than intended or where the emulsion is too weak due to water being added to the sump instead of premixed emulsion.

Taper turning

Many components have a taper, which may be turned on a lathe by any of the four methods described below.

1 Compound rest method

The top slide on the lathe saddle may be set at angle θ to the axis, where 2θ is the angle of the taper. The method can be used for any angle of taper, but hand feed must be used and the length of travel is limited, and so is the degree of accuracy which can be achieved.

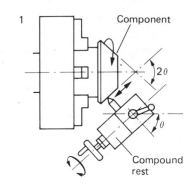

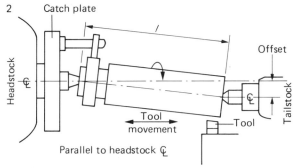

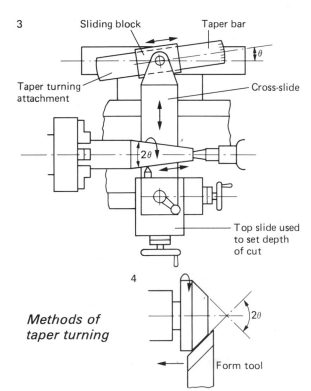

Methods of taper turning

2 Offsetting the tailstock

By offsetting the tailstock as shown, the small diameter of the taper will be at the tailstock end. The angle of taper is limited, due to the offset travel amount of the tailstock.

If the offset is x mm, then the diameter at the tailstock end will be $(2 \times x)$mm less than the diameter at the headstock end.

If the length *between centres* is 1 mm, the *taper on diameter* per unit length

$$= \frac{2 \times x}{1}$$

If $x = 3$ mm and $1 = 240$ mm, then the taper on diameter per unit length

$$= \frac{2 \times 3 \text{ mm}}{240 \text{ mm}} = \frac{1}{40}, \text{ i.e. 1 in 40.}$$

Due to the driving dog it is impossible to obtain a taper for the whole length of the job between centres.

3 Taper turning attachment

Many modern lathes have a taper bar fitted at the back of the bed which can be adjusted through a range of angles to the spindle axis. The bar carries a sliding block which, during taper turning, is attached to the cross-slide. This means that before such attachments can be used, the cross-slide must be disconnected from its actuating screw, to enable it to move across the taper bar and the sliding block. This is generally done by removing a screw located about in the centre of the upper face of the cross-slide.

The length of the taper bar allows large degree divisions on its degree scale, which enable accurate settings to be carried out, an angle vernier often being incorporated. The taper is produced by the movement of the saddle under power feed, giving improved and controllable surface finish, and a long taper is possible. It is, however, limited to semi-angles of taper of about 15° (30° included angle).

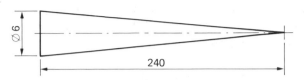

Offsetting the tailstock

4 Form tool

The cutting face has to be straight and set at half the included taper angle. This method of taper turning is used a great deal, e.g. on capstan and turret lathes where large numbers of components are made.

Questions

1   Calculate the tailstock setover or offset to turn the following tapers.

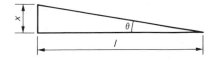

(a) a taper of 1 in 10 on a job 300 mm long,

(b) a taper of 1 in 15 on a job 200 mm long,

(c) a taper of 1 in 18 on a job 360 mm long.

2   For each of the tapers in question **1**, what are the taper included angles? Make use of the following right-angle triangle formula:

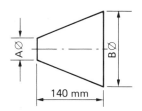

$$\text{Tan } \theta = \frac{x}{l}$$

3   Calculate the included angle of the taper for each of the following:

(a) A = 30 mm;   B = 80 mm,

(b) A = 40 mm;   B = 75 mm,

(c) A = 45 mm;   B = 135 mm.

4   Calculate the following angles for the turned bar:

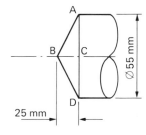

(a) the angle BAC of the conical turned end of a bar,

(b) the angle ABD.

Screw thread cutting methods

The principles of generating and forming have already been discussed. Screwcutting on a lathe combines the two processes, the thread shape being formed by the tool, and the helix being generated by the lathe motion. The large range of threads which may be required involve (as already seen) a gearbox which, in practice is commonly a quick change one.

The Quick-change gearbox

This box contains several different size gears any of which can be quickly engaged, to give the proper ratio between the rotation of the work spindle and the lead screw. On a plate, secured to the box, is a table of the various pitches to be cut and the corresponding positions of the levers.

Setting up a gear train

If two gear wheels of the same size and the same number of teeth are selected, one placed on the work spindle and one on the lead screw; by placing an idler gear between, the ratio between the spindle and lead screw remains the same. The pitch of the thread cut will be the same as the pitch of the lead screw, the lead screw being single-start.

Then $\dfrac{\text{Work spindle turns}}{\text{Lead screw turns}} = \dfrac{1}{1}$

If the ratio is $\dfrac{\text{Work spindle turns}}{\text{Lead screw turns}} = \dfrac{2}{1}$

then the pitch cut will be one-half of the lead screw pitch.

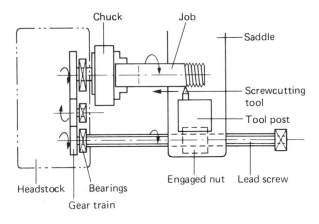

Single point screwcutting, right-hand thread

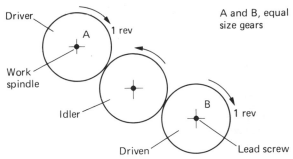

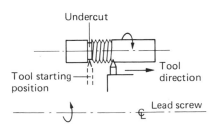

Single point screwcutting, left-hand thread

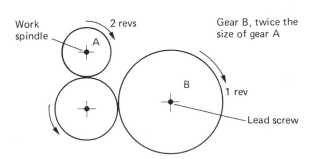

A ratio $\frac{4}{1}$ means that the pitch will be one-quarter of the lead screw pitch.

Then $\dfrac{\text{Work spindle turns}}{\text{Lead screw turns}}$

$= \dfrac{\text{pitch to be cut}}{\text{pitch of lead screw}}$

or $\dfrac{\text{Driver}}{\text{Driven}} = \dfrac{\text{pitch to be cut}}{\text{pitch of lead screw}}$

For a multi-start thread the tool movement must be equal to the *lead*, not the pitch. Then the formula is modified to

$$\frac{\text{Driver}}{\text{Driven}} = \frac{\text{Lead to be cut}}{\text{Lead of lead screw}}$$

Square-threading tool calculations

A square screwcutting tool must be ground so that it fits into the helical groove. It must have the same slope as the helix angle α, and clearance on both sides, so that the sides do not rub the work.

$$\tan\alpha = \frac{\text{Lead}}{\text{Circumference}}$$

Example

Given that the major diameter of a square-threaded shaft is 38 mm, thread 6 mm pitch, two-start, calculate (a) the helix angle and (b) the ground shape of the tool, allowing 5° clearance angles.

Pitch dia. $= 38 - 3 = 35$ mm.

Lead $= 6 \times 2 = 12$ mm.

$\text{Tan}\,\alpha = \dfrac{12\text{ mm}}{3\frac{1}{7} \times 35\text{ mm}} = 0.1091$

Helix angle $= 6°13'$

Leading angle $= 6°13' + 5° = 11°13' = F$

Following or

Tracking angle $= 6°13' - 5° = 1°13' = E$

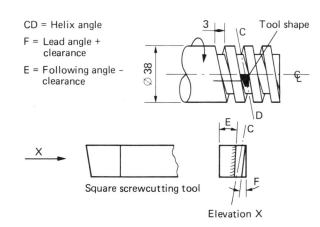

CD = Helix angle

F = Lead angle + clearance

E = Following angle − clearance

Square screwcutting tool

Elevation X

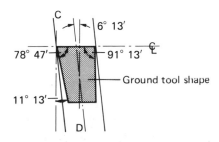

Arrangement drawing of the tool shape, Cutting a square thread of 6 mm pitch, two start

The unified thread

The unified thread adopted by the ISO has a 60° angle form and has rounded roots and rounded or flat crests. It is available in three classes of fit: UNF for fine precision threads, UNM for medium general use and UNC for coarse work. The threads can be produced by several methods, such as rolling, grinding, milling, by the use of taps and dies and by screwcutting on a lathe.

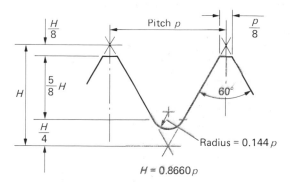

150 standard thread form

Method of screwcutting an internal right-hand unified thread in a blind hole

1 Set the internal screwcutting tool on centre, and square, using the screw gauge located on the outside diameter of the turned work.
2 With the work stationary, move the tool into the blind hole to the position shown dotted.
3 Mark the saddle position on the bed slide with chalk.
4 Move the tool out of the bore. Pick up the bore with the tool and set the cross-slide dial to zero.
5 With the work revolving at a slow speed, engage the lead screw nut and take the first cut.
6 Disengage quickly when the saddle reaches the chalk mark and stop the lathe.
7 Move the tool out of the thread towards the middle of the bore and remove to the right, clear of the job.
8 Put a further cut on the tool, engage the nut at the right position and cut. Repeat **6**, **7** and **8**.
9 To obtain the correct form of thread, use a tap or an internal chaser. Check with an *external screw gauge* or with the *external threaded bolt* to suit the work.

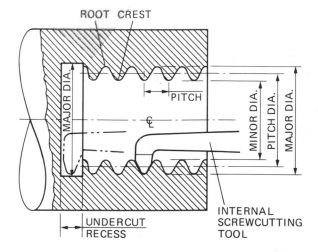

Method of screwcutting an internal left-hand unified thread

1 The lead screw is made, by changing gears, to rotate in the opposite direction when compared with cutting a right-hand thread.
2 The procedure is the same as when cutting a right-hand, except that the cut is taken starting in the undercut recess. The tool now moves from left to right.

Method of screwcutting an external right-hand unified thread

1 Set the compound slide at 29°.
2 Index the tool post so that the 60° tool angle on centre is located squarely in the screw gauge. The screw gauge is on centre and horizontal. Lock the tool post.
3 Move the tool to touch the outside diameter of the work. Set both the compound slide and cross-slide collar to zero.
4 Back off the tool and move the saddle so that the tool is clear of the end of the work and turn the cross-slide to zero.
5 Set the depth of cut with the compound slide.
6 With the work at a slow speed engage the nut on the lead screw.
7 Disengage the nut quickly and stop the lathe.
8 Withdraw the tool with the compound slide handle and move the saddle to the starting position.
9 Feed the tool into the previous reading and add another small cut.
10 Repeat **6**, **7**, **8** and **9** until the minor diameter is nearly obtained. ·
11 To obtain the correct form of thread, use a die or an external thread chaser. Check with a *ring nut* or the *mating nut*.

Note:
With the compound rest set to 29°, a slight shaving action occurs on the trailing edge of the tool and tends to produce a better finish.

A further method is the *plunge feed* method, whereby the cuts are applied by the *cross-slide* handle.

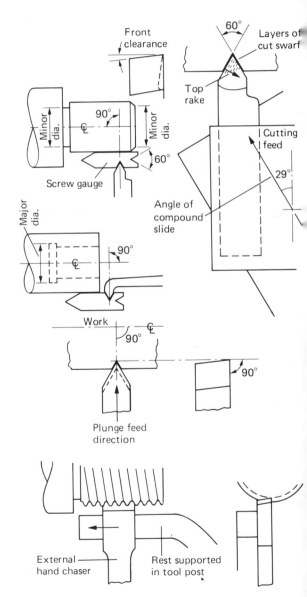

Unified thread

Acme threads

The acme thread form is generally replacing the square thread because:

(a) it is stronger,
(b) it is easier to cut on a lathe, and
(c) it can be made with taps and dies.

This thread has a clearance of 0.250 mm at the crest and root of mating parts.

The hole for an internal acme thread is cut 0.5 mm larger than the minor diameter of the screw, while the major diameter of the internal thread is 0.5 mm larger than the screw. Taps for acme threads are 0.5 mm larger than the major diameter of the screw.

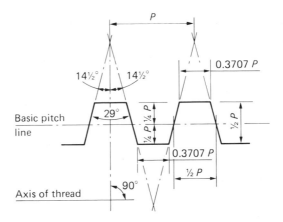

Basic form of acme thread

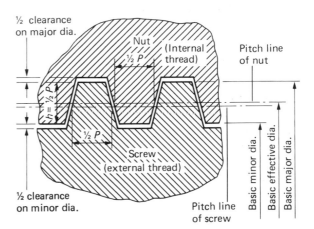

Design forms of acme threads

Method of cutting a right-hand acme external thread

1 Grind the cutting tool to fit the 29° angle in a thread gauge. As with a square screw-cutting tool, allow the necessary clearance angles for the leading and trailing cutting edges.

2 Grind the point flat until it fits the proper slot.

3 Set the compound slide to 14½°.

4 Set the cutting tool square with the work and on centre.

5 Cut the thread to depth using the compound slide, taking many cuts to achieve this depth.

It may be advantageous to rough-cut the thread with a square thread cutting tool, and use the acme tool to finish-cut.

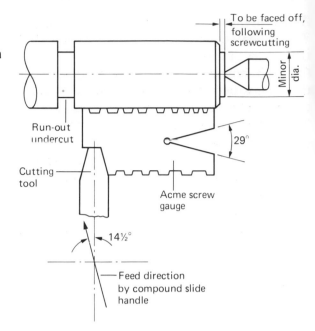

Locating the tool in the thread

When screwcutting, the work spindle and the lead screw must be in the same relative position for each successive cut. If not, then cross-cutting occurs and the work is spoilt. The methods used to follow the same thread are as follows.

1 *Constant engagement of the saddle split nut with the lead screw*

(a) When a cut has been completed, and the tool withdrawn clear of the work, the lead screw can be reversed.

(b) With the cutting tool well clear of the start of the thread to be cut, a feed can be put on to the tool and a cut taken.

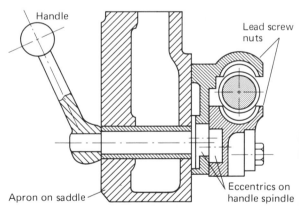

By moving the handle, the top half of the nut moves down, and the bottom half moves up

2 *The thread chasing Dial*

(a)   The worm wheel, when meshing with the lead screw, revolves.

(b)   When the first cut has been taken, the position of one of the graduations on the dial relative to the zero mark on the saddle is noted.

(c)   After the completion of this cut, the tool is withdrawn, the split nut disengaged and moved to the right, clear of the starting position.

(d)   With another cut set, the lead screw is engaged at the same dial to zero position as in (b).

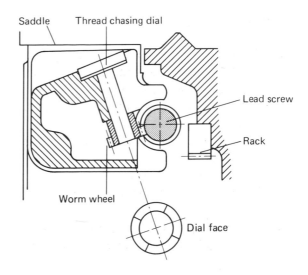

3 *Chalk-marking the lathe*

(a)   With the tool at the starting position, the lead screw nut engaged and the machine at rest, chalk-mark the chuck and the corresponding position in the headstock casing.

(b)   Chalk-mark the lead screw and a corresponding position on the fixed casing.

(c)   On the right of the saddle, locate and clamp on end stop to the bed slide.

(d)   Take a cut.

(e)   Stop the lathe and disengage the nut. Withdraw the tool and move the saddle to the right to the end stop.

(f)   Engage the nut when the two pairs of chalkings are in line and put a further cut in the tool.

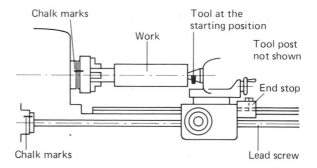

Multi-start threads

The methods used to cut a two start thread are as follows.

1 *By setting the compound slide parallel to the bed of the lathe.*

(a) With the saddle nut still engaged with the lead screw, following the completion of cutting one thread, withdraw the tool clear of the work.

(b) Place slip gauges equal to the pitch, on the side of the tool post.

(c) Locate and register a clock gauge on the slip gauges.

(d) Remove the slip gauges and move the tool post, by the compound slide handle, to the same reading on the clock gauge.

Note: The screwcutting tool must be fed into the work with the *crossfeed handle*.

2 *The gear train method*

(a) When a tooth of A is meshing in a tooth space in B mark both gears with chalk. Also mark B to C, with the saddle nut still engaged with the lead screw.

(b) Taking A to have an even number of teeth, say 30, slide the idler gear out of mesh and rotate the work spindle gear A, half a rev, i.e. 15 teeth places.

(c) Replace the idler with all the chalk lines lined up.

3 *The indexed catch plate*

(a) The work, mounted between centres, will be rotated by a driving dog located in a slot.

(b) With the saddle nut still engaged with the lead screw, remove the work and the dog, and index the dog in the slot dia-metrically opposite to its original position.

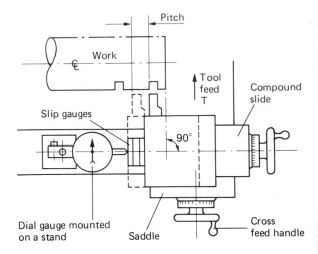

Two start square thread

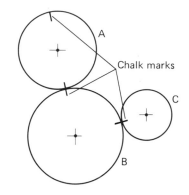

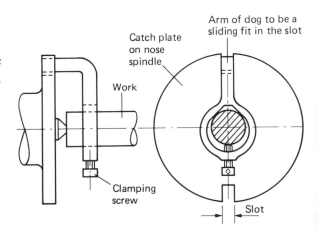

Grinding wheels

A grinding wheel is a circular cutting tool with a very large number of teeth, each of which removes minute chips of metal. The individual cutting points are provided by many small hard grains called the *grit* which are embedded in a matrix known as the *bond*. In the bond are many small air spaces which help to provide clearance for the chips cut away by the grit.

Two types of grit are (a) *aluminium oxide* and (b) *silicon carbide*.

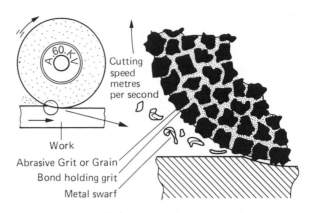

Grinding wheel removing metal

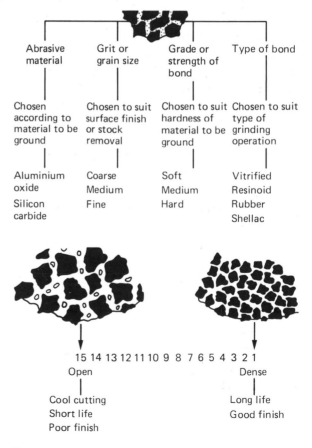

Abrasive material	Grit or grain size	Grade or strength of bond	Type of bond
Chosen according to material to be ground	Chosen to suit surface finish or stock removal	Chosen to suit hardness of material to be ground	Chosen to suit type of grinding operation
Aluminium oxide	Coarse	Soft	Vitrified
	Medium	Medium	Resinoid
Silicon carbide	Fine	Hard	Rubber
			Shellac

15 14 13 12 11 10 9 8 7 6 5 4 3 2 1

Open	Dense
Cool cutting	Long life
Short life	Good finish
Poor finish	

Properties of a grinding wheel

Aluminium oxide (fused alumina) is prepared in an electric furnace from bauxite (hydrated aluminium oxide). It is reddish brown in colour and is used on tough, strong materials such as steel. Examples of makers' trade names are Aloxite, Alundum, Oxaluma and Bauxilite.

Silicon carbide is a chemical combination of carbon and silicon and is made in a resistance-type electric furnace. Silicon carbide is greenish-black in colour and is harder than aluminium oxide and is therefore used on hard, non-ductile materials. As silicon carbide is more easily fractured, new cutting points are provided without undue wheel wear when grinding low resistance materials. The makers' trade names are Carborundum, Carbolite, Crystolon and Unirundum.

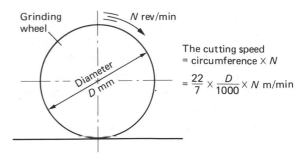

The cutting speed
= circumference × N

$$= \frac{22}{7} \times \frac{D}{1000} \times N \text{ m/min}$$

Types of grinding	Average cutting or wheel speeds
Cylindrical	1600 − 2000 m/min
Surface	1300 − 1600 m/min
Internal	600 − 2000 m/min

The bond
The bond is the substance which when mixed with the abrasive grit or grain, holds them together, so enabling the mixture to be shaped. Suitable treatment then takes place, giving to the wheel the correct mechanical strength for its work. The proportion of bond in a wheel varies from about 10 per cent to 30 per cent of its total volume.

Grade
The degree of hardness possessed by the bond is called the grade of the wheel. A soft bond permits the grains, when they become dulled or glazed, to break away easily. A hard bond retains the abrasive grains longer and should be used on soft materials — hard wheel for soft work and soft wheel for hard work.

Wheel selections
Manufacturers will supply suitable grinding wheels provided the following information is given:
1   The type and material of work to be ground.
2   The make of the machine and its condition.
3   The work speed.
4   The personal factor — whether a skilled or semi-skilled operator is to use the wheel.
5   Use of a coolant. If grinding is to be carried out with coolant supplied, then a hard wheel will be used. Without a coolant a softer and freer cutting wheel will be necessary.

A tag or label attached to a wheel indicates the composition of wheel, conforming to BS:4481.

Glazing and loading

A *glazed wheel* is one in which the grains are being broken but not released, and therefore the grains are practically level with the bond surface. The wheel has a 'shiny' or glazed appearance. In this state it has a poor cutting action and can burn the work. The wheel should be 'dressed' and then a reduced speed used.

Dressing is a process of cleaning and opening up the face of a grinding wheel. Sometimes wheels are dressed with a solid lump of abrasive crystals, or a small wheel of the same material mounted on a spindle with handles at each end for holding. Another method is by using a hand tool, called a *star wheel dresser*. It has a number of star-shaped metal wheels, which revolve in the tool when pressed into the grinding wheel face and, by so doing, dig away the bond and release the dulled grains.

These methods are suitable for hand grinding and certain classes of machine grinding in which a precision finish is not necessary. For cylindrical surface grinding the diamond in its holder is used.

A *loaded wheel* is one to which chips of metal have adhered, thus clogging up the voids in the bond. The wheel must be 'dressed', the wheel speed increased, if this is permissible, and more coolant used.

In both cases the correct solution may be to use a softer wheel.

Effect of lack of balance in grinding wheels

When any rotating wheel, including a grinding wheel, is out of balance, the centre of the mass of the wheel is not on its centre of rotation. When rotating, the centrifugal force set up can cause the wheel to disintegrate. An internal grinding wheel can rotate at 60 000 rev/min. Damage could also be caused to the bearings due to the 'hammering' effect of the centrifugal force as it acts above and below the centre of the spindle as it rotates.

Trueing and dressing grinding wheels

This operation is necessary when a wheel is first mounted and also if the wheel wears out of shape. The tool used is an industrial diamond set into a spindle and taken across the face of the wheel parallel to the horizontal axis. The angle of between 3° and 15° prevents the diamond 'digging' in. On a surface grinder the diamond holder is held by the magnetic chuck and cross-transversed. On a cylindrical grinder, the diamond holder is set into the tailstock, and the wheel is trued up by the operator moving the table from side to side. If the diamond does not follow the correct path, it is possible to have a conical or concave shape to the wheel face.

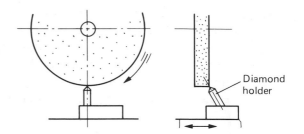

Surface grinding

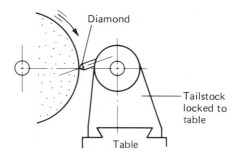

Dressing of a grinding wheel for cylindrical grinding

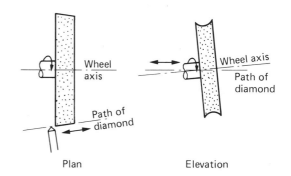

Dressing errors

Grinding wheel mounting and balancing

The procedure is as follows:

1   Fix the two balancing weights in the wheel flange diametrically opposite to each other and lock them in place. Assemble the grinding wheel on the machine spindle and lock it in position. True the wheel.

2   Remove the wheel flange, grinding wheel and lock nut assembly and set them on the balancing mandrel.

3   Set the balancing stand level using the spirit level provided.

4   Place the assembly on the knife edges of the stand and allow the assembly to roll, due to its 'out of balance', until it stops. Mark the top centre of the wheel with chalk.

5   Move the balance weights to 90° from the mark and diametrically opposite.

6   Repeat the roll test, moving the balance weights equally towards the marks, about 5 mm at a time, until the assembly remains static in any position.

7   Remount the assembly onto the wheelhead and redress wheel.

8   Grind a specimen on the grinding machine and inspect the surface finish produced.

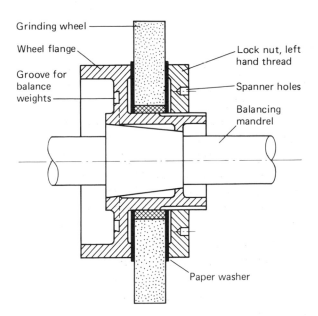

Grinding wheel assembly for balancing

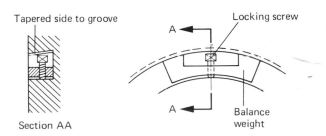

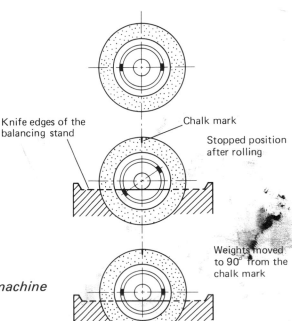

Wheel and balance weights on the machine spindle

Questions

1 Explain the difference between the terms:
(a) trueing and (b) dressing, when
applied to grinding wheels.
2 On a precision grinding wheel, how is the
wheel surface restored to its original
efficient condition?
3 State the effect of grinding with the wheel
out of balance as regards to surface finish
and effect on the machine.
4 What is meant by the operation faults:
(a) loaded and (b) glazing?
5 What are the probable causes of loading
and glazing?
6 What effects do loading and glazing have
on the work finish?

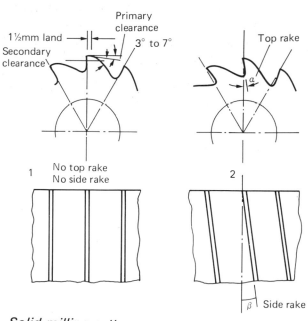

Solid milling cutters

Cutter teeth on milling cutters

The teeth of solid milling cutters are generally
of the fluted type. Fluted teeth have a shape of
the type shown and are sharpened by grinding
the narrow top land of the cutting edge. If the
front of the tooth is made radial as at **1**, the
cutting takes place without top rake, but by
deposing the flute as at **2** a top rake of $\alpha°$ is
introduced. Side rake is introduced by cutting
the teeth on a helix as at **3**.

Primary and secondary clearance angles on milling cutters

Face, side and face cutters, all have the narrow
land ground on the teeth to form the cutting
edge. It is ground at a primary clearance angle
of 6° to 7° for cutters up to 75 mm diameter.
Over 75 mm it is 4° to 5°, and end teeth of end
mills, 3° to 5°.

To avoid the heel of the land rubbing the
work, a *secondary* clearance angle is necessary.
For cutting mild steel the secondary clearance
angle is 5° to 7°. For cutting high carbon steel
it is 3° to 5°. For cutting brass and aluminium,
10° to 12°.

Setting of a fluting cutter when milling a blank to obtain α° top rake

The first stage in the manufacture of a milling cutter is to cut the main recesses in a circular blank of steel by using a *fluting cutter*. The blank will be held in a universal dividing head.

In order to obtain a top rake the fluting cutter is offset by the distance BC.
In the right-angled triangle ABC

$$\text{Sin } \alpha = \frac{BC}{CA} \text{ but CA} = R, \text{ then sin } \alpha = \frac{\text{offset}}{R}$$

.. Offset = sin α × R.

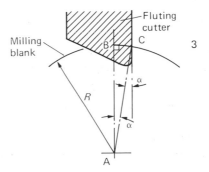

Set-up for milling flutes to give α° top rake

Disc wheel grinding to grind the face primary clearance angle

The procedure for setting up on a tool and cutter grinder is as follows:
1   Set the grinding wheel and the cutter centres level and parallel to each other.
2   Clamp the tool rest to the table and adjust the rest to the centre height by the use of a height gauge.
3   Raise the wheel centre the calculated amount. In the right-angled triangle ABC, the clearance angle = BÂC; AC = radius R of the grinding wheel; BC = height that the grinding wheel is raised then

$$\sin \hat{BAC} = \frac{BC}{AC} \text{ also BC} = \sin \hat{BAC} \times AC.$$

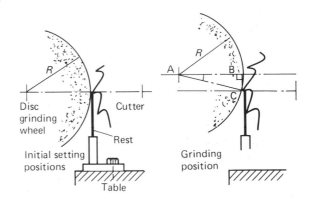

Set-up for grinding cutter teeth with a disc wheel

Cup wheel grinding to grind the face primary clearance angle

The procedure for setting up on a tool and cutter grinder is as follows:
1   Set the grinding wheel centre about central with the cutter centre. It does not need to be on absolute centre.
2   Clamp the tool rest to the table; the end of the rest must be level with the cutter centre.

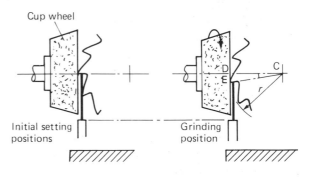

Face — set-up for grinding cutter teeth with a cup wheel

3 Lower the end of the rest by the calculated amount. In the right-angled triangle CDE; CE = cutter radius r; the clearance angle = $D\hat{C}E$; DE = distance that the rest is lowered.

$$\text{Sin } D\hat{C}E = \frac{DE}{CE} \text{ then } DE = CE \times \sin D\hat{C}E$$

Grinding side cutting edges

The procedure for setting up is as follows:

1 Use a small cup wheel.

2 Set the cutter axis to the primary clearance angle.

3 Clamp the post to the table.

Form relieved cutters

Note:

(a) Only the front face to be ground.

(b) The radial distance from the centre to the cutting edges must be exactly the same.

(c) The pitches on the diameter must be exactly the same.

The procedure for setting up is as follows:

Radial tooth front cutter

1 Set an *index disc* on the cutter arbor. The disc must be accurately machined so that all disc teeth are spaced at an angle A degrees, the same angle as the cutter teeth spacing.

2 Set the grinding face on the vertical centre of the cutter, and move the first tooth face to the cutter.

3 Secure the disc to the cutter mandrel shaft, with the rest in position.

Offset tooth cutter

The procedure is similar to the radial tooth except that first of all the grinding wheel must be offset relative to the vertical centre of the cutter.

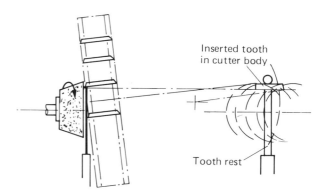

Set-up for grinding side cutting edges

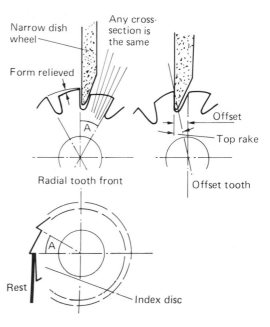

Grinding cutting edges

Face — The procedure is to:

1   Mount the cutter approximately in the centre of the headed mandrel. This is done by arranging the collar.
2   Screw on the knurled nut and finger tighten the assembly.
3   Mount the assembly between centres on the tool and cutter grinder.
4   Clamp the tool rest to the table and locate the rest on centre.
5   Switch on the cup wheel and by oscillating the table across the cup wheel, move the wheel in to grind. At the same time with the left hand, exert a slight turning effect on the collars and mandrel so as to keep the tooth to be ground in contact with the rest.
6   Immediately contact is made, stop the feed in, but continue to traverse the cutting edges across the cup wheel.
7   Switch off the machine and, when the cup wheel has stopped, rotate the cutter to the next tooth to be ground.
8   Repeat 5, 6 and 7 for each of the cutter teeth.

Helical slab mill cutting edges

The procedure is the same as the above except for 4. Clamp the tool rest onto the wheel head housing. As the table and cutter move across the cup wheel a slight rotation of the cutter will result. This is due to the inclined cutter blade passing over the fixed rest.

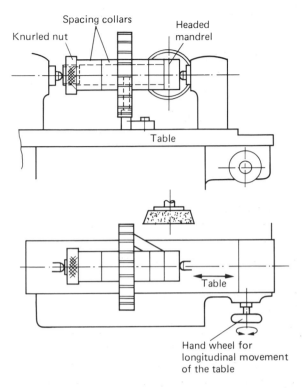

Set-up for grinding milling cutter face teeth

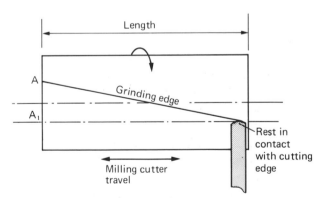

When the slab mill has travelled a distance equal to its length point A will turn through arc AA_1.

Files

Files are described by their length, section and cut.

Length is normally the measurement from the shoulder above the tang to the point. The exception is the needle file where the total length is measured. The length of file required for any job generally corresponds to the size of the workpiece.

Section describes the actual shape of the section of steel from which a file is made, e.g. round, square, half round, knife, etc. In some cases, files are described by the use for which they are intended, e.g. warding for filing locks, chainsaw for sharpening chain saws, magnets for cleaning electrical contacts, gardeners for sharp-ending spades, shears, etc.

Cut of a file (whether single or double) varies from coarse to extremely smooth. The fineness (or coarseness) of the cut also varies with the length of the file. The three grades of cut are:

1 *Bastard* for heavy removal of material leaving a rough finish.
2 *Second cut* for general purpose light removal with a fair finish.
3 *Smooth* for fine finishing work.

Single cut files are normally used with light pressure to produce a smooth finish or a sharp edge on cutting tools. *Double cut* files are normally used with heavier pressure for fast removal where a rough finish is acceptable.

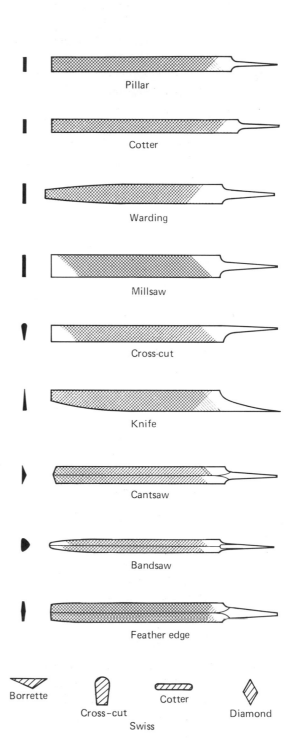

Pillar

Cotter

Warding

Millsaw

Cross-cut

Knife

Cantsaw

Bandsaw

Feather edge

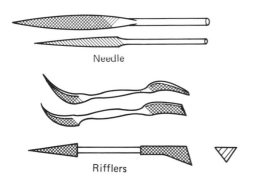

Needle

Rifflers

Borrette

Cross-cut
Swiss

Cotter

Diamond

Special files

Type	Uses
Pillar	For filing slots and keyways. One edge plain.
Cotter	For filing slots and keyways. Cut on both edges.
Warding	For filing keyways, working on press tools and gauge marking.
Millsaw	For radiusing slots, e.g. in toolmaking and diesinking, and sharp-ending the teeth on circular saws.
Cross-cut	For filing the teeth on wood saws.
Knife	To produce small angle vee grooves for toolmaking, die sinking, and in sheet metal.
Cantsaw	By using the acute cutting angle on the file, teeth on a saw of less than 60° angle can be filed.
Bandsaw	For sharpening bandsaw blades. Again the acute angle is used.
Feather edge	As the name suggests, the very small angle on the file enables filing to be carried out in very small angle vee grooves.
Swiss	Numerous cross-sections are obtainable to suit high precision work, for example in toolmaking. The files are small in length.
Needle	Similar to Swiss files but complete with handles. The needle and Swiss files are operated with gentleness and great skill.
Rifflers	Can be obtained in many shapes. For filing the inside of curved surfaces of tools and dies and where the previous straight files would be unsuitable.

Hand scraping

A *flat scraper* can be made from a large flat file. It must be forged to shape the cutting edge end and then ground, hardened and tempered. Honing then produces a sharp cutting edge.

The *three plate method*, to produce three square plates by hand scraping, is as follows:

1 Thinly coat the surface of plate A with prussian marking blue.
2 Rub plate B with plate A.
3 The plate B will now be marked with blue on its high spots. Plate A will be rubbed clean on its high spots.
4 Scrape the high spots on A and B and repeat the procedure.
5 Coat the surface of plate A with blue and rub with plate C. Scrape all high spots on plates A and C and repeat the procedure.
6 Coat the surface of plate B with blue and rub with plate C. Scrape all high spots on plates B and C and repeat the procedure.

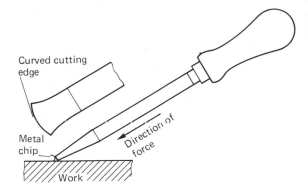

Flat scraper

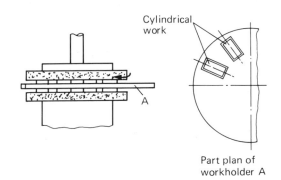

Mechanical lapping

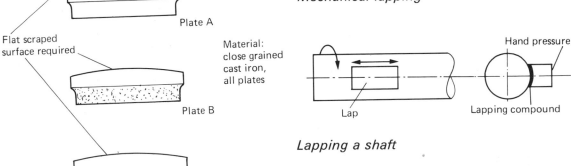

Material: close grained cast iron, all plates

Three plate method

Lapping a shaft

Lapping

This is an operation of placing an abrasive powder between two surfaces which rub on each other, thus wearing down the surfaces. Oil and thin grease absorb and spread the lapping powders, which can be silicon carbide, aluminium oxide or diamond dust. The lapping compound is placed on a *lap* which is usually softer than the surface to be lapped. Hardened steel may be lapped with a lap of grey cast iron and soft steel by a lap made of copper or lead. Lapping is done by hand or by machines. The process differs from grinding, since the speed is slow, the pressure is light, there is a larger area of contact and the work is not clamped down.

Advantages of lapping as compared to grinding

1 No cracking of the surface as is possible due to the heat of grinding.
2 Better surface finish whether it is flat or round work.
3 Better flatness.
4 Improved sharpness of cutting tool edges.

Lapping plate

Surface plates can be finished by hand lapping on a lapping plate. A lapping plate is usually made of soft cast iron, and has small vee grooves machined in the surface. When the surface is coated with lapping paste and the surface plate lapped, the vee grooves act as a reservoir for the paste.

Half-round scraper

This is chiefly used in scraping bearings to 'bed-in' a shaft.

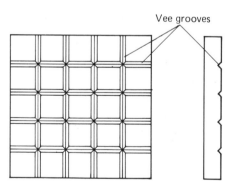

Lapping plate

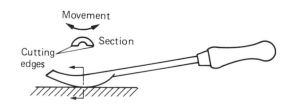

Half round scraper

Honing

Honing, unlike lapping, can remove a surface very rapidly. To finish the surface of bored holes a *honing head* can be used. The head carries six abrasive 'sticks' of composition similar to a fine grinding wheel, which by means of a cone expander can increase or decrease the head's diameter. The head, connected by a universal joint, means that the head can 'float'. The head, rotating at a surface speed between 15 m/min and 60 m/min, according to the hardness of the work, is also moved axially backwards and forwards.

Long horizontal machines are used for gunbores, whilst engine cylinder blocks require vertical multi-spindle machines.

External honing consists of passing two honing sticks in an axial direction while the shaft rotates.

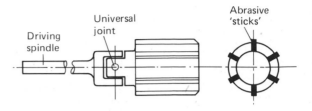

Internal honing head

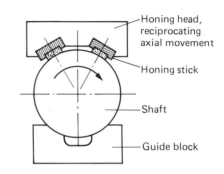

External honing head

Optical flats

These are made of *quartz* in plate form and a useful size is 60 mm diameter by 15 mm thick. By holding the edge between thumb and finger, it is seen to be perfectly transparent and colourless. The two faces are very highly polished, perfectly flat and parallel to each other to a high degree of accuracy. When an optical flat is placed on a perfectly flat surface, then nothing would be seen.

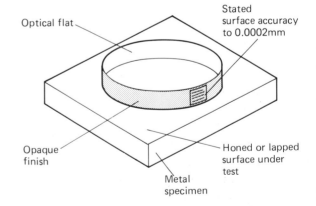

As the surface of AB is perfectly flat, a ray from the source S would (ignoring refraction effects) pass through the flat to the point E, which is equally on the flat surface AB and the lower surface of the flat CD. So there is only one return ray from E reaching the eye.
1 However, assume a speck of dust, or a tiny irregularity in the surface AB causes CD to rest at an angle to AB as shown, greatly exaggerated, in 2.

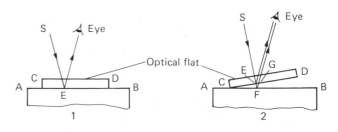

This time, a ray from S would be partly reflected from E on the face CD; but some light would pass through to F on AB and be reflected back to the eye, passing through the lower surface CD at G. Thus, the eye would receive two reflected rays, one having travelled a distance EFG farther than the other. These two rays of light interfere, producing a pattern of light and dark bands. As the very small angle of separation between AB and CD changes, so does the spacing between the bands. The number of bands produced, and their movement, provides an accurate method for measuring very small changes in flatness. Also, characteristic patterns enable particular changes of flatness to be recognised, e.g. *convex* or *concave* surfaces.
2 Concentric bands would indicate either a *convex* or *concave* surface. Pressing on the centre of the prism, or imparting a slight rocking movement, would determine the surface shape.
3 The curved band shapes could indicate either a valley or a ridge running approximately north to south.
4 A small convex or concave shape near the north edge of the optical flat.
Finger pressure will determine the correct surface form for 3 and 4.

Knowledge of contour lines on a map, conveys to one the shapes of the surface when using an optical flat.

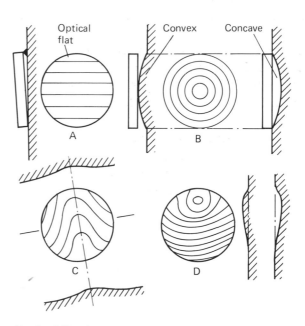

Optical flat images

Reamers

When a hole with a good finish and a true cylindrical shape is required, the following operations are carried out:

1   The hole is first of all opened-out, by more than one drill if required, to a size slightly smaller than the finish size.
2   A reamer, at a much slower speed but a faster feed than for drilling, is then fed through the hole. Other than for cast iron, a lubricant must be used.

Parallel hand reamer
1   This is operated by hand with a tap wrench.
2   For about a quarter of its length it is slightly tapered. This body clearance gives a lead into the drilled hole.
3   The minimum of metal should be left by the drill for the reamer — about 0.05 to 0.12 mm.
4   The shank diameter is always smaller than the cutting diameter.

Parallel machine reamer
1   The taper shank fits into a drill spindle or the tailstock barrel on a lathe.
2   The left-hand spiral flutes, varying from 4° to 8°, tend to push the reamer into its holder when cutting.
3   If the flutes were right-handed the reamer would tend to screw into the hole and pull out of its holder.
4   It is manufactured from carbon steel or high speed steel.

Taper reamer
Assemblies, such as collars or pulleys on shafts are secured with tapered pins. A drill slightly smaller than the small diameter of the pin is put through the assembly. The hole is then reamed out using the taper reamer until the pin fits.

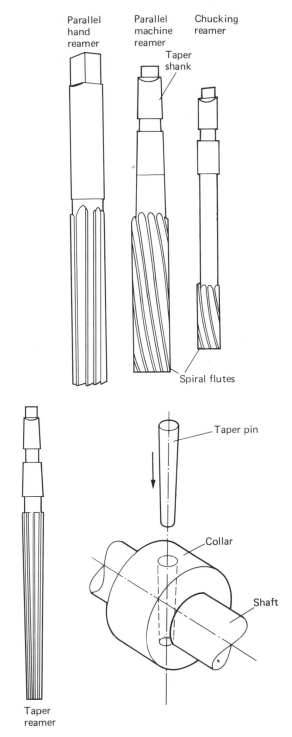

Parallel hand reamer

Parallel machine reamer

Chucking reamer

Taper shank

Spiral flutes

Taper reamer

Taper pin

Collar

Shaft

Chucking reamers

1 A *rose* reamer has a full diameter at the end of the reamer and tapers to a smaller diameter at the shank end, called *body clearance*. This reamer can remove greater amounts of metal than a *fluted* reamer but is not so accurate. In some cases cored holes can also be reamed.

2 A *fluted* chucking reamer cuts on the flutes in the same way as an ordinary solid reamer.

When fluting reamers, it is necessary to 'break up the flutes', i.e. to space the cutting edges unevenly around the reamer. The difference in spacing is about two degrees either way. It obviates 'chatter', so producing a smooth finish.

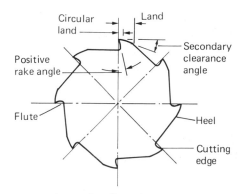

Cross-section of a fluted reamer

Plain shell reamer

A shell reamer is a finishing reamer and is held onto an arbor provided with driving lugs. The flutes can be parallel or left-handed helical. The shanks can be parallel or tapered. This reamer is used a great deal on capstan and turret lathes.

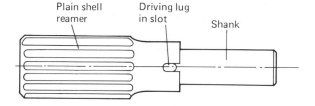

Expanding shell reamer

The blades can be adjusted to give different diameters. It has a long life as compared with a shell reamer.

Adjustable reamer

Fixed solid reamers are ground to a particular size. This size is stamped or engraved on the reamer. Adjustable reamers can cater for a variety of sizes. A set of adjustable reamers can cover most of the sizes encountered in the normal workshop.

The principle of construction is as follows:
1 The solid body has a shank and a screwed portion.
2 Six slots parallel to the reamer's axis are milled through the turned portion.
3 The bottom of the slots are at an angle to the axis.
4 Six blades with parallel cutting edges are inserted into the slots and held captive by the two end nuts.
5 When an increased diameter of the reamer is required, the nuts are adjusted for the blades to slide up to the shank end. At the correct diameter the two nuts are tightened up.
6 Inserting six different blades with a number of cutting edges arranged helically provides a greater number of cutting edges. 'Chatter' is eliminated and easier reaming is possible.

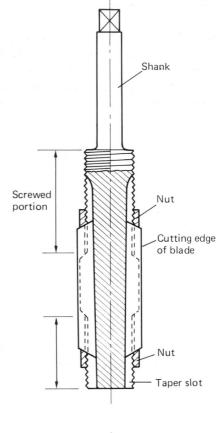

Expanding reamer

Floating reamer attachment

Reamers, when held in a floating holder, give better holes. It allows the reamer to pick-up the previously drilled or cored hole, naturally and without restraint.

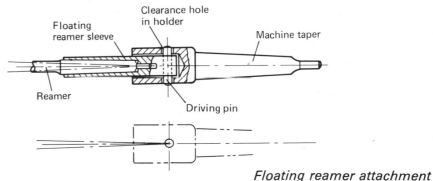

Floating reamer attachment

Thread-cutting taps

The vast majority of internal threads are produced by tapping. The operation removes metal from a hole by a series of cuts of increasing depth. The cutting edges move axially with the hole centre, and at the same time travel along the axis.

Manufacture and design of taps
1   The cutting edges of a tap are provided by milling a number of flutes equi-spaced around its periphery.
2   The periphery is threaded to provide cutting edges with the correct profile.
3   The rake angles necessary for cutting are provided by the shape of the flute. The flutes also provide temporary but adequate storage space for swarf.
4   The start of the taps are chamfered.
5   The web or core to be strong enough to resist the torsional forces on the tap when cutting.

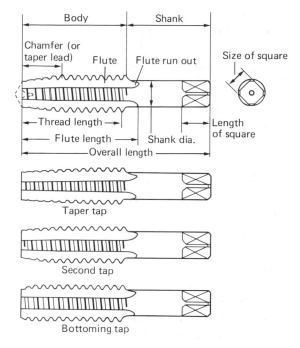

Standard set of hand taps

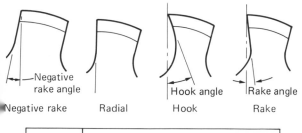

Form	Material being cut
Negative rake	Brass
Radial	Soft brass and fibre
Hook	Aluminium, copper, gun metal, cast iron, MS and stainless steel
Rake	Bakelite, hard brass, ebonite, cast iron, cast steel, phosphor bronze

Tap flute forms

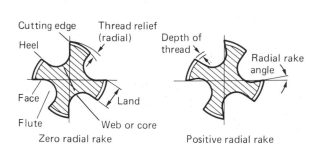

Radial relief

Carbon steel hand taps, 1.15 to 1.25 per cent carbon, with approximately 0.25 per cent vanadium added, gives the taps toughness as well as improving the cutting qualities.

High-speed steel hand taps are of 0.60 to 0.75 per cent carbon and from 17 to 19 per cent tungsten. They are used extensively for production tapping, with *cut threads* for a general line of work, and *ground threads* where greater accuracy is essential.

When taps are worn they can be reground on the faces. Due to the thread relief (radial), too much grinding of the faces will reduce the diameter of the tap.

The relationship between tap and the hole size

1 The hole to be tapped must be the correct size.
2 The tap and hole must be concentric and the axis mutually aligned.
3 When tapping blind holes, clearance would be provided in the bottom to accommodate swarf.
4 The speed of tapping is important and this evolves with experience.
5 The correct cutting lubricant is essential.
6 The correct tapping drill size is obtained from tabulated charts.

The chart shows tapping drill sizes for ISO metric threads.

Metric course				*Metric fine*		
Nominal diameter	Pitch	Tapping drill size		Nominal diameter	Pitch	Tapping drill size
3.0	× 0.50	2.50		3.0	× 0.35	2.65
4.0	× 0.70	3.30		4.0	× 0.50	3.50
6.0	× 1.00	5.00		6.0	× 0.75	5.20
10.0	× 1.50	8.50		10.0	× 1.00	9.00
16.0	× 2.00	14.00		16.0	× 1.50	15.00

Deep hole drilling

Tubular drill

1 Deep drilling is done by using a drill consisting of a tube, the length of which is determined by the depth of the hole.
2 A drill bit is brazed into the tube which must be of a similar cross-section, i.e. circular with a vee groove running for its length.
3 The work is rotated by a machine, the drill being held stationary.
4 A high pressure supply of coolant is forced down the tube to the point of the drill. It:
   (a) prevents overheating of the drill lips,
   (b) lubricates the chips, thereby aiding chip clearance, and
   (c) washes the chips from the drill lips and ejects them from the drill flutes.

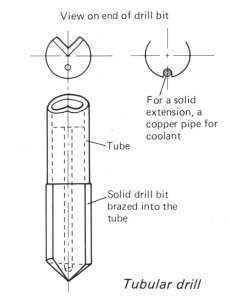

Tubular drill

Crankshaft-type drills

1 They are used for drilling deep holes of small diameter.
2 The reinforced parallel web gives the drill maximum rigidity.
3 A specially sharpened point forms cutting edges on the chisel edge.

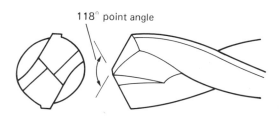

Crankshaft type drill — quick

Progressive stage method (series length drilling)

Series length drilling is a process of deep drilling, which is carried out by using a range of drills all of the same diameter, but each in turn of longer overall length.

1 The number of drills in each 'series' depends upon the diameter and depth of hole required.
2 In progressive stage drilling the drill for the first stage is usually a standard drill.
3 The second stage of the hole is then drilled with a special drill with an increased plain cylindrical portion. This gives a drill of greater rigidity than would be obtained with a drill having flutes for the full length of the body.

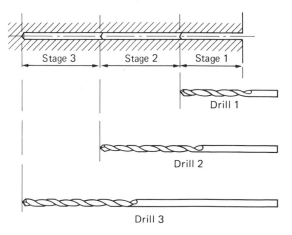

Progressive stage method

4 Succeeding stages follow the same
principle.
5 Total withdrawal of the drill out of the hole
to allow the chips to be removed is
necessary. This prevents the flutes
becoming clogged up and consequent drill
breakage.

Oil-tube drills
1 For holes above 13 mm, the use of the oil-
tube drill is recommended.
2 Two oil tubes are situated in the body
periphery between the land and the heel,
connecting with a central hole in the
shank.
3 Cutting lubricant under pressure is
supplied through these tubes to the point
of the drill.

Drill bits
1 For large holes it may be found more
economical to use drills mounted in a bar.
2 The drill bit can fit into a straight fluted
bar or a spiral fluted bar.
3 Lubricant tubes or some other method of
lubrication is necessary.
4 This type of construction is sometimes
used in capstan and turret lathes for
repetition drilling.

Drilling of cored holes
The disadvantage of using a two-flute drill to
open out a cored hole is that it tends to dig in,
because the cutting edges are diametrically
opposite to each other. Three- or four-fluted
drills are used.

Advantages
1 The multi-lipped point centres itself.
2 The cutting is shared by more cutting
edges and proceeds trouble free.
3 The tool life is longer.
Note: These drills cannot drill from the solid.

The table shows cutting tool angles and
speeds for machining thermoplastics.

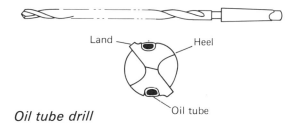

Oil tube drill

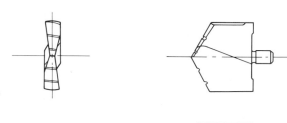

Typical drill bit

Drill bit and straight-fluted bar

Drill bit and spiral-fluted bar

			Turning	Milling	Drilling
Material	Rake	Clearance	Cutting speed m/s	Cutting speed m/s	Cutting speed m/s
Nylon	0 to − 10°	20° to 30°	2.5 to 5	5	2 to 5
PTFE	0 to − 5°	20° to 30°	1 to 2.5	5	1.25 to 5
Polystyrene	0 to − 5°	20° to 30°	1.5 to 5	5	0.5 to 10
PVC (rigid)	0 to − 10°	20° to 30°	1.5 to 5	5	2.5 to 30

Notes:
1 Feed (mm/rev) for turning and drilling can vary from 0.05 to 0.75.
2 Feed (mm/s) for milling can be up to 4.
3 Coolants, to avoid burning or melting of plastics: use air jet, water or soluble oil solution.
4 Rigid PVC to be annealed before machining.
5 When machining PTFE, it has a transition point at 20°C. It undergoes a dimensional change of 3%. It must be machined and measured at temperatures above this.
6 No smoking when machining PTFE. At the temperature of burning tobacco the swarf can break down to give off toxic vapours which are harmful. Hands to be washed after work.

Plastics

Thermoplastics soften under heat and harden upon cooling. Examples are perspex, nylon, polytetrafluoroethylene (PTFE), polypropylene and PVC (rigid polyvinyl chloride). They have very good machining properties and very good chemical resistance.

Recommendations when drilling plastics

1 Drills, of high-speed steel, to have the standard helix.
2 Wide flutes to minimise clogging of the swarf.
3 Narrow lands to minimise abrasion and heat generation.
4 The point angle to be 90° included. Lip clearance angle can vary from 8° to 16°.
5 On thin sheets the point angle to be 100° and reduce the clearance angle to 3° in order to make a clean break through.
6 Support the plastic on a piece of wood, beneath the drill, to overcome the breaking away at the edge of the hole.
7 When drilling thick plastic, withdraw the drill frequently to clear the swarf.
8 Use a jet of compressed air directed to the drill and hole. Heat is reduced, and increases the life and efficiency of the drill.
9 When drilling abrasive plastics, and also in repetition drilling, carbide-tipped drills are recommended.
10 Slow feed rate.

7 Planning

Objectives

(a) The student should be able to draw up an orderly list of operations, so that a workpiece or an assembly can be made efficiently.

(b) The student will be able to list the measuring instruments, machine tools and accessories required for particular operations.

(c) The student should be able to state the fitting processes, heat treatment, allowance for grinding, inspection requirements and recommendation of speeds and feeds for workpieces or assemblies.

When a craftsman has a drawing of a component he has to prepare an *operation sheet*. His planning of this sheet will depend on the availability of:

1 the machine tools,
2 the machine tool accessories,
3 the cutting tools,
4 the measuring equipment,
5 the fitting procedures,
6 the finishing processes, e.g. grinding and heat treatment.

Operation planning sheet

	Operation sequence	Machine equipment	Cutting tools	Measuring equipment
1	Place bar in a 3 jaw chuck Face end A	3 jaw chuck	Facing tool	Rule
2	Rough turn to $\varnothing$ 28 $\times$ 28 Finish turn to limits $\times$ 30 Finish turn to $\varnothing$ 38 $\times$ 12		Roughing tool Finishing tool Knife tool	External micrometer Depth micrometer
3	Centre drill Drill $\varnothing$ 10 right through Drill $\varnothing$ 17 $\times$ 23	Drill chuck Tapered sleeves	Centre drill 10 and $\varnothing$ 17 drills	
4	Bore to limits $\times$ 25		Boring tool	Vernier calipers
5	Part off a length 37 from end A Reverse bearing in chuck and face flange to 5		Parting off tool Facing tool	Vernier calipers

A complete planning sheet comprises:
1 an operation sequence,
2 machine equipment,
3 cutting tools,
4 speed of tools
5 feed of tools,
6 measuring equipment.

As an example, consider the production of the *flanged bearing*, as shown on the drawing, and for which the operation planning sheet is provided.

Flanged bearing

The component is to be machined on a centre lathe in a sequence of five operations.

By following the operation planning sheet, through from sequence number **1** to sequence number **5**, the component can be made quickly and efficiently.

By knowing the cutting tool material, operating on brass, and using the recommended cutting speeds (from the maker's catalogue on cutting tools), a further column can be added showing the lathe speeds in rev/min. The formula to be used would be:

$$N = \frac{1000 \times S}{\pi \times d}$$

A column 'feed/rev' could be added for the turning, boring and drilling operations by making reference to the table.

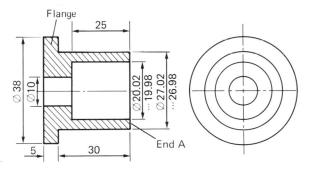

Material size: $\varnothing$ 40 × 70 long brass

Limits ± 0.50 unless otherwise stated

Flanged bearing

Machine reamer

A machine reamer is to be produced from a bar of high carbon steel, ∅ 32 mm × 205 mm long.

In planning the production of the reamer the stages will be:
1 turning the blank,
2 milling the flutes and the tang,
3 heat treatment,
4 grinding the teeth, and
5 inspection.

Construction of a planning sheet for Stage 1 — Turning the blank

From the tables on cutting speeds for HSS tools cutting high carbon steel, the cutting speed for roughing cuts is 14 m/min and the feed 0.25 mm/rev.

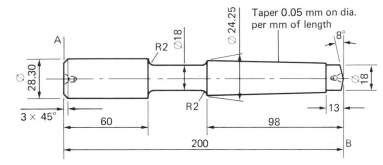

Stage 1: Machine reamer blank-turning operations

The tables give suitable tool angles, cutting speeds and feeds for a range of common engineering materials.

Cutting angles for HSS and cemented carbide tools

Materials	High speed steel		Cemented carbide	
	Top Rake	Clearance	Top Rake	Clearance
Mild steel	20°	6°	8°	4°–6°
High carbon steel	10°	4°	3°–4°	4°–6°
Soft cast iron	10°	8°	4°–8°	4°–6°
Chilled iron	0°	4°	0°	2°–4°
Copper	12°	10°	13°	4°–6°
Brass	0°–6°	10°	3°	4°–6°
Aluminium	30°	10°	16°	6°–8°

Cutting speed in metres per minute

Material	HSS tools		Cemented carbide	
	Roughing	Finishing	Roughing	Finishing
Mild steel	40	60	60	90
High carbon steel	14	18	60	120
Soft cast iron	18	23	60	105
Chilled iron	3	5	5	10
Copper	60	60	120	210
Brass	75	120	120	210
Aluminium	90	120	150	300

To calculate the rev/min to turn the bar

The bar diameter is 32 mm and the finished turned diameter is 28.3 mm. The approximate average diameter is 30 mm, which is equal to d in the formula,

$$N = \frac{1000 \times S}{\frac{22}{7} \times d}.$$

If the $\frac{22}{7}$ is rounded off to a value of 3 it makes the calculation for the rev/min much easier,

$$N = \frac{1000 \times 14}{3 \times 30} = 156 \text{ rev/min.}$$

It is probable that the exact speed is unobtainable on the lathe; therefore, it will be necessary to engage the nearest higher speed.

Feeds in millimetres per revolution

Material	HSS and cemented carbide tools	
	Roughing	Finishing
Mild steel	0.25	0.18
High carbon steel	0.25	0.18
Soft cast iron	0.33	0.20
Chilled iron	0.20	0.12
Copper	0.50	0.20
Brass	0.50	0.20
Aluminium	0.33	0.18

Construction of a planning sheet for stage 2 — Milling the flutes and the tang

To mill flutes with teeth unevenly spaced but diametrically opposite, set dividing head on a 39 hole circle and proceed as follows:

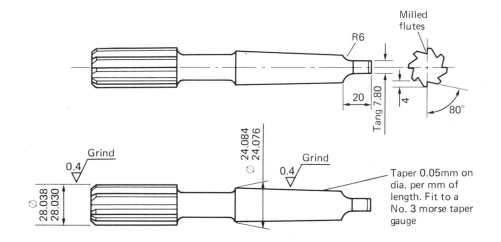

Stage 2: Milling operations

1 Set cutter relative to workpiece — mill flute 1.
2 Index 4 turns, 29 spaces — mill flute 2.
3 Index 5 turns, 10 spaces — mill flute 3.
4 Index 4 turns, 34 spaces — mill flute 4.
5 Index 5 turns, 5 spaces — mill flute 5.
6 Index 4 turns, 29 spaces — mill flute 6.
7 Index 5 turns, 10 spaces — mill flute 7.
8 Index 4 turns, 34 spaces — mill flute 8.

Following the milling operations, *stage 3 — heat treatment* must take place. This entails hardening and tempering operations.

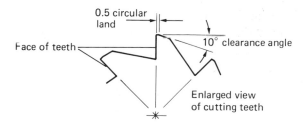

Stage 4: Grinding operations

Construction of a planning sheet for stage 5 — inspection

With the reamer located between spring-loaded centres, the roundness of the cutter teeth diameter and the taper can be inspected by using a dial test indicator and rotating the reamer. A constant reading denotes a true roundness.

A constant reading on the indicator, when it travels along the length of the circular land on the teeth, indicates parallelism of the cutting edge to the axis of the reamer.

By setting a comparator with appropriate slip gauges the diameter of the teeth of the reamer can be inspected.

Similarly, the large diameter of the taper can be inspected for roundness.

Stage 1 — Turning — operation planning sheet

Operation sequence	Machine equipment	Cutting tools	Measuring equipment
Place bar in a 3-jaw chuck. Face end A and centre drill. Face end B, to finished length of 200 mm, and centre drill.	3-jaw chuck. Drill chuck. Lathe.	Centre drill. No. 19 facing tool.	300 mm rule. 25 — 50 mm outside micrometer.
Place bar between centre S. With end A at tailstock centre, turn to ⌀ 28.30 × 120. Turn ⌀ 18. Chamfer end A.	Catch plate. Driving dog. Pair of centres.	No. 37 straight. No. 45 and 46 R2 light turning. No. 29 square nose turning.	300 mm rule. 0 — 25 mm outside micrometer.
With end B at tailstock centre, taper turn. Turn ⌀ 18 × 13.		No. 37 straight rougher. No. 7 knife cutting.	300 mm rule. 0 — 25 mm outside micrometer.

Stage 2 — Milling — operation planning sheet

Operation sequence	Machine equipment	Cutting tools	Measuring equipment
Place end B of blank in a 3-jaw chuck on a universal dividing head. End A on the tailstock centre mill flutes.	Horizontal milling machine. Universal dividing head. Tailstock centre.	80° angle milling cutter.	
Set between centres, end B on the tailstock centre. End mill one side of the tang at B. Rotate 180° and end mill other side of tang.	Catch plate. Driving dog.	End mill R6.	0 — 25 mm outside micrometer.

Stage 4 — Grinding — operation planning sheet

Operation sequence	Machine equipment	Cutting tools	Measuring equipment
Set reamer between centres. Grind face of teeth. Grind teeth ⌀ 28.038 28.030. Grind 10° clearance angle. Grind No. 3 morse taper shank.	Universal cylindrical grinding machine. Catch plate. Driving dog. Finger indexing post.	Disc grinding wheel. Cup grinding wheel.	0 — 25 mm outside micrometer. Internal No. 3 morse taper gauge.

Stage 5 — Inspection — operation planning sheet.

Operation sequence	Machine equipment	Objective	Measuring equipment
Set reamer between centres. Rotate reamer against dial test indicator for: (a) teeth, and (b) taper.	Bench centres. Surface table.	Test for cylindricity.	Comparator. Slip gauges. Dial test indicator.
With reamer at rest, run the indicator along the land.		Test for parallelism of the cutting edge with the axis.	
Set the comparator with 'high' and 'low' readings to suit: (c) teeth diameter, and (d) large taper diameter.		To check that diameters fall within the stated limits.	
Hardness readings on teeth clearance land, taper and tang.	Hardness testing machine.	To obtain the actual tensile strength in the three areas.	

Tapered component

A small quantity of the tapered component is to be manufactured using the seven operations listed A to G.

Complete the process planning sheet by inserting the operation reference letters in their correct order.

Note:

1 Material — 0.7% carbon steel bar stock ⌀ 60.
2 Heat treatment — harden and temper.
3 General tolerance ± 0.5.

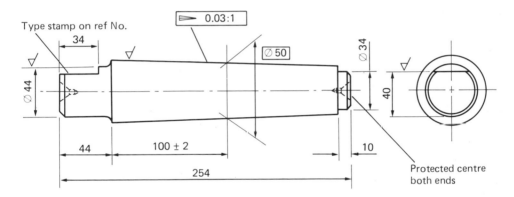

Tapered component

OPERATIONS	REF.
Turn ⌀ 34 by 10 long Turn taper to ⌀ 50 + 004 − 003	A
Type stamp ref. number on flat	B
Mill flat to 40 dimension	C
Face and centre one end Turn ⌀ 44 by 44 long and chamfer	D
Grind taper ⌀ 50 ▷ .03 : 1	E
Harden and temper	F
Face to 254 long and centre end	G

CORRECT OPERATION SEQUENCE	OPERATION REFERENCE LETTER
1	
2	
3	
4	
5	
6	
7	

Process planning sheet

Index